fundamentals of mathe-matics

fundamentals of
mathe-
matics

Bevan K Youse

Emory University

Dickenson Publishing Company, Inc.
belmont, california

L. C. Cat. Card No.: 67-16451

Printed in the United States of America

preface

This text presents in the modern spirit the essential topics of algebra and trigonometry as well as an introduction to analytic geometry and calculus. Every attempt is made to accomplish the following goals:

1. To provide a correct presentation of the material for the student in an interesting and comprehensible manner.
2. To spread the introduction of new ideas as evenly as possible throughout the text.
3. To present the material in a fashion that allows considerable latitude in the selection of topics to be studied.

Chapter 1, *Sets,* covers the "language of mathematics" needed in the study of the rest of the book. Although parts of this material will be familiar to some students, many of the exercises selected should provide the student with an interesting challenge. Chapter 2 is an extensive, though non-axiomatic, study of the real number system; emphasis is placed on the ordered field properties and the completeness property. After the concepts of inequalities and absolute value are introduced in Chapter 3, a detailed discussion of relations, functions, and graphs is given in Chapter 4. The first four chapters form an integral part of the book, and the material in them is a prerequisite to the other chapters. Chapters 5 and 6 develop the elementary transcendental functions. A discussion of mathematical induction is given in Chapter 7, followed by a discussion of sequences and the sigma notation in Chapter 8. The other chapters are: *Probability, Complex Numbers, Elementary Theory of Equations, Analytic Geometry,*

Linear Equations and Determinants, Vector Algebra, Introduction to Differential Calculus, and *Introduction to Integral Calculus.*

    Every effort has been made to maintain a continuity in the presentation of topics; however, the material in each chapter was developed so as to allow considerable flexibility in the selection of topics to be studied. The following chart indicates the chapters that are prerequisites to other chapters.

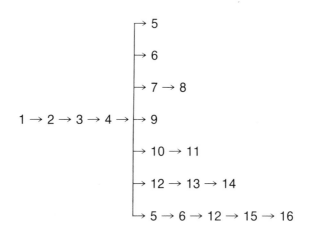

$$1 \to 2 \to 3 \to 4 \to \begin{cases} \to 5 \\ \to 6 \\ \to 7 \to 8 \\ \to 9 \\ \to 10 \to 11 \\ \to 12 \to 13 \to 14 \\ \to 5 \to 6 \to 12 \to 15 \to 16 \end{cases}$$

    Certain sections and some problems within the exercise sets have been designated as "optional." In the case of exercise problems, this has been done by means of an asterisk. These items should provide a challenge for interested students.

    I wish to acknowledge with gratitude the assistance given in the preparation of the manuscript by the following people: Professor John D. Neff, Georgia Institute of Technology, who wrote Chapter 9, *Probability*; Professor Trevor Evans, Emory University, who wrote Chapter 13, *Linear Equations and Determinants*; Professor F. Lane Hardy, Armstrong College of Savannah, who read the manuscript and made many valuable suggestions for improvement; Mrs. Peggie Wiegand, who read the material in its early stages of development, made numerous helpful suggestions, and participated in class-testing much of the material in the pre-calculus course at Emory University; Mrs. Janice Astin, Mr. John Spellmann, Mr. Thomas Tredway, and Mr. Homer Carlisle, who also class-tested the material and contributed to its improvement; Mr. David Clark, who read the book in galley stages and made significant contributions for improvement; and Mrs. Hetty Levy and Mrs. Catherine C. Wilburn, who provided the excellently typed final version of the manuscript. I would be remiss if I did not give special thanks to Mr. Richard Hansen, President of Dickenson Publishing Company, for his encouragement and utmost willingness to help during each stage in the development of the text.

Bevan K Youse

contents

fundamentals of mathe- matics

sets

1

The study of any mathematical system begins with certain undefined terms. We consider *set*, *element*, and *element of a set* as the undefined terms in our study of set theory. The usual way to gain an intuitive idea of the meaning of undefined terms is to state familiar synonyms for them and to give specific examples to clarify their meaning.

A *set* is a collection of objects; the individual objects are called *elements*, or *members*, of the set. For example, the numbers 3 and 16 are elements of the set of positive integers. We speak of the set of letters in the Roman alphabet; a, b, and c are three of the elements of this set. In algebra, we speak of the *solution set* of the equation $x^2 - x - 6 = 0$. The solution set of this equation contains the elements -2 and 3, the values for x that make the equation a true statement.

One method of defining a set is to list the elements in the set; this is called the *tabulation*, or *roster*, method. When defining a set in this manner, we use braces { } to enclose the names of the objects in the set. The set with positive integers 1, 2, 3, 4, 6, and 12 as elements is denoted by {1, 2, 3, 4, 6, 12}. This set can also be denoted by {3, 6, 4, 12, 2, 1}, since the order of listing the elements is immaterial when defining a set.

It is convenient to use letters to denote sets. For example, we might let S denote the set $\{1, 2, 3, 4, 6, 12\}$; thus, $S = \{1, 2, 3, 4, 6, 12\}$. If a letter, such as u, is used to denote any one of the elements in a given set S, then u is called a *variable on the set S*. The symbol ϵ is used to stand for "is an element in," or "belongs to"; thus, $u \epsilon S$ means that u is an element in the set S. If t represents an element not in S, we express this by $t \notin S$. For the set defined by $S = \{1, 2, 3, 4, 6, 12\}$, $2 \epsilon S$, $6 \epsilon S$, $23 \notin S$, etc.

Two sets S and T are said to be *equal* if and only if every element in S is an element in T and every element in T is an element in S; that is, two equal sets S and T have exactly the same elements. If set S is equal to a set T, then $S = T$ expresses this fact. If S and T do not contain exactly the same elements, then the sets are said to be *unequal*; we write $S \neq T$.

A method different from listing the elements to define a set is to specify a distinguishing property (or properties) of the elements in the set. For example, let $S = \{1, 2, 3, 4, 6, 12\}$. The set S may also be described as the set which has as its elements the positive factors of 12. We will now discuss the symbolism used for defining a set by this second method.

A sentence such as "x is a positive factor of 12" is called an *open sentence*. If x is a variable on the set of positive integers, then the truth or falsity of the given open sentence depends on the integer x represents. If $x = 2$, "x is a positive factor of 12" is a true statement; if $x = 5$, the statement is false. The set S consisting of exactly those positive integers that make the open sentence "x is a factor of 12" a true statement upon substitution for x is defined by $\{x \mid x$ is a positive factor of $12\}$—which is read, "the set of all x such that x is a positive factor of 12." If $P = \{x \mid x$ is a positive integer having exactly two positive factors$\}$, then P is the set of positive *prime* numbers; $2 \epsilon P$, $3 \epsilon P$, $5 \epsilon P$, $7 \epsilon P$, $11 \epsilon P$, etc.

exercises

1. State which of the following statements are true and which are false.
   (a) $5 \epsilon \{2, 4, 6, 8\}$
   (b) $37 \notin \{x \mid x$ has exactly two positive factors$\}$
   (c) $35 \epsilon \{x \mid x$ has exactly four positive factors$\}$
   (d) $28 \epsilon \{y \mid$ the sum of the positive factors of y is $2y\}$
   (e) $128 \epsilon \{y \mid$ the sum of the positive factors of y is $2y\}$
   (f) $496 \notin \{y \mid$ the sum of the positive factors of y is $2y\}$
   (g) $7,747 \epsilon \{t \mid t$ is a multiple of $37\}$
   (h) $3 \notin \{x \mid x^4 - 5x^3 + 2x^2 - 112x + 6 = 0\}$

2. Define the following sets by listing the elements in each.
   (a) $\{t \mid t$ is a prime number less than $100\}$
   (b) $\{y \mid y$ is a positive integer less than 30 and the sum of the positive factors of y is $2y\}$
   (c) $\{x \mid x$ is a positive integer less than 10 and $2^x - 1$ is a prime number$\}$

(d) {m|m was a president of the United States with H as last initial}
(e) {x|x is a positive factor of 128}
(f) {u|u is a prime (positive) factor of 128}
(g) {x|x is a letter in the title of this book}
(h) {y|y is a Hindu-Arabic numeral}

3. Define the following sets by stating properties of the elements.
(a) {a, e, i, o, u}
(b) {1, 1/2, 1/3, 1/4, 1/5, 1/6, 1/7}
(c) {2, 4, 8, 16, 32, 64}
(d) {1, 4, 9, 16, 25, 36, 49, 64, 81, 100}
(e) {John Nance Garner, Henry Agard Wallace, Harry S Truman}
(f) {1, 3, 5, 7, 9, 11, 13, 15, 17}
(g) {3, 9, 15, 21, 27, 33, 39, 45}
(h) {I, V, X, L, C, D, M}

4. List the elements in each of the following sets.
(a) $\{x|2x+11=15\}$
(b) $\{x|x^2-7x-8=0\}$
(c) $\{x|x^2=x\}$
(d) {x|x is twice its square}

5. Define the following sets of real numbers by the tabulation method.
(a) $\{x|6x+11=2x+15\}$
(b) $\{x|x^4-5x^2+6=0\}$
(c) $\{t|t^3=t\}$
(d) $\left\{w\left|\dfrac{w-2}{w+3}=3\right.\right\}$

6. Let $S=\{t|t$ is a positive factor of a prime number $p\}$. List the elements of S.

7. Let $W=\{x|x$ is a positive factor of the number $2^{p-1}(2^p-1)$ where (2^p-1) is a prime number}. List the elements of W.

1–2 subsets

definition: A set A is said to be a *subset* of a set B if, and only if, every element of A is an element of B.

If A is a subset of B, we say that A is included in B and use the symbol $\subseteq$ to denote set inclusion; thus, $A \subseteq B$—which is read "A is a subset of B"—if and only if $x \in A$ implies $x \in B$. The set of even integers is a subset of the set of integers; {2, 3} is a subset of {1, 2, 3, 4}; and the set of prime factors of 128 is a subset of the set of factors of 128. Not only is {2, 3} $\subseteq$ {1, 2, 3, 4} but also {2} $\subseteq$ {1, 2, 3, 4}. We should be careful to distinguish between {2} $\subseteq$ {1, 2, 3, 4} and $2\epsilon\{1,2,3,4\}$; "{2} $\subseteq$ {1,2,3,4}" states that the set with only the one element 2 is a subset of {1, 2, 3, 4} and "2 ϵ {1, 2, 3, 4}" states that 2 is an element of the set {1, 2, 3, 4}. Furthermore, it should be noted that as a consequence of the definition of subset, {1, 2, 3, 4}

⊆ {1, 2, 3, 4}. In general, if A is any set then $A \subseteq A$ since every element in A is in A.

As a consequence of the definitions of set equality and of subset, $A = B$ where A and B are sets if, and only if, $A \subseteq B$ and $B \subseteq A$. If A is a subset of B and if B contains at least one element not in A, we say that A is a *proper subset* of B and express the fact by $A \subset B$. Thus, A is a proper subset of B if and only if $A \subseteq B$ and $A \neq B$.

Suppose we consider the prime numbers between 900,000 and 900,268. Have we actually described a set? That is, are there any prime numbers between the two given numbers? If we insist that a set must have at least one element, it is necessary to produce one prime number between the two numbers to show that a set has been defined. In general, when defining a set by describing the properties of its elements, we must either produce at least one element having the given properties or agree to having a set with no elements. It is more convenient to take the latter course. A set with no elements is called the *empty, null,* or *void* set and is denoted by $\emptyset$. We have $\emptyset = \{x | x$ is an integer and $2x = 3\}$, or $\emptyset = \{x | x \neq x\}$. Since the empty set has no elements, it follows that each of its elements is in any given set A. Thus, the empty set is a subset of any set; that is, $\emptyset \subseteq A$.

The set $\{1,2,3\}$ has eight subsets; they are $\{1\}$, $\{2\}$, $\{3\}$, $\{1,2\}$, $\{1,3\}$, $\{2,3\}$, $\{1,2,3\}$, and $\emptyset$. All subsets of $\{1,2,3\}$ other than the set $\{1,2,3\}$ are proper subsets of the given set. Note that $\{1\} \subset \{1,2,3\}$, $\emptyset \subset \{1,2,3\}$, and $1 \epsilon \{1,2,3\}$; however, $\{1\} \notin \{1,2,3\}$ and $\emptyset \notin \{1,2,3\}$. If T is the set of subsets of $\{1,2,3\}$, then

$$T = \{\{1\}, \{2\}, \{3\}, \{1,2\}, \{1,3\}, \{2,3\}, \{1,2,3\}, \emptyset\}.$$

Note that $\{2,3\} \epsilon T$, $\emptyset \epsilon T$, $\{1\} \epsilon T$, but $2 \notin T$.

1–3   equivalent sets

Let $A = \{1, 2, 3\}$ and $B = \{4, 5, 6\}$. Although $A \neq B$, these two sets have the same number of elements. Let us discuss what "same number of elements" or "same size" for two sets implies mathematically.

Let S and T be two sets. If there exists any method of pairing every element of S with one and only one element of T and every element of T with one and only one element of S, the two sets are said to be in *one-to-one correspondence*.

definition: Two sets S and T that can be put into one-to-one correspondence are said to be *equivalent;* equivalence of S and T is expressed by $S \sim T$.

For example, a one-to-one correspondence of $A = \{1, 2, 3\}$ and $B = \{4, 5, 6\}$ is exhibited by the following pairing:

$$A \sim B$$
$$1 \leftrightarrow 4$$
$$2 \leftrightarrow 5$$
$$3 \leftrightarrow 6$$

Sets A and B could be proved equivalent by exhibiting other one-to-one correspondences between the sets. Another one-to-one correspondence is exhibited as follows:

$$A \sim B$$
$$1 \leftrightarrow 6$$
$$2 \leftrightarrow 4$$
$$3 \leftrightarrow 5$$

Although equivalent sets may not be equal, it should be noted that equal sets are equivalent.

For $A = \{1, 2, 3\}$, if we let $n(A)$ denote the number of elements in the set A then $n(A) = 3$. If $B = \{3, 4, 5\}$, then $n(B) = 3$. All sets that are equivalent to set A have the *same number* of elements and are said to be the *same size*. Three is said to be the *cardinal number* of sets A and B. All equivalent sets have the same cardinal number.

Let $\aleph_0$ (aleph null) denote the cardinal number of the set of all positive integers. If N is the set of all positive integers and E is the set of all even integers, then E can be proved equivalent to N by the following one-to-one correspondence:

$$E \sim N$$
$$2 \leftrightarrow 1$$
$$4 \leftrightarrow 2$$
$$6 \leftrightarrow 3$$
$$8 \leftrightarrow 4$$
$$\cdots \cdots$$
$$2n \leftrightarrow n$$

Since E is equivalent to N, E has cardinal number $\aleph_0$ and is the same size as set N. Notice that E is equivalent to N and E is a proper subset of N; this situation is impossible for two sets with only a finite number of elements. We use this distinguishing property to define *infinite set*: An infinite set is one that can be put into one-to-one correspondence with a proper subset of itself.

Since $\aleph_0$ is not the cardinal number of a finite set, it is called a *transfinite number*. An extensive study of transfinite numbers is not within the scope of this text; however, an interesting theory in this area awaits the student in *An Introduction to Transfinite Mathematics* by John E. Yarnelle, D. C. Heath and Company, 1964.

exercises

1. (a) List all the subsets of $\{1, 2\}$.
   (b) List all the subsets of $\{1, 2, 3\}$.

(c) List all the subsets of $\{1, 2, 3, 4\}$.

(d) How many subsets are there of a set with five elements?

(e) Conjecture the number of subsets of a set with n elements.

2. Let N be the set of positive integers and let T be the set of odd positive integers. Prove that N is equivalent to T. (Exhibit a one-to-one correspondence between the elements in each set.)

3. Let $T = \{x | x$ is a positive factor of $30\}$ and let S be the set of subsets of T. State which of the following statements are true and which are false.

(a) $2 \in T$ (b) $\emptyset \in T$ (c) $11 \subseteq T$

(d) $\emptyset \subseteq T$ (e) $\{1, 3, 5, 10\} \subset T$ (f) $\emptyset \subset T$

(g) $\{3, 5\} \subset S$ (h) $\{3, 5\} \in S$ (i) $\{\emptyset\} \subset S$

(j) $\{\emptyset\} \in S$ (k) $\emptyset \in S$

4. Prove that the set of perfect squares has cardinal number $\aleph_0$.

5. (a) Let $S_2 = \{1, 2\}$ and $T_2 = \{a, b\}$. Exhibit all the one-to-one correspondences between the two sets.

(b) Let $S_3 = \{1, 2, 3\}$ and $T_3 = \{a, b, c\}$. Exhibit all the one-to-one correspondences between the two sets.

(c) How many one-to-one correspondences exist between the two sets $S_4 = \{1, 2, 3, 4\}$ and $T_4 = \{a, b, c, d\}$?

(d) Conjecture the number of one-to-one correspondences between two sets with n elements each.

6. Let $T = \{x | x$ is a positive factor of $24\}$ and let S be the set of subsets of T. State which of the following statements are true and which are false.

(a) $6 \in T$ (b) $\{6\} \in T$ (c) $\{\{2, 3\}, \{6\}\} \subset S$

(d) $T = \{1, 2, 3, 4, 6, 12, 24\}$ (e) $n(T) = 24$ (f) $n(S) = 128$

(g) $\emptyset \in S$ (h) $\{\emptyset\} \in T$ (i) $\emptyset \subset S$

(j) $\emptyset \subset T$

7. Let $S = \{x | x$ is a positive multiple of 3 less than $100\}$ and let $P = \{x | x$ is a prime number less than $20\}$. What is $n(S) + n(P)$?

8. If $T = \left\{ x \left| \dfrac{x+5}{x-7} - 5 = \dfrac{4x - 40}{13 - x} \right. \right\}$, is T the empty set? Justify your answer.

9. Is $\{x | x^2 - 5x - 6 = 0\} \subseteq \{x | x^4 - 5x^3 - 2x^2 - 20x - 24 = 0\}$?

°10. Let $S = \{(m, n) | m$ and n are positive integers$\}$. Prove S has $\aleph_0$ as cardinal number.

1-4   union, intersection, and complement

A *binary operation* on two sets is a procedure for constructing a new set from two given sets. One binary operation on two sets is *union*.

definition: The *union* of two sets A and B is the *set* consisting of all elements in A, in B, or in both A and B; the union of sets A and B is expressed by $A \cup B$, read "A union B." Symbolically, $A \cup B = \{x | x \in A \text{ or } x \in B\}$.

For example, if $A = \{1, 2, 3\}$ and $B = \{4, 5\}$, then $A \cup B = \{1, 2, 3, 4, 5\}$; if $A = \{1, 2, 3\}$ and $C = \{2, 3, 4\}$, then $A \cup C = \{1, 2, 3, 4\}$. If $S = \{1, 2, 3, 4\}$ and $T = \{1, 4\}$, then T is a subset of S and $S \cup T = \{1, 2, 3, 4\}$; this is an example of the general property that if $T \subseteq S$ then $S \cup T = S$.

definition: The *intersection* of two sets A and B is the set consisting of all elements in both A and B; the intersection of sets A and B is expressed by $A \cap B$, read "A intersection B." Symbolically, $A \cap B = \{x | x \, \epsilon \, A \text{ and } x \, \epsilon \, B\}$.

If $A = \{1, 2, 3\}$ and $B = \{2, 3, 4\}$, then $A \cap B = \{2, 3\}$. If $S = \{1, 2, 3, 4\}$ and $T = \{1, 4\}$, then T is a subset of S and $S \cap T = \{1, 4\}$; this is an example of the general property that if $T \subseteq S$ then $S \cap T = T$.

The existence of the empty set allows us to state that the intersection of any two sets is a set. For example, if $A = \{1, 2, 3\}$ and $B = \{4, 5\}$, then $A \cap B = \emptyset$. Sets that have no elements in common are said to be *disjoint*. The set E of even integers and the set F of odd integers are disjoint sets and $E \cap F = \emptyset$.

Let $B = \{1, 2, 3, 4, 5, 6, 7\}$ and let $A = \{1, 3, 5, 7\}$. The set of elements in B and not in A is called the *complement of A relative to B* and is denoted by A'_B; thus, $A'_B = \{2, 4, 6\}$.

definition: If $A \subseteq B$ then the complement of A relative to B is the set of all elements in B not in A; symbolically, $A'_B = \{x | x \, \epsilon \, B \text{ and } x \, \notin \, A\}$.

Often throughout a discussion we consider only subsets of a particular given set; in this case, the given set is called the *universal set*. If we are to consider only subsets of the set R of real numbers, then R is the universal set and it is customary to write S' instead of S'_R for the complement of a subset S relative to R and to call S' the complement of S.

If I is the set of positive integers and E is the set of even positive integers, then E'_I is the set of odd positive integers. For any set S, since S'_S contains all elements in S not in S, $S'_S = \emptyset$. Similarly, since $\emptyset'_S$ contains all elements in S not in the empty set, $\emptyset'_S = S$.

Let A and B be subsets of some universal set C. We prove that $(A \cup B)' = A' \cap B'$. This property of sets is stated as follows. The complement of the union of two sets is the intersection of the complements of the two sets. To *prove* that two sets S and T are equal, we need to prove that every element in S is in T *and* every element in T is in S; in other words, we need to prove $S \subseteq T$ and $T \subseteq S$.

theorem 1–1:   If A and B are subsets of some universal set C, then $(A \cup B)' = A' \cap B'$.

proof: *Part* 1.   We first prove that $(A \cup B)' \subseteq (A' \cap B')$ by showing that every element in $(A \cup B)'$ is in $(A' \cap B')$. Let x be any element in $(A \cup B)'$. Then, $x \notin (A \cup B)$ by the definition of complement. If $x \notin (A \cup B)$, then $x \notin A$ and $x \notin B$ by the definition of union of two sets. Thus, $x \in A'$ and $x \in B'$. Consequently, $x \in (A' \cap B')$ by the definition of the intersection of two sets. Hence, $(A \cup B)' \subseteq (A' \cap B')$.

Part 2.   Now, we prove that $(A' \cap B') \subseteq (A \cup B)'$. Let x be any element in $(A' \cap B')$. Then, $x \in A'$ and $x \in B'$ by definition of intersection; thus, $x \notin A$ and $x \notin B$, which implies that $x \notin (A \cup B)$. Consequently, $x \in (A \cup B)'$ and $(A' \cap B') \subseteq (A \cup B)'$.

Parts 1 and 2 imply $(A \cup B)' = A' \cap B'$.

   We conclude our discussion of sets by proving one more theorem concerning the properties of sets.

theorem 1–2:   Let A, B, and C be sets. Then

$$A \cap (B \cup C) = (A \cap B) \cup (A \cap C).$$

proof: *Part* 1.   We first prove $A \cap (B \cup C) \subseteq [(A \cap B) \cup (A \cap C)]$. Let x be any element in $A \cap (B \cup C)$. Then, $x \in A$ and $x \in (B \cup C)$. Since $x \in (B \cup C)$, $x \in B$ or $x \in C$. If $x \in B$, then $x \in (A \cap B)$ since x is in both A and B. We conclude that $x \in [(A \cap B) \cup (A \cap C)]$. Note that if $x \in (A \cap B)$ then x is in the union of $(A \cap B)$ and any set. If $x \notin B$, then $x \in C$ and we conclude $x \in (A \cap C)$; thus, $x \in [(A \cap B) \cup (A \cap C)]$. Consequently, $A \cap (B \cup C) \subseteq (A \cap B) \cup (A \cap C)$.

Part 2.   We now prove that $[(A \cap B) \cup (A \cap C)] \subseteq A \cap (B \cup C)$. Let x be any element in $(A \cap B) \cup (A \cap C)$. Then, $x \in (A \cap B)$ or $x \in (A \cap C)$. If $x \in (A \cap B)$, $x \in A$ and $x \in B$. Thus, $x \in (B \cup C)$ and $x \in [A \cap (B \cup C)]$. If $x \in (A \cap C)$, $x \in A$ and $x \in C$. Thus, $x \in (B \cup C)$ and $x \in [A \cap (B \cup C)]$. Consequently, $[(A \cup B) \cap (A \cup C)] \subseteq A \cap (B \cup C)$.

Parts 1 and 2 prove the theorem.

exercises

1. Let $A = \{x | x$ is a positive factor of $128\}$ and $B = \{x | x$ is a positive factor of $80\}$.
    (a) List all the elements of A.
    (b) List all the elements of B.
    (c) List all the elements of $A \cup B$.
    (e) List all the elements of $A \cap B$.
    (e) Is $\{16, 32, 64\} \subseteq A$?
    (f) If $T = \{x | x$ is a positive factor of $32\}$, what is $T \cup A$? $A \cap T$? $T \cup B$? $T \cap B$?

2. Consider the sets defined as follows.
    $K = \{x | x^2 - 7x + 6 = 0\}$
    $I = \{x | x^2 = 1\}$

$H = \{x | x$ is a positive factor of 6$\}$
$S = \{x | x$ is a positive multiple of 2$\}$
$T = \{-2, -1, 0, 1, 2\}$
(a) List the elements of $I \cup K$.
(b) List the elements of $H \cap K$.
(c) List the elements of $H \cap T$.
(d) List the elements of $S \cap H$.
(e) Show that $K \cup (T \cap I) = (K \cup T) \cap (K \cup I)$.
(f) Show that $K \cap (T \cup I) = (K \cap T) \cup (K \cap I)$.

3. Let A and B be sets with a finite number of elements. If $n(A) = a$, $n(B) = b$ and $n(A \cap B) = c$, how many elements are in $A \cup B$?

4. Assume there is a group of 500 students who enjoy watching football or basketball games. If only 407 enjoy watching basketball and only 386 enjoy watching football, how many enjoy watching both games? See Exercise 3.

5. Let $S = \{1, 2, 3, 4, 5, 6, 7, 8, 9\}$, $A = \{1, 2, 3, 4, 5\}$, $B = \{3, 5, 7, 8\}$, and $C = \{7, 8, 9\}$. List the elements in each of the following sets.
   (a) A_S'　　　　　(b) B_S'　　　　　(c) C_S'　　　　　(d) $(A \cap B)_S'$
   (e) $A_S' \cup B_S'$　　(f) $A_S' \cap C$　　(g) $A \cap (B \cap C)$
   (h) $(A \cup B)_S'$　　(i) $A_S' \cap B_S'$　　(j) $(A \cup B)_S' \cap (B \cup C)_S'$
   (k) $(A_S' \cup C_S')_S'$

6. Prove that if $A \subseteq B$, then $A \cup B = B$.

7. Prove that if $A \subseteq B$, then $A \cap B = A$.

8. Prove that if A and B are subsets of some universal set C, then $(A \cap B)' = A' \cup B'$.

9. Prove if A, B, and C are sets, then $A \cup (B \cap C) = (A \cup B) \cap (A \cup C)$.

10. Let A and B be sets. We define $A - B$ to be $\{x | x \in A$ and $x \notin B\}$.
    (a) If $A = \{1, 2, 3, 4, 5\}$ and $B = \{4, 5, 6, 7\}$, list the elements in $A - B$.
    (b) List the elements in $B - A$.
    (c) Under what conditions is $A - B = B_A'$?

11. Let N be the set of positive integers. If S is a set of positive integers such that $S_N' = \emptyset$, what can you conclude about the set S?

12. Let $A \subseteq B$, $n(A) = a$ and $n(B) = b$. What is $n(A_B')$?

13. Let $A = \{1, 2, 3, 4, 5, 6\}$, $B = \{x | x$ is a positive factor of 6$\}$, and $C = \{4, 6, 7, 8\}$. Define each of the following sets by the tabulation method.
    (a) $A \cup B$　　　　(b) $A \cap B$　　　　(c) $A \cup C$　　　　(d) $A \cap C$
    (e) $B \cap C$　　　　(f) $A \cap (B \cup C)$

*14. Let P be the set of (positive) prime numbers and let $S = \{t | 2^t - 1$ is a prime$\}$. Prove $S \subseteq P$. (Hint: Show if $x \notin P$ then $x \notin S$.)

*15. Let A, B, and C be sets. Prove that $n(A \cup B \cup C) = n(A) + n(B) + n(C) - n(A \cap B) - n(A \cup C) - n(B \cup C) + n(A \cap B \cap C)$.
    Hint: See Exercise 3.

the real number system

2

2–1 introduction

In mathematics, one deals with many different sets of objects; one of the most important of these sets is the set of *real numbers*. Before listing the distinguishing properties of this set, let us discuss the properties of some of its important subsets. This detailed examination of various subsets of the set of real numbers will enhance our understanding of the structure of the real number system.

2–2 integers

One of the important subsets of the set of real numbers is the set of positive integers—$\{1, 2, 3, 4, 5, 6, \ldots\}$. The use of numbers to measure depends on the concept of associating a number with a point on a line. To construct a correspondence (pairing) between positive integers and points on a line, we begin by marking off equal segments to the right of the origin P of a given ray. (See Figure 2–1.)

Positive integers

FIGURE 2–1

We associate "1" with the right endpoint of the first segment, "2" with the right endpoint of the second segment, etc. This method associates with each positive integer a point on the given ray. The number associated with a point on the ray is called the *coordinate* of the point. Although a point on the ray is associated with each positive integer, there are points on the ray not associated with any positive integer.

Addition of two positive integers is an abstraction of finding the total number of objects in two disjoint sets. Addition may be considered a prescribed *method* by which a number called the *sum* is associated with any given *pair* of numbers; addition is a binary operation. We are familiar with the fact that the sum $2+3$ equals the sum $3+2$. In general, if a and b are positive integers, then $a+b = b+a$; this is called the *commutative property of addition*.

The set of positive integers is said to be *closed with respect to addition;* this means that the sum of any two positive integers is itself a positive integer. More generally, any set is said to be *closed with respect to a given binary operation* if an element in the set always results from performing the operation on any two given elements in the set. For example, since the sum of two even integers is an even integer, the set of even integers is closed with respect to addition. Since the sum of two prime numbers is not necessarily a prime number, the set of prime numbers is not closed with respect to addition.

Multiplication is another binary operation that associates a number, called the *product*, with a given pair of numbers; the product of numbers a and b is denoted by ab, or $a \times b$. If a and b are positive integers, then $ab=ba$; this is called the *commutative property of multiplication*. Since the product of two positive integers is a positive integer, the set of positive integers is closed with respect to multiplication.

Parentheses and other such symbols are the punctuation marks of mathematics. For example $(2+3)+7$ represents the sum of 5 and 7, while $2+(3+7)$ represents the sum of 2 and 10. Another important property of the set of positive integers is that if a, b, and c are positive integers, then $(a+b)+c=a+(b+c)$; this is called the *associative property of addition*. It is also true that $(ab)c=a(bc)$; this is called the *associative property of multiplication*. The associative property allows us to avoid excessive use of parentheses. We usually omit parentheses when only one of the operations of addition or multiplication is involved; that is, we write $2+3+7$ instead of $(2+3)+7$ or $2+(3+7)$. Furthermore, parentheses can be avoided when both addition and multiplication are involved by agreeing that multiplication has precedence over addition; that is, $mn+n$ represents $(mn)+n$ rather than $m(n+n)$.

Consider the product $3(4+5)$. From the interpretation of multiplication for positive integers as repeated addition, we have

$$3(4+5) = (4+5) + (4+5) + (4+5).$$

By the associative and commutative properties of addition, we have

$$(4+5) + (4+5) + (4+5) = (4+4+4) + (5+5+5)$$

so that

$$3(4+5) = (4+4+4) + (5+5+5)$$
$$= (3 \times 4) + (3 \times 5).$$

In general, if a, b, and c are positive integers, then $a(b+c)=ab+ac$. This is called the *distributive property*. The distributive property is the important basic property that involves both the operations of addition and multiplication.

The operations of subtraction and division are defined in terms of addition and multiplication. If a and b are any two numbers and if there exists a unique (one and only one) number c such that $a+c=b$, then c is called the *difference* of b and a, or the difference b *minus* a. We say that b minus a is c and write $b-a=c$. For example, since $2+9=11$, 9 is the difference of 11 and 2; that is, $11-2=9$. It should be noted that there is no positive integer c such that $15+c=7$; consequently, the set of positive integers is not closed with respect to subtraction.

If a and b are any two numbers and if there exists a unique number c such that $ac=b$, then c is called the quotient of b by a, or the quotient of b divided by a. We say b divided by a is c and write $b \div a=c$. For example, since $7 \times 8=56$, $56 \div 8=7$. No positive integer c exists such that $3c=11$; thus $11 \div 3$ is not an integer, and the set of positive integers is not closed with respect to division. It should be obvious that subtraction and division are not commutative operations; that is, in general, $a-b \neq b-a$ and $a \div b \neq b \div a$. The operations of addition, subtraction, multiplication, and division are called the *rational operations*; each rational operation is a binary operation.

definition: For any two numbers a and b, a is said to be *less than* b if and only if there exists a *positive number* x such that $a+x=b$; this is expressed by $a<b$. If a is less than b, we say that b is *greater than* a; symbolically, $b>a$.

For example, $2<7$ since there exists a positive number, namely 5, such that $2+5=7$; furthermore, $7>2$. The expressions $a<b$ and $b>a$ are called *inequalities*.

A geometric interpretation of the less-than relation is quite simple. Let P and Q be points on the number line with coordinates x and y, respectively. With the standard orientation for the number line, $x < y$ if and only if point P is to the left of point Q.

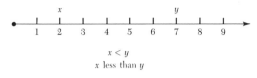

$x < y$

x less than y

FIGURE 2–2

An important property of the set of positive integers is that if a and b are any two positive integers, one and only one of the following is true: $a < b$, $a = b$, or $a > b$; this is called the *trichotomy property*. Geometrically, the trichotomy property is obvious. If a and b are the coordinates of two points on the number line, then a represents a point to the left of the point represented by b, a and b represent the same point, or a represents a point to the right of the point represented by b.

We write $a \leq b$ to indicate that the number a is less than or equal to the number b. Similarly, $c \geq d$ implies that either $c > d$ or $c = d$.

Let S be any set of numbers. If there exists a number t in S less than *every other* number in S, then t is called the *least* number in S. In other words, t is the least number in S if $t \in S$ and $t \leq x$ for *every* x in S. For example, if $S = \{3, 8, 17, 84\}$, then 3 is the least element in S. If there exists a number u in S greater than every other number in S, then u is called the *greatest number* in S. In other words, u is the greatest number in a set S if $u \in S$ and $u \geq x$ for every x in S. In $\{3, 8, 17, 84\}$, the greatest number is 84.

Although the set of even positive integers does not contain a greatest number, this set does contain a least number, namely 2. An important property of the number system is that every non-empty set of positive integers contains a least number; this is called the *well-ordering property*. The well-ordering property can be used to justify an important method of proof known as mathematical induction. (See chapter 7.)

The set consisting of the positive integers and zero is called the *non-negative integers*, or *whole numbers*. The integer 0 is associated with the origin of the number line. We are familiar with the fact that $a + 0 = 0 + a = a$. Since the sum of 0 and any number a is a, the number 0 is called the *additive identity*. Similarly, since $a \times 1 = 1 \times a = a$, the number 1 is called the *multiplicative identity*. The set of non-negative integers is closed with respect to the operations of addition and multiplicaton; however, this set is not closed with respect to either subtraction or division.

As a consequence of the definition of subtraction, it follows that $0-0=0$ since $0+0=0$. Let us consider the set of non-negative integers and some important consequences of the definition of division. First, since $8 \times 0 = 0$, we have by the definition of division that $0 \div 8 = 0$. In fact, if $a \neq 0$, we have $0 \div a = 0$ since $a \times 0 = 0$. Second, since the product of any number and zero is zero, there is no number that we can multiply by 0 to get a product of, say 15; hence, $15 \div 0$ is meaningless, or undefined. In general, if $a \neq 0$, then $a \div 0$ is undefined. Third, since *any* number times zero is zero (see theorem 2–15), there is no *unique* number to multiply by 0 to have the product 0; hence, $0 \div 0$ is undefined. Thus, *division by zero is an excluded operation* for the number system.

Consider 0 and a positive integer a. There exists a positive integer c such that $0 + c = a$, namely, $c = a$; thus, by the definition of the less-than relation, $0 < a$. In other words, if a is positive then $a > 0$. Conversely, if $a > 0$, then a is positive.

The integers

FIGURE 2–3

For a positive integer such as 6 there exists a number x such that $6 + x = 0$; the number x is called a *negative integer* and is denoted by -6. If the number line is extended to the left of the origin, marking off equal segments to the left of 0 gives points with which to associate the set of negative integers. (See Figure 2–3.) The set consisting of the positive integers, zero, and the negative integers is called the *integers*.

We are familiar with such addition and multiplication facts as $(-8) + (-7) = -15$ and $(-3)(-8) = 24$. Since the sum of two negative integers is a negative integer, the set of negative integers is closed with respect to addition; however, since the product of two negative integers is a positive integer, the set of negative integers is not closed with respect to multiplication. The fact that the set of positive integers is closed with respect to multiplication while the set of negative integers is not closed with respect to multiplication is an important distinguishing property between these two sets.

Since there is a positive integer c such that $(-6) + c = 0$, it follows from the definition of the less-than relation that $-6 < 0$. In general, if a is any negative integer, then $a < 0$; conversely, if $a < 0$, then a is negative.

For any integer x, the integer y such that $x + y = 0$ is called the *additive inverse* of x. Since $8 + (-8) = (-8) + 8 = 0$, the integer -8 is the additive inverse of 8 and, conversely, 8 is the additive inverse of -8. Furthermore, since $0 + 0 = 0$, the additive inverse of 0 is 0.

The set of integers is closed with respect to addition, subtraction, and multiplication, but the set is not closed with respect to division. Furthermore, the set of integers has the commutative property of addition and multiplication, the associative property of addition and multiplication, the distributive property, and the trichotomy property.

exercises

1. Name the rational operations.

2. Use integers to illustrate the validity of each of the following:
   (a) $(x+y)+z = x+(y+z)$.
   (b) $x(yz) = (xy)z$.
   (c) $x(y+z) = xy+xz$.

3. Is the set of positive integers closed with respect to addition? Subtraction? Multiplication? Division?

4. Is the set of integers closed with respect to addition? Subtraction? Multiplication? Division?

5. Is the set of perfect squares—$\{1, 4, 9, 16, 25, \ldots\}$—closed with respect to addition? Subtraction? Multiplication? Division?

6. Is the set of prime numbers closed with respect to addition? Subtraction? Multiplication? Division?

7. Is the set of positive multiples of 3 closed with respect to addition? Subtraction? Multiplication? Division?

8. Is the set $\{0, 1, -1\}$ closed with respect to addition? Subtraction? Multiplication? Division?

9. Which of the following are true? Justify your answer.
   (a) $2 < 8$ (b) $3 > 7$ (c) If $x < y$, then $x \leqslant y$.
   (d) If $x \leqslant y$, then $x < y$.

10. Perform the indicated operations.
    (a) $[(2)(3)-11]\,6+27$
    (b) $5[(2)(-7)+8]-(-5)(6)$
    (c) $(0 \times 8)-(0 \div 16)$
    (d) $[(8)(7)-6] \div (-5)$

11. Discuss the following "proof." If there are integers x and y such that

$$x-2 = y,$$

then

$$(x-2)^2 = y(x-2).$$

Subtracting y^2,

$$(x-2)^2 - y^2 = y(x-2) - y^2.$$

Hence,

$$(x-2-y)(x-2+y) = y(x-2-y)$$

by factoring, and

$$x-2+y=y$$

by cancellation property of multiplication. Thus,

$$x-2=0$$

and

$$x=2.$$

Consequently, the only integer x such that $x-2=y$ is $x=2$.

12. What is the least element in each of the following sets of positive integers?
    (a) $\{p|p$ is a prime$\}$
    (b) $\{n|n$ is a multiple of 6, 12, and 35$\}$
    (c) $\{n|n$ is a multiple of 14 and 15$\}$
    (d) $\{n|4n^2 < 2^n\}$.

2–3   rational numbers

A set of numbers closed with respect to all of the rational operations, except division by zero, is the set of *rational numbers*. A rational number can be expressed as a fraction p/q where p and q are integers and $q \neq 0$. A rational number p/q can be expressed in notations other than the fractional notation. For example, the rational number denoted by the fraction 17/2 can also be written in mixed numeral notation $8\frac{1}{2}$, decimal notation 8.5, and decimal fraction notation 85/10. It is expected that the reader is familiar with these various notations for rational numbers and with the techniques for adding, subtracting, multiplying, and dividing rational numbers using these notations.

Let us consider the method for associating any rational number with a point on the number line. To find the point on the number

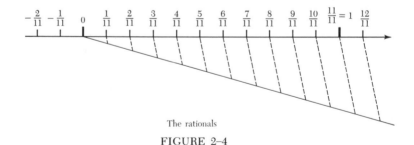

The rationals

FIGURE 2–4

line associated with the rational number 23/11, we divide each of the unit segments (between 0 and 1, between 1 and 2, between 0 and

−1, etc.) into eleven equal segments. Next, since 23/11 is positive, we count twenty-three segments to the right of the origin and associate 23/11 with the right-hand endpoint of the twenty-third such segment. The rational number −23/11 is associated with the left endpoint of the twenty-third such segment to the left of 0. Although this procedure gives a method for associating every rational number with a point on the number line, not every point on the number line has a rational number associated with it. (See Section 2–4.) The points on the number line associated with rational numbers are called *rational points*.

The set Q of rational numbers has the following basic properties:

1. If x and y are in Q, then the sum $x+y$ is a unique number in Q. This is called the *closure property of addition*.

2. If x, y, and z are in Q, then $(x+y)+z=x+(y+z)$. This is called the *associative property of addition*.

3. There is a number in Q, denoted by 0, such that for any x in Q we have $x+0=x$. The number 0 is called the *additive identity*.

4. For every x in Q, there exists a number in Q, denoted by $-x$, such that $x+(-x)=0$. The number $-x$ is called the *additive inverse of x*.

5. If x and y are in Q, then $x+y=y+x$. This is called the *commutative property of addition*.

6. If x and y are in Q, then the product xy is a unique number in Q. This is called the *closure property of multiplication*.

7. If x, y, and z are in Q, then $(xy)z=x(yz)$. This is called the *associative property of multiplication*.

8. There is a number in Q different from 0, denoted by 1, such that for every x in Q we have $x \cdot 1=x$. The number 1 is called the *multiplicative identity*.

9. For every x in Q, except $x=0$, there exists a number in Q, denoted by x^{-1}, such that $x \cdot x^{-1}=1$. The number x^{-1} is called the *multiplicative inverse of x*.

10. If x and y are in Q, then $xy=yx$. This is called the *commutative property of multiplication*.

11. If x, y, and z are in Q, then $x(y+z)=xy+xz$. This is called the *distributive property*.

The word *field* is the special name given to any set having these properties; therefore, the set of rational numbers is often referred to as the *rational number field*. As we shall see later, other sets of numbers have the field properties. It should be noted that the set of integers has all the field properties except Property 9, the existence of multiplicative inverses.

We make certain assumptions about the (undefined) concept of *positiveness* for the set of rational numbers. It is assumed that there is a subset of the set of rational numbers called the set of positive numbers which has the following properties: (1) If x and y are positive, then $x+y$ and xy are positive. (2) The number 0 is not positive. (3) If $x \neq 0$, then x is positive or $-x$ is positive, but not both. A rational number $x \neq 0$ which is not positive is called a *negative* number. Since we have already defined the "less-than" relation in terms of positiveness, we are now able to prove various properties of this relation for rational numbers.

theorem 2–1:   Let a and b be rational numbers. One and only one of the following is true: $a < b$, $a = b$, or $a > b$.

proof: Let $x = (-a) + b$. Thus,

$$a + x = a + [(-a) + b] = [a + (-a)] + b = 0 + b = b.$$

From $a + x = b$, it follows that

$$(a + x) + (-x) = b + (-x)$$
$$a + [x + (-x)] = b + (-x)$$
$$a + 0 = b + (-x).$$

Consequently,

$$a = b + (-x).$$

If $x = 0$, then $a = b$. Furthermore, if $x = 0$, then x is not positive and $-x$ is not positive; hence, $a < b$ and $a > b$ are false. If $x \neq 0$, then x is positive or $-x$ is positive, but not both. If x is positive, $a + x = b$ implies $a < b$ by definition of the less-than relation. If x is negative, then $(-x)$ is positive. From $a = b + (-x)$, we conclude that $a > b$.

If a, b, and c are rational numbers such that $a < b$ and $b < c$, then we may conclude that $a < c$; this is called the *transitive property of inequalities*. We shall prove this property even though the transitive property is geometrically obvious: If a, b, and c are rational points on the number line such that a is to the left of b and b is to the left of c, then a is to the left of c.

theorem 2–2:   If a, b, and c are rational numbers such that $a < b$ and $b < c$, then $a < c$.

proof: Since $a < b$, there is a positive number x such that $a + x = b$. Since $b < c$, there is a positive number y such that $b + y = c$. (The number represented by y is not necessarily different from the number represented by x, but since the numbers may be different it is necessary to use different letters.) Now,

$$(a + x) + y = b + y \qquad \text{since } a + x = b.$$
$$(a + x) + y = c \qquad \text{since } b + y = c.$$
$$a + (x + y) = c \qquad \text{by the associative property.}$$

Since x and y are positive, the sum $(x+y)$ is positive. Hence, $a < c$ as a consequence of the definition of the less-than relation.

Any set having both the trichotomy property and the transitive property of inequality is called an *ordered set*. The set of rational numbers and the set of positive integers are two examples of ordered sets.

Two additional important properties of inequalities are stated in the following theorems.

theorem 2–3: Let a, b, and c represent rational numbers. If $a < b$, then $a + c < b + c$.

proof: Since $a < b$, there is a positive number x such that $a + x = b$. Thus,

$(a+x) + c = b + c$ since $a + x = b$.
$a + (x+c) = b + c$ by the associative property of addition.
$a + (c+x) = b + c$ by the commutative property of addition.
$(a+c) + x = b + c$ by the associative property of addition.

Since x is a positive number, it follows from the definition of the less-than relation that $a + c < b + c$.

Theorem 2–3 states that we can add the same number to both sides of an inequality without changing the validity of the inequality. We now prove that we can multiply both sides of an inequality by the same *positive* number without changing the validity of the inequality.

theorem 2–4: Let a, b, and c represent rational numbers. If $a < b$ and $c > 0$, then $ac < bc$.

proof: Since $a < b$, there is a positive number x such that $a + x = b$. Thus,

$(a+x)c = bc$ since $a + x = b$.
$c(a+x) = bc$ by the commutative property of multiplication.
$ca + cx = bc$ by the distributive property.
$ac + cx = bc$ by the commutative property of multiplication.

Since c and x are positive, the product cx is positive. Hence, it follows from the definition of the less-than relation that $ac < bc$.

An *ordered set* having both the field properties and the properties expressed in Theorems 2–3 and 2–4 is called an *ordered field*. Since the set of rational numbers has the properties of an ordered field, we often speak of the ordered field of rational numbers. Although the set of integers does not have the properties of an ordered field, the set does have the properties stated in Theorems 2–1, 2–2, 2–3, and 2–4.

If P and Q are rational points on the number line with coordinates x and y, respectively, such that $x \leqslant y$, then the non-negative rational number $y - x$ is called the *distance* between P and Q. If P has coordi-

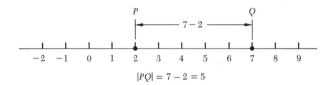

$$|PQ| = 7 - 2 = 5$$

FIGURE 2–5

nate 2 and Q has coordinate 7, then the distance between P and Q. denoted by $|PQ|$, is $7 - 2 = 5$; that is, $|PQ| = 5$.

Let us consider the method for finding the coordinate of the midpoint between two rational points P and Q on the number line. If x and y are the coordinates of two distinct points P and Q, respectively, then, since $x \neq y$, either $x < y$ or $x > y$. There is no loss in generality in assuming that P is to the left of Q on the number line; that is, we assume $x < y$. The distance between P and Q is $y - x$; thus, half the distance is $(y - x)/2$. If M represents the midpoint of the line segment

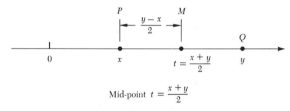

Mid-point $t = \dfrac{x + y}{2}$

FIGURE 2–6

PQ, its coordinate t is given by the sum of x and $(y - x)/2$. Hence,

$$t = x + \frac{(y - x)}{2};$$

thus,

$$t = \frac{x + y}{2}.$$

The coordinate of the midpoint of two points on the number line is half the sum of the two coordinates of the given points. If x and y are rational numbers, then $(x + y)/2$ is a rational number; consequently, there is a rational number between any two different rational numbers. In fact, it follows that there are infinitely many rational numbers between any two given rational numbers; to express this fact, we say the set of rational numbers is *dense*. Although the set of rational numbers is dense, we shall see in the next section that points still exist on the number line that are not associated with rational numbers. However, an important consequence of the density property of the set of rational numbers is that the length of any segment can be approximated to any degree of accuracy by a rational number.

Let us prove that the set of positive rational numbers has the same cardinal number as the set of positive integers. To find a one-to-one correspondence between the set of positive rationals and the set of positive integers, we need only to find some method to "order" the rationals sequentially; that is, if we can discover a method of listing *all* the positive rational numbers so that it will be possible to identify the first, second, or nth in the list, then the set of positive rational numbers will be in one-to-one correspondence with the set of positive integers.

Since every positive rational number may be written as p/q where p and q are integers and $q \neq 0$, we can arrange the positive rationals

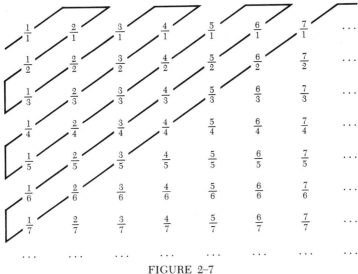

FIGURE 2–7

in an (infinite) rectangular array as in Figure 2–7, where p/q is in the pth column and qth row. For example, the rational 5/6 is in the fifth column and sixth row. Next we write down sequentially the rational numbers obtained by the diagonal process indicated in Figure 2–7; that is, 1/1, 2/1, 1/2, 1/3, 2/2, 3/1, 4/1, 3/2, ... If we delete from this sequence each fraction whose numerator and denominator have a factor other than 1 in common, we obtain the sequence 1/1, 2/1, 1/2, 1/3, 3/1, 4/1, 3/2, 2/3, ... This sequence will contain every positive rational number once and only once. Thus, we could find the rational number corresponding to, say, 106 by finding the 106th term in this sequence. Conversely, we could find the positive integer corresponding to, say, 123/17 by finding which position in the sequence is occupied by 123/17.

Since the set of positive rational numbers can be made to correspond in a one-to-one fashion with the set of positive integers, the cardinal number of the set of positive rationals is the same as the set of positive integers; therefore, the cardinal number of the set of positive rational numbers is $\aleph_0$.

exercises

1. If x is any given rational number, is it true that $x \div x = 1$?

2. Let p and n be positive integers. Is the set of rational numbers of the form $p/2^n$ closed with respect to addition? Subtraction? Multiplication? Division?

3. Find the distance between each of the following pairs of points and give the coordinate of the midpoint of the segment with the two given points as endpoints.
   (a) 11 and −17
   (b) 2/3 and 11/3
   (c) $2\frac{1}{3}$ and $-4\frac{5}{8}$
   (d) 5/7 and −13/3

4. Let points P, Q, and R have coordinates 3, $7\frac{2}{3}$, and $-4\frac{1}{5}$ respectively.
   (a) Is $|PQ| + |QR| = |PR|$?
   (b) Under what conditions is $|AB| + |BC| = |AC|$ for any three different points, A, B, and C on the coordinate line? (Consider all possible arrangements of points.)
   (c) Is it true that $|AB| + |BC| \geqslant AC$ for any three points on the coordinate line?

5. If x and y are rational numbers such that $x < y$, prove that $(2x + y)/3$ is the coordinate of the point one-third the distance from the point with coordinate x to the point with coordinate y.

6. Let P and Q be two rational points with coordinates x and y, respectively, such that $x < y$. If the line segment PQ is divided into five equal segments, what are the coordinates of the division points?

7. Let P and Q be two rational points with coordinates x and y, respectively, such that $x < y$. If the line segment PQ is divided into n equal segments where n is a positive integer greater than 1, find the coordinate of the point at the end of the kth segment from P. See Exercises 5 and 6.

8. List the fifteen basic properties of the ordered field of rational numbers.

9. Is $-3/5 > -16/27$? Justify your answer.

10. Prove if a and b are rational numbers such that $a < b$, then $a - c < b - c$.

11. Prove if a, b, and c are rational numbers such that $a + c < b + c$, then $a < b$.

12. Is the following true? For rational numbers a, b, and c, if $ac < bc$ then $a < b$. Justify your answer.

13. Assume a, b, c, and d are integers. Prove that if a rational number x/y exists such that $a/b + x/y = c/d$ then $(xbd)/y$ is an integer.

14. (a) Exhibit a one-to-one correspondence (different from the one given in this section) between the set of positive rationals and the set of positive integers. (*Hint:* 1/1, 2/1, 2/2, 3/1, 3/2, 3/3, 4/1, 4/2, 4/3, 4/4, 5/1, 5/2, 5/3, 5/4, 5/5, 6/1, 6/2, 6/3, 6/4, 6/5, 6/6, etc.) After each term in your correspondence insert its multiplicative inverse.
   (b) In your correspondence, what rational corresponds to 25?
   (c) In your correspondence, what integer corresponds to 3/8?

2–4   real numbers

In arithmetic, the basic operations are the rational operations. In algebra, the additional operation of taking roots is introduced. The operations of addition, subtraction, multiplication, division, and extracting roots are called the *algebraic operations*.

Prior to the second century B.C., Euclid proved that no rational number exists whose square is 2; that is, no rational number x exists such that $x^2 = 2$. To prove this fact, we assume there *is* a rational number whose square is 2 and show this assumption leads to a contradiction. In other words, we give an indirect proof.

theorem 2–5:   There is no rational number whose square is 2.

proof: (Recall that any rational number can be expressed as a fraction in lowest terms; that is, any rational number can be expressed in the form p/q where p and q are integers, q is not zero, and p and q have no common factors except 1.)

Assume that there is a rational number whose square is 2. Let p/q be the fraction in lowest terms representing this number. Thus,

$$\left(\frac{p}{q}\right)^2 = 2.$$

Hence,

$$p^2 = 2q^2. \tag{A}$$

Since q is an integer, q^2 is an integer and $2q^2$ is an even integer. Since $p^2 = 2q^2$, p^2 is even. (Since the square of every odd integer is odd, p is an even integer.) Since p is even, it can be expressed as $p = 2t$ where t is some integer. Substituting in Equation (A),

$$(2t)^2 = 2q^2$$
$$4t^2 = 2q^2$$
$$2t^2 = q^2.$$

Since $2t^2$ is an even integer, by an argument similar to the one above we conclude that q is an even integer. Therefore, p and q have a common factor of 2, a contradiction to our original assumption. Hence, our assumption that there is a rational number whose square is 2 is false; the theorem is proved.

We use "$\sqrt{2}$" to denote the positive *irrational* (not rational) number whose square is 2. Irrational numbers arise naturally in geometry; for example, $\sqrt{2}$ is the length of the hypotenuse of an isosceles right triangle having the remaining two sides each one unit in length. The number π is also an irrational number; this is not easy to prove. It can be proved that if n is not a perfect square, no rational square root of n exists; for any integer that is not a perfect cube, no rational cube root exists; etc. Thus, $\sqrt{5}$, $\sqrt[3]{11}$, $\sqrt[5]{17}$, $\sqrt[8]{39}$, and $\sqrt[9]{41}$ are irrational numbers. It follows from the above statement that the set of irrational numbers does not contain a finite number of elements; it is an *infinite set*.

In high school, we learned how to perform various operations on irrational numbers; no attempt is made here to give a precise definition of these numbers or to prove the various stated properties. Although irrational numbers played a useful role in the development of both geometry and algebra, it was not until the nineteenth century that a satisfactory definition of irrational numbers was given; this was first accomplished by the German mathematician Richard Dedekind (1831–1916). Other mathematicians have since given different methods to develop the irrational numbers. The reader should look forward to studying one or more of these rigorous developments of the number system. (See Bevan K Youse, *The Number System*, Dickenson Publishing Company, Inc., 1965.)

The set consisting of all the rational and irrational numbers is called the set of *real numbers*; that is, the set of real numbers is the union of the set of rational numbers and the set of irrational numbers. It can be proved that the set of real numbers has the properties of an ordered field. The real numbers are assumed to be in one-to-one correspondence with the points on the number line; that is, it is assumed that there is exactly one point on the number line associated with every real number, and exactly one real number associated with every point on the number line. The number line, then, is a graphic representation of the set of real numbers.

The set of real numbers is an infinite set; but what is the cardinal number of this infinite set? If the set of real numbers can be put into one-to-one correspondence with the set of positive integers, then, by our definition of transfinite cardinals, the set of real numbers would have cardinal number $\aleph_0$. However, the set of real numbers does not have cardinal number $\aleph_0$; the proof of this fact is rather subtle but not extremely difficult. (See Courant and Robbins, *What Is Mathematics?* Oxford University Press, 1941, pp. 79–83.)

2–5 completeness property

As already indicated, both the set of real numbers and the set of rational numbers have the properties of an ordered field. Let us now consider the important differences between these two ordered fields. First, there is a proper subset of the set of real numbers (namely, the set of rational numbers) having the ordered field properties; no proper subset of the set of rational numbers has the properties of an ordered field. Second, the set of real numbers has what is called the *completeness property*; the set of rational numbers does not have this property. Let us consider this second important distinguishing property of the set of real numbers.

Let S be a subset of any set F of numbers having the properties of an ordered field. Suppose there exists a number $t \in F$ such that $x \leqslant t$ for every x in S; then, the number t is called an *upper bound* for the set S. For example, if $S = \{1/3, 10, -3, 26\}$, then since every number in S is less than 38 we conclude that 38 is an upper bound of S; 43 and 26 are also upper bounds of S. If $T = \{x|x \text{ is real and } x < 3\}$, then any real number greater than or equal to 3 is an upper bound of T. If $W = \{x|x \text{ is real and } x \leqslant 3\}$, then any real number greater than or equal to 3 is an upper bound of W. Note that the set of upper bounds for the two different sets T and W is the same.

definition: If the set of upper bounds of a set S has a least number z in it, then z is said to be the *least upper bound of S*.

In other words, if $S \subseteq F$, then a number z is the least upper bound of S, expressed by $z = \text{lub } S$, if and only if the following are true:
  (i) z is an upper bound of S.
  (ii) If t is any upper bound of S, then $z \leqslant t$.
In the three preceding examples, the least upper bound of set S is 26, the least upper bound of T is 3, and the least upper bound of W is 3. It should be noted that the least upper bound of a given set may or may not be a member of the set.

A set of numbers need not have an upper bound. For example, consider the set of positive integers or the set of rational numbers; neither of these sets has an upper bound. If a set of real numbers does have an upper bound, then the set has a least upper bound. This is assured by the completeness property of the real numbers.

completeness property: For every non-empty set of real numbers with an upper bound, a least upper bound exists.

In the further study of mathematics, the importance of the completeness property will become evident; we must be satisfied now with the fact that this property is an important distinguishing feature between the set of rational and set of real numbers. Although we assume the set of real numbers has the completeness property, we prove that a bounded set of rational numbers need not have a rational least upper bound.

Let $S = \{x | x$ is a positive rational and $x^2 < 2\}$. This set is not empty since, for example, 1 is in S. The set has an upper bound; for example, 3 is an upper bound of S. We now prove the assumption that S has a rational number as a least upper bound leads to a contradiction.

Suppose z is the *rational* least upper bound of S. If z is in S, then by definition of S we conclude that z is positive and $z^2 < 2$. If

$$z^2 < 2,$$

then

$$z^2 + 2 < 4$$

by adding 2 to both sides. Thus,

$$(z^2 + 2)z < 4z$$

by multiplying by a positive number z. Dividing by the positive number $z^2 + 2$,

$$z < \frac{4z}{z^2 + 2}.$$

If we let

$$t = \frac{4z}{z^2 + 2},$$

then t is a rational number such that $z < t$. Furthermore,

$$\begin{aligned}
2 - t^2 &= 2 - \frac{16z^2}{(z^2 + 2)^2} \\
&= \frac{2(z^2 + 2)^2 - 16z^2}{(z^2 + 2)^2} \\
&= \frac{2}{(z^2 + 2)^2} \cdot (z^4 + 4z^2 + 4 - 8z^2) \\
&= \frac{2(z^2 - 2)^2}{(z^2 + 2)^2}.
\end{aligned}$$

Since

$$\frac{2(z^2 - 2)^2}{(z^2 + 2)^2}$$

is positive, $2 - t^2 > 0$. Hence $t^2 < 2$, and we conclude that t is in S. Furthermore, since t is *greater* than z, this contradicts the assumption that the least upper bound z is in S. If z is the least upper bound but not in S, then z is a positive number such that $z^2 = 2$ or $z^2 > 2$. Since we proved that no rational number has 2 as its square, the only remaining possibility for the rational least upper bound z is that $z^2 > 2$. If $z^2 > 2$, then $2z^2 > 2 + z^2$ by adding z^2 to both sides. Hence,

$$z > \frac{2+z^2}{2z}$$

by dividing by the positive number $2z$. If we let

$$u = \frac{2+z^2}{2z},$$

then u is a positive rational number and $u < z$. If we can show that $u^2 > 2$, then u would be an upper bound of S less than the (assumed) least upper bound z; this is impossible.

$$\begin{aligned} u^2 - 2 &= \frac{(2+z^2)^2}{4z^2} - 2 \\ &= \frac{4 + 4z^2 + z^4 - 8z^2}{4z^2} \\ &= \frac{(2-z^2)^2}{4z^2}, \quad \text{a positive number.} \end{aligned}$$

Thus, $u^2 - 2 > 0$ and $u^2 > 2$. We have proved if the set S had a rational number z as a least upper bound, then the rational number z^2 is not less than 2, equal to 2, nor greater than 2; this contradicts the trichotomy property for the rational numbers. Hence, the set S has no rational number as a least upper bound.

The set T of positive *real numbers* whose squares are less than 2 has an upper bound and by the axiom of completeness has a least upper bound. In fact, the least upper bound is the irrational (real) number $\sqrt{2}$.

exercises

1. Prove that there is no rational number whose square is 3. (You may use the fact that if p is a prime factor of the product ab where a and b are integers, then p is a factor of a or p is a factor of b.)

2. If $T = \{x \mid x$ is a positive rational and $x^2 < 3\}$, prove that T does not have a rational number as a least upper bound.

   Hint: Assume z is the rational least upper bound and let

   $$t = \frac{6z}{z^2 + 3} \quad \text{and} \quad u = \frac{z^2 + 3}{2z}.$$

*3. Prove that z is the least upper bound of a set S if and only if the following are true: (i) z is an upper bound of S, (ii) for any $a > 0$, there exists an $x \in S$ such that $x > z - a$.

*4. Let S be a set of real numbers. Assume there is a real number t such that $x \geq t$ for every x in S; the number t is called a *lower bound* of S. If T is the set of all lower bounds of S and if T contains a greatest number u, then u is called the greatest lower bound of S. Prove that a non-empty set of real numbers S with a lower bound has a greatest lower bound. Hint:

Let $W=\{-x \,|\, x \in S\}$ and prove that if t is a lower bound of S then it is an upper bound of W. Use the completeness property.

2–6   ordered field properties (optional)

In this section, we exhibit that various properties of the rational and real numbers are consequences of the ordered field properties. We assume only that we have a set F with the following properties:

1. *Addition.* For every pair x and y in F, an element in F called the sum is uniquely determined; it is denoted by $x+y$.

2. *Commutative property of addition.* $x+y=y+x$ for every x and y in F.

3. *Associative property of addition.* $x+(y+z)=(x+y)+z$ for every x, y, and z in F.

4. *Additive identity.* There exists an element in F, denoted by 0 and called an additive identity, such that $x+0=x$ for every x in F.

5. *Additive inverses.* For every element x in F, there exists an element y in F called an additive inverse of x such that $x+y=0$.

6. *Multiplication.* For every x and y in F, an element in F called the product is uniquely determined; it is denoted by xy, or $x \cdot y$.

7. *Commutative property of multiplication.* $xy=yx$ for every x and y in F.

8. *Associative property of multiplication.* $x(yz)=(xy)z$ for every x, y, and z in F.

9. *Multiplicative identity.* There exists an element in F, distinct from 0 and denoted by 1, called a multiplicative identity such that $x \cdot 1=x$ for every x in F.

10. *Multiplicative inverses.* For every element $x \neq 0$ in F, there exists an element y in F called a multiplicative inverse of x such that $xy=1$.

11. *Distributive property.* $x(y+z)=xy+xz$ for every x, y, and z in F.

12. There is a subset of F whose elements are called positive for which the following are true: (a) If x and y are positive, then $x+y$ and xy are positive. (b) The element 0 is not positive. (c) If $x \neq 0$, then x is positive or $-x$ is positive, but not both.

The less-than relation is defined in F in terms of the positive elements (as we have done earlier). Since these assumptions are generalizations of the properties of the set of rational numbers, the trichotomy (Theorem 2–1) and transitive (Theorem 2–2) properties of inequality and Theorems 2–3 and 2–4 are immediate consequences of them. We now turn our attention to proving other properties of an ordered field.

theorem 2–6:   There is only one additive identity in a set with the field properties.

proof: Let 0 and 0^* be additive identities. Then $0+0^*=0$ since 0^* is an additive identity, and $0+0^*=0^*$ since 0 is an additive identity. Consequently, $0=0^*$; the additive identity is unique.

theorem 2–7: There is only one multiplicative identity in a set with the field properties.

proof: Left as an exercise for the student.

theorem 2–8: *Cancellation property of addition.* Let x, y, and z be elements in a field. If $x+z=y+z$, then $x=y$.

proof: Let t be an additive inverse of z; thus, $z+t=0$.

Since $x+z=y+z$, we have

$$(x+z)+t=(y+z)+t$$

and

$$x+(z+t)=y+(z+t) \qquad \text{by the associative property.}$$

Hence,

$$x+0=y+0$$

and

$$x=y.$$

theorem 2–9: *Cancellation property of multiplication.* Let x, y, and z be elements in the field. If $xz=yz$ and $z\neq 0$, then $x=y$.

proof: Left as an exercise for the student.

theorem 2–10: For any element x in a field, there is only one additive inverse of x.

proof: Assume s and t are additive inverses of x. Then,

$$x+s=0$$

and

$$x+t=0.$$

Thus,

$$x+s=x+t$$

and

$$s=t \qquad \text{by the commutative property of addition and Theorem 2–8.}$$

theorem 2–11: For any $x\neq 0$ in a field, there is only one multiplicative inverse of x.

proof: Left as an exercise for the student.

theorem 2–12: Let x and y be elements of an ordered field and let $-x$ and $-y$ be their additive inverses, respectively. If $x<y$, then $-x>-y$.

proof: Left as an exercise for the student.

theorem 2–13: If x is any element of a field, then $x\cdot 0=0$.

proof: Since
$$0+0=0,$$
$$x(0+0)=x \cdot 0.$$
But,
$$0+x \cdot 0 = x \cdot 0 \qquad \text{since 0 is the additive}$$
Thus,   identity.
$$x \cdot 0 + x \cdot 0 = 0 + x \cdot 0$$

and
$$x \cdot 0 = 0 \qquad \text{by Theorem 2–8.}$$

theorem 2–14:   If x and y are elements of a field, then $(x)(-y) = -(xy)$.

proof: Since $y+(-y)=0$, we conclude that
$$x[y+(-y)] = x \cdot 0.$$
Then, by the distributive property and Theorem 2–13
$$xy + x(-y) = 0.$$
Since xy is an element of the field, it has an additive inverse $-(xy)$ such that
$$xy + (-(xy)) = 0.$$
Hence,
$$xy + x(-y) = xy + (-(xy)).$$
Consequently,
$$x(-y) = -(xy) \qquad \text{by the commutative property of}$$
addition and Theorem 2–8.

It should be noted that Theorem 2–14 does not say that the product of a positive and negative number is negative. Rather, it states that a given number times the additive inverse of a second number is the additive inverse of the product of the two numbers. Of course, if x and y are positive numbers, $-y$ is negative and $-xy$ is negative.

theorem 2–15:   Let x, y, and z be elements of an ordered field. If $x < y$ and $z < 0$, then $xz > yz$.

proof: If $z < 0$, then $-z > 0$. If $x < y$ and $-z > 0$, then
$$x(-z) < y(-z)$$
by Theorem 2–4. By Theorem 2–14,
$$-xz < -yz,$$
and by Theorem 2–12,
$$xz > yz.$$

theorem 2–16: Let x be an element of an ordered field. If $x \neq 0$, then $x^2 > 0$.

proof: If $x \neq 0$, then $x < 0$ or $x > 0$ by the trichotomy property. If $x > 0$, then $x^2 > x \cdot 0$ by Theorem 2–4 and $x^2 > 0$ by Theorem 2–13. If $x < 0$, then $x^2 > 0$ by Theorems 2–15 and 2–13.

We call any element t of an ordered field positive if and only if $t > 0$; thus, Theorem 2–16 states that the square of any element different from 0 in an ordered field is positive.

exercises

1. Prove that if x and y are elements of a field and if $xy = 0$, then $x = 0$ or $y = 0$.

2. Prove Theorem 2–7.

3. Prove Theorem 2–9.

4. Prove Theorem 2–11.

5. Prove Theorem 2–12.

6. Prove that if x and y be elements of a field, then $(-x)\,(-y) = xy$.

7. Prove that $1 > 0$.

8. Let x and y be elements of an ordered field. Prove that if $x > 0$ and $y > 0$, then $xy > 0$.

Prove each of the following implications:

9. If x^{-1} is the multiplicative inverse of x and if $x > 0$, then $x^{-1} > 0$.

10. If $x > 0$, $y > 0$, and $x < y$, then $1/x > 1/y$ where $1/x = x^{-1}$, and $1/y = y^{-1}$.

11. If $x < y$ and $w < z$, then $x + w < y + z$.

12. If $x > 0$, $y > 0$, $w > 0$, $z > 0$, $x < y$, and $w < z$, then $xw < yz$.

13. If x is an element of a field and $x \neq 0$, prove that the multiplicative inverse of x^{-1} is x.

14. If x is an element of a field, prove that $-(-x) = x$.

15. If $x < 0$, $y < 0$, and $x < y$, then $1/x > 1/y$.

inequalities and absolute value

3

In Chapter 2 we discussed various properties of the less-than relation for an ordered field. Below is a partial list of the most important of these properties. Let a, b, and c be real numbers.

1. One and only one of the following is true: $a < b$, $a = b$, or $a > b$.
2. If $a < b$ and $b < c$, then $a < c$.
3. If $a < b$, then $a + c < b + c$ and $a - c < b - c$.
4. If $a < b$ and $c > 0$, then $ac < bc$.
5. If $a > 0$ and $b > 0$, then $ab > 0$. If $a < 0$ and $b < 0$, then $ab > 0$.
6. If $a < b$ and if $ab > 0$, then $1/a > 1/b$.
7. If $a < b$ and $c < d$, then $a + c < b + d$.
8. If $a < b$ and $c < 0$, then $ac > bc$.
9. If $a \neq 0$, then $a^2 > 0$.
10. If $a > 0$, $b > 0$, $c > 0$, $d > 0$, $a < b$, and $c < d$, then $ac < bd$.

The set of real numbers greater than 2 and less than 5 is equivalent, geometrically, to all the points on the number line between 2 and 5.

This set of real numbers x such that $x > 2$ and $x < 5$ is called an *open interval* and it is denoted by $2 < x < 5$, or by $(2, 5)$; 2 and 5 are called

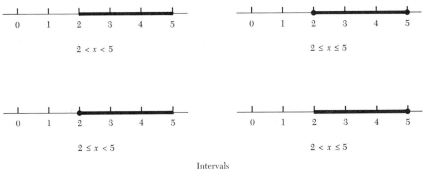

Intervals

FIGURE 3–1

the *endpoints of the interval.* The collection of points on the number line with coordinates less than 5 and greater than 2 is called the *graph* of the open interval. In general, if $a < b$, then the open interval with a and b as endpoints is $\{x | a < x < b\}$.

The set of all real numbers x such that $x \geq 2$ and $x \leq 5$ is called a *closed interval.* This closed interval is denoted by $2 \leq x \leq 5$, or by $[2, 5]$. In general, $[c, d] = \{x | c \leq x \leq d\}$. The set of real numbers x such that $2 \leq x < 5$ (or $2 < x \leq 5$) is neither a closed nor an open interval; it is sometimes called a half-open interval. The set of all real numbers not in the closed interval $[2, 5]$ is the set of all x such that $x < 2$ *or* $x > 5$; this set is not an interval and the interval notation is not used. Sometimes the set of real numbers less than 2 is denoted by $(-\infty, 2)$ and the set of real numbers greater than 5 is denoted by $(5, +\infty)$. Thus, the set of real numbers not in the closed interval $[2, 5]$ can be denoted by $(-\infty, 2) \cup (5, +\infty)$.

An inequality such as $2x + 1 < 7$ is often called a *conditional inequality* since the truth of the inequality depends on the number that x represents. The *solution set* of a conditional inequality is the set of numbers that makes the inequality a true statement. This is similar to the concept of the solution set of a conditional equality (conditional equation) such as $2x + 1 = 7$. Finding the solution set of a linear inequality such as $2x + 1 < 7$ is similar to finding the solution set of the linear equation $2x + 1 = 7$.

If there is any real number x satisfying $2x + 1 < 7$, then this real number satisfies the inequality $2x < 6$. We multiply both sides of the inequality by the positive number $1/2$; any number satisfying the inequality $2x < 6$ also satisfies the inequality $x < 3$. Therefore, we have proved that any number satisfying $2x + 1 < 7$ satisfies $x < 3$. Since all the steps in our proof are "reversible," it is true that if $x < 3$ then $2x + 1 < 7$. Hence, the solution set of the conditional inequality is $\{x|x<3\}$; this solution set may also be denoted by $(-\infty, 3)$.

To find the solution set of the inequality $x+(1/x) \geqslant 2$, we proceed as follows. Obviously, $x \neq 0$. If $x < 0$, then $1/x < 0$ and the sum $x+1/x$ is negative; thus, since $x+(1/x)$ is to be positive, there are no negative solutions. Assume there is a positive x such that

$$x+\frac{1}{x} \geqslant 2;$$

thus,

$$x^2+1 \geqslant 2x.$$

Consequently,

$$x^2-2x+1 \geqslant 0,$$
$$(x-1)^2 \geqslant 0.$$

Since any real number squared is non-negative and since the steps in the argument are reversible provided x is positive, we conclude that the solution set is the set of positive real numbers; that is, the solution set is $\{x|x>0\}$.

To find the solution set of the inequality

$$(3x+1)^2-2x > 9x^2+4x+11,$$

we proceed as follows. If there is a real number x such that

$$(3x+1)^2-2x > 9x^2+4x+11,$$

then

$$9x^2+6x+1-2x > 9x^2+4x+11.$$

Consequently, $1 > 11$. Since we have *proved* that $1 > 11$ if there is any real number satisfying the given inequality, we conclude that there is no real number satisfying the inequality. Hence, the solution set is the empty set $\emptyset$.

examples

1. Find the solution set of $3x-17 > 8x+14$.

> *Solution:*　　$3x-17 > 8x+14$
>
> $3x-8x > 17+14$
>
> $-5x > 31$
>
> $x < -31/5.$

The solution set is all real numbers less than $-31/5$: symbolically, $\{x|x<-31/5\}$.

2. Solve　　$\dfrac{3x+1}{x} \leqslant 1.$

Solution: Obviously $x \neq 0$; dividing the numerator by the denominator on the left side of the inequality, we obtain the following.

$$3 + 1/x \leq 1.$$

Thus,
$$1/x \leq -2.$$

Since there are obviously no positive numbers satisfying $1/x \leq -2$, assume $x < 0$. Thus, by Property 6, page 32, $x \geq -1/2$; the solution set is $\{x | -1/2 \leq x < 0\}$.

3. Solve $\dfrac{7x+2}{x} < 5.$

Solution: (Although this inequality is similar to Example 2, we exhibit another method used to solve this type of inequality.) Obviously, $x \neq 0$.

I. $\dfrac{7x+2}{x} < 5.$

II. $\dfrac{7x+2}{x} < 5.$

If $x > 0$, then multiplying both sides of the inequality by x, we obtain

$$7x + 2 < 5x.$$

Hence,
$$2x < -2$$
and
$$x < -1.$$

We have proved that if x is positive and satisfies the inequality, then $x < -1$, a contradiction. Thus, the inequality has no positive solutions.

If $x < 0$, then multiplying both sides of the inequality by x, we obtain

$$7x + 2 > 5x.$$

Hence,
$$2x > -2,$$
and
$$x > -1.$$

If $x > -1$, and $x < 0$, then the steps are reversible; consequently, negative real numbers greater than -1 satisfy the inequality. The solution set is $\{x | -1 < x < 0\}$.

4. Solve $\dfrac{5x+2}{3x-11} < 3.$

First solution:

I. Assume $3x - 11 > 0$.

Thus, $5x + 2 < 9x - 33$

$$-4x < -35$$

$$x > \frac{35}{4}.$$

Since $3x - 11 > 0$, $x > 11/3$. Any real numbers that make both $x > 35/4$ and $x > 11/3$ true statements will satisfy the given inequality. Hence, any real number greater than the larger of the two will be a solution.

$$x > \frac{35}{4}$$

II. Assume $3x - 11 < 0$.

Thus, $5x + 2 > 9x - 33$

$$-4x > -35$$

$$x < \frac{35}{4}.$$

Since $3x - 11 < 0$, $x < 11/3$. Any real numbers that make both $x < 35/4$ and $x < 11/3$ true statements will satisfy the given inequality. Hence, any real number less than the smaller of the two will be a solution.

or $$x < \frac{11}{3}.$$

Second solution:

$\dfrac{5x+2}{3x-11} < 3$ if and only if $\dfrac{5x+2}{3x-11} - 3 < 0.$

$$\frac{5x+2-9x+33}{3x-11} < 0$$

$$\frac{-4x+35}{3x-11} < 0$$

The quotient is negative if and only if either

$-4x+35 < 0 \quad and \;\; 3x-11 > 0 \quad or \quad -4x+35 > 0 \quad and \;\; 3x-11 < 0$
$-4x < -35 \;\; and 3x > 11 \quad -4x > -35 \;\; and 3x < 11$
$x > \dfrac{35}{4} \;\; and x > \dfrac{11}{3}. \quad x < \dfrac{35}{4} \;\; and x < \dfrac{11}{3}.$

The numbers that make both $x > 35/4$ and $x > 11/3$ true statements are those such that

$$x > \frac{35}{4}.$$

The numbers that make both $x < 35/4$ and $x < 11/3$ true statements are those such that

$$x < \frac{11}{3}.$$

Solution set: $\{x \mid x > \dfrac{35}{4} \text{ or } x < \dfrac{11}{3}\}.$

5. Solve

$$-\frac{1}{10} < \frac{x+1}{x} - \frac{4}{3} < \frac{1}{10}.$$

Solution:

$$-1/10 \;\; < 1+\frac{1}{x}-\frac{4}{3} < \;\; 1/10$$

$$-1/10 \;\; < \;\; \frac{1}{x}-\frac{1}{3} \;\; < \;\; 1/10$$

$$1/3-1/10 < \;\; 1/x \;\; < 1/3+1/10$$

$$7/30 \;\; < \;\; 1/x \;\; < \;\; 13/30.$$

Since $1/x$ must be positive to satisfy this inequality, we use the fact that if $0 < a < b$, then $1/a > 1/b$.
Thus,

$$30/7 > x > 30/13.$$

The solution set is

$$\{x \mid \frac{30}{13} < x < \frac{30}{7}\}.$$

6. Find a positive real number d such that if $-d < x-2 < d$, then $-0.1 < (3x+1)-7 < 0.1.$

Solution: We first find what real numbers satisfy $-0.1 < (3x+1)-7 < 0.1.$

$$-0.1 < (3x+1) - 7 < 0.1.$$
$$-0.1 < 3x - 6 < 0.1$$
$$5.9 < 3x < 6.1$$
$$59/30 < x < 61/30.$$

Subtracting 2,

$$-1/30 < x - 2 < 1/30.$$

Since all steps are reversible, if $d = 1/30$, then all x satisfying $-1/30 < x$ $-2 < 1/30$ also satisfies $-0.1 < (3x+1) -7 < 0.1$. Of course, any positive real number less than $1/30$ would be a solution. (The solution could be simplified considerably by noting that division of the first inequality by 3 gives the desired solution.)

exercises

Solve each of the inequalities in Exercises 1 through 13.

1. $3x + 17 < x + 12$

2. $5x - 16 < 15x + 11$

3. $x + 2/3 \geqslant 3/4 + 11x$

4. $\dfrac{2x+1}{x} \leqslant 5$

5. $(3x+1)(2x-5) < 0$

6. $(3x+2)(2x-1) < 0$

7. $\dfrac{6x+11}{17x+2} > 0$

8. $\dfrac{3x+1}{2x-5} > 6$

9. $\dfrac{8x+3}{2x} < 2$

10. $\dfrac{3x+7}{5x-6} < -3$

11. $\dfrac{2x+13}{5x-2} < \dfrac{2x+7}{5x+1}$

12. $\dfrac{3x+6}{3x-1} < \dfrac{3x-5}{3x+8}$

13. $(3x+2)(5x-4)(x+8) > 0$

14. Find a positive real number d such that if $-d < x-3 < d$, then $-1/100 < (2x+5) - 11 < 1/100$.

*15. Find a real number $d < 0$ such that if $-d < x-3 < d$ then $-1/100 < \dfrac{x+1}{x} - \dfrac{4}{3}$ $< 1/100$. (See Example 4.)

3-2 absolute value

If P is a point on the number line with x as coordinate and if $x > 0$, then the distance of P from the origin is x. If P is to the left of the origin, then its coordinate x is less than 0; the distance of P from the origin in this case is $0 - x = -x$. (Note that $-x$ is positive.) If P is any point on the number line with x as coordinate, then the distance of P from the origin is called the *absolute value* of x and it is denoted by $|x|$. More precisely, the absolute value of a real number x is defined as follows:

definition: For any real number x,

$$|x| = x \text{ if } x \geqslant 0$$

and

$$|x| = -x \text{ if } x < 0.$$

It follows from the definition that the absolute value of any real number is not negative.

If T is the set of real numbers x such that $|x| < 3$, then each number in T represents a point whose distance from the origin is less than 3. In other words, T is the set of all x such that $-3 < x < 3$. In general, if a is any positive real number, then the set of real numbers x such that $|x| < a$ is the open interval $-a < x < a$. Similarly, the real numbers x such that $|x| \leqslant a$ is the closed interval $-a \leqslant x \leqslant a$.

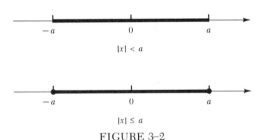

$$|x| < a$$

$$|x| \leqslant a$$

FIGURE 3-2

If P and Q are two points on the number line with coordinates x and y, respectively, the non-negative number $|x - y|$ is the distance between P and Q. This follows from our definitions of absolute value and of distance between two points on the number line since if $x \leqslant y$ then $|x - y| = -(x - y) = y - x$ and if $y \leqslant x$ then $|x - y| = x - y$.

Let us consider the set of real numbers x satisfying the inequality $|x - 3| < 5$; this is the set of real numbers x satisfying $-5 < x - 3 < 5$. Hence,

$$-5 < x - 3 \quad \text{and} \quad x - 3 < 5;$$
$$-2 < x \qquad \text{and} \quad x \quad < 8.$$

That is,
$$-2 < x < 8.$$

Geometrically, $|x-3|$ represents the distance between the points whose coordinates are x and 3, and the real numbers satisfying $|x-3| < 5$ are the coordinates of all the points on the number line whose distances from 3 are less than 5. Hence, the solution set of $|x-3| < 5$ represents the points in the open interval $-2 < x < 8$.

Any real number x satisfying the inequality $|x+8| < 11$ also satisfies $-11 < x+8 < 11$. Hence, the open interval $-19 < x < 3$ is the solution set. Since $|x+8| = |x-(-8)|$, the real numbers satisfying $|x+8| < 11$ are the same as those satisfying $|x-(-8)| < 11$. Geometrically, this represents the set of real numbers whose distances from -8 are less than 11; that is, the open interval $-19 < x < 3$.

The real numbers x such that $|x| > 5$ represents the points on the number line whose distances from the origin are greater than 5; thus, if $|x| > 5$, then $x > 5$ or $x < -5$. The solution set of $|x| > 5$ is not an interval; it is $(-\infty, -5) \cup (5, +\infty)$, the union of two disjoint sets.

$$|x| > 5$$

FIGURE 3–3

Consider the set of real numbers x such that $|x-3| > 5$. This is the set of real numbers x such that either $x-3 > 5$ or $x-3 < -5$; that is, $x > 8$ or $x < -2$. Geometrically, the solution set of $|x-3| > 5$ represents all the points on the number line whose distances from 3 are greater than 5.

Since $|x| = -x$ if $x \le 0$ and $|x| = x$ if $x \ge 0$, we have $-|x| = x$ if $x \le 0$ and $x = |x|$ if $x \ge 0$. Hence, for any real number x we conclude

$$-|x| \le x \le |x|. \tag{A}$$

Similarly, for any real number y we conclude

$$-|y| \le y \le |y|. \tag{B}$$

Consequently, by adding inequalities (A) and (B),

$$-(|x| + |y|) \le x + y \le (|x| + |y|);$$

this is equivalent to the inequality

$$|x+y| \le |x| + |y|$$

since $-t < s < t$ for $t > 0$ is equivalent to $|s| < t$. The inequality $|x+y| \le |x| + |y|$ is called the *triangular inequality*; the triangular inequality is used in the proof of many important mathematical theorems.

1. Graph the solution sets of each of the following inequalities.

   (a) $|x| < 6$ (b) $|x| \geq 3$ (c) $|x-5| < 7$
   (d) $|3x-5| < 13$ (e) $|x+3| \geq 6$ (f) $|5x+7| \geq 2$

2. Prove if a and b are real numbers then $|a| \cdot |b| = |ab|$.

3. Prove if a and b are real numbers and $b \neq 0$ then $|a| / |b| = |a/b|$.

4. Prove if $a < c < b$ and $a < d < b$ then $|c-d| < b-a$. Interpret geometrically.

   Find the solution sets in Exercises 5 through 13 if x is a variable on the set of real numbers.

5. $|x+4| = 7$

6. $|3x+11| = 4$

7. $|5x-17| = 13$

8. $|x+1| + |x| = 7$

9. (a) $|x+1| + |x| > 3$ (b) $|3-x| + |2x+1| < 2$

10. (a) $|2x+3| - |3x+1| = 15$ (b) $|3x-2| + |3x+1| = 3$

11. $|x^2+4| + |x^2+9| > 10$

12. $|x+1| \, |x-3| = 2$

13. $|2x-1| \, |3x+5| > 14$

14. Find a positive real number d such that $|x-5| < d$ implies $|(3x+1) - 16| < t$ where t is any positive real number.

15. Find a real number d such that $|x-3| < d$ implies

$$\left| \frac{2x+5}{x} - \frac{11}{3} \right| < t$$

   where $0 < t < 5/3$.

16. If x and y are real numbers, prove $|x| - |y| \leq |x-y|$. Hint: $x = y + (x-y)$. Use triangular inequality.

17. If x and y are real numbers, prove $|x| - |y| \leq |x+y|$.

18. If x and y are real numbers, prove $| \, |x| - |y| \, | \leq |x-y|$.

19. Prove that $|x|^2 = x^2$.

20. Is $\sqrt{x^2} = |x|$? Justify your answer.

relations and functions

4

We shall now consider sets whose elements are ordered pairs of real numbers. An *ordered pair* is denoted by (x, y); the element x is called the *first coordinate* and the element y is called the *second coordinate*. The ordered pair (x, y) is defined to be equal to the ordered pair (u, v) if and only if $x = u$ and $y = v$.

The set S of ordered pairs of real numbers whose coordinates satisfy the equation $2x + y = 7$ is often denoted by

$$S = \{(x, y) \mid x \text{ and } y \text{ are real numbers and } 2x + y = 7\}$$

read "S is the set of ordered pairs (x, y) such that x and y are real numbers and $2x + y = 7$." Since $2(3) + 1 = 7$, the ordered pair $(3, 1)$ is an element in S. The set S contains an infinite number of ordered pairs of real numbers; for example, $(1, 5) \in S$, $(0, 7) \in S$, $(7/2, 0) \in S$, $(\sqrt{3}, 7 - 2\sqrt{3}) \in S$, etc. Since $2(5) + 3 \neq 7$, $(5, 3) \notin S$.

definition: If A and B are sets, then the set of all ordered pairs (x, y) where $x \in A$ and $y \in B$ is called the *Cartesian product* of A and B; symbolically,

$$A \times B = \{(x, y) \mid x \in A \text{ and } y \in B\}.$$

If $A = \{1, 2, 3\}$ and $B = \{4, 5\}$, then

$$A \times B = \{(1,4), (2,4), (3,4), (1,5), (2,5), (3,5)\}$$

and

$$B \times A = \{(4,1), (4,2), (4,3), (5,1), (5,2), (5,3)\}.$$

Notice that $A \times B \neq B \times A$. If $T = \{1, 2\}$, then

$$T \times T = \{(1,1), (1,2), (2,1), (2,2)\};$$

this is called the Cartesian product of the set T with itself.

A method has already been discussed for associating real numbers with points on a line; we now consider a method for associating ordered pairs of real numbers with points in a plane. That is, if R is the set of real numbers we discuss a method to represent geometrically the Cartesian product $R \times R$.

Draw two number lines in the plane, one horizontal and one vertical, and intersecting at right angles at their origins. The standard orientation is to have the positive direction to the right for the horizontal number line and the positive direction up for the vertical num-

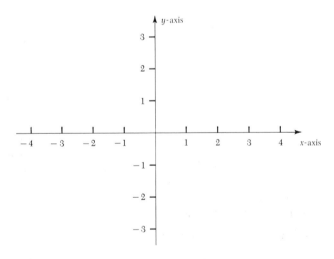

Rectangular coordinate system

FIGURE 4–1

ber line. The two number lines are called *coordinate axes*. The horizontal coordinate axis is called the *x-axis*, or *first coordinate axis*, and the vertical coordinate axis is called the *y-axis*, or *second coordinate axis*.

If x is the real number associated with a given point on the x-axis (the horizontal number line), then the ordered pair $(x, 0)$ is associated with this point. If y is the real number associated with a given point on the y-axis, then the ordered pair $(0, y)$ is associated with this point. If P is a point in the plane not on either of the coordinate axes, if $(x, 0)$ represents the point at the foot of the perpendicular drawn from P to the x-axis, and if $(0, y)$ represents the point at the foot of the per-

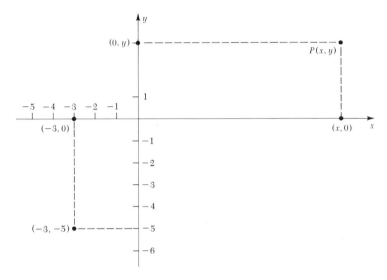

FIGURE 4–2

pendicular drawn from P to the y-axis, then the ordered pair (x, y) is associated with the point P. Thus, we have a method for associating an ordered pair of real numbers with every point in the plane. Furthermore, this correspondence associates a point in the plane with every ordered pair of real numbers. The first number of the ordered pair (x, y) is called the *x-coordinate*, or *abscissa*, of the point and the second is called the *y-coordinate*, or *ordinate*.

An association of points in the plane with pairs of real numbers is called a *coordinate system*. The coordinate system just described was developed by René Descartes, a French mathematician who lived from 1596 to 1650; it is called the *rectangular* coordinate system, or *Cartesian* coordinate system. Although we restrict our study of coordinate systems to the rectangular coordinate system, it should be noted that there are other methods, such as polar coordinates, for associating points in the plane with ordered pairs of real numbers.

Let P and Q be two distinct points in the plane with Cartesian coordinates (x_1, y_1) and (x_2, y_2), respectively. We are interested in a method to find the distance between P and Q. (See Figure 4–3.) The

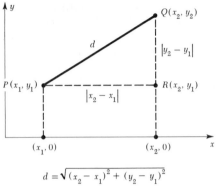

$$d = \sqrt{(x_2 - x_1)^2 + (y_2 - y_1)^2}$$

FIGURE 4–3

distance between P and R is $|x_2 - x_1|$ and the distance between R and Q is $|y_2 - y_1|$. Since PQ is the hypotenuse of a right triangle, it follows from the Pythagorean Theorem that

$$d = |PQ| = \sqrt{(x_2 - x_1)^2 + (y_2 - y_1)^2}.$$

This is called the distance formula.

To form the right triangle in Figure 4–3, it was necessary to assume that the line containing P and Q was not parallel to either axis. If $y_1 = y_2$ the line containing P and Q (that is, the line PR) is parallel to the x-axis and the distance between (x_1, y_1) and (x_2, y_2) is obviously $|x_2 - x_1|$. Since $\sqrt{(x_2 - x_1)^2} = |x_2 - x_1|$, the distance formula is valid when $y_1 = y_2$. Similarly, the formula is valid when $x_1 = x_2$. If P and Q are not distinct points, the distance is defined to be 0; in this case $x_1 = x_2$ and $y_1 = y_2$ and the distance formula gives the desired result.

definition: A *relation F* is a set of ordered pairs of elements; symbolically $F = \{(x, y)\}$. The set of all first elements in a relation F, denoted by D_F, is called the *domain* of the relation F, and the set of all second elements, denoted by R_F, is called the *range* of F.

For example, the set $\{(1,2),(-2,3),(1/2,3)\}$ is a relation; the domain of this relation is the set $\{1,-2,1/2\}$ and the range is $\{2,3\}$. That is, $D_F = \{1,-2,1/2\}$ and $R_F = \{2,3\}$.

If the domain and range of a relation F are sets of real numbers, then F is a subset of $R \times R$ where R is the set of real numbers. The set of all points in the coordinate system determined by the ordered pairs of real numbers in the relation F is called the *graph* of the relation. More precisely, the point determined by the ordered pair of real numbers (x, y) is a part of the graph of a relation F if and only if the ordered pair (x, y) is a member of the set F.

examples

1. If $F = \{(2, 3), (3, -7), (\sqrt{28}, 3), (-4, 8)\}$, then F is a relation. Domain of F: $D_F = \{2, 3, \sqrt{28}, -4\}$; range of F: $R_F = \{3, -7, 8\}$; graph of F: see Figure 4–4.

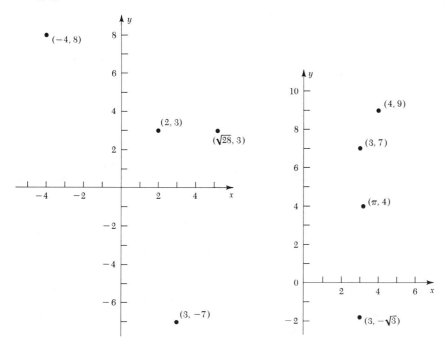

$F = \{(2,3),(3,-7),(\sqrt{28},3),(-4,8)\}$ $G = \{(3,7),(\pi,4),(3,-\sqrt{3}),(4,9)\}$

FIGURE 4–4

2. If $G = \{(3, 7), (\pi, 4), (3, -\sqrt{3}), (4, 9)\}$, then G is a relation. Domain of G: $D_G = \{3, \pi, 4\}$; range of G: $R_G = \{7, 4, -\sqrt{3}, 9\}$; graph of G: see Figure 4–4.

3. If $H = \{(2, 7), (-4, 8), (6, 11), (8, 1/2)\}$, then H is a relation. Domain of H: $D_H = \{2, -4, 6, 8\}$; range of H: $R_H = \{7, 8, 11, 1/2\}$; graph of H: see Figure 4–5.

4. If $S = \{(x, y) \mid x \text{ and } y \text{ are real numbers and } x^2 + y^2 = 25\}$, then S is a relation. Considering the right triangle with the origin, the point $(x, 0)$, and the point (x, y) as vertices, it is obvious that $x^2 + y^2 = 25$ if the point (x, y) is on the circle of radius 5 with center at the origin. Domain of S: $D_S = \{x \mid -5 \leqslant x \leqslant 5\}$; range of S: $R_S = \{y \mid -5 \leqslant y \leqslant 5\}$; graph of S: see Figure 4–5.

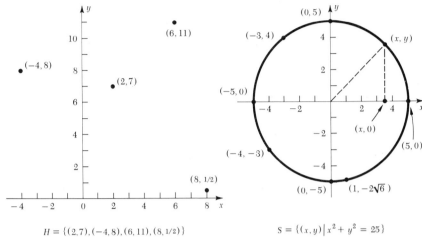

$H = \{(2,7),(-4,8),(6,11),(8,1/2)\}$

$S = \{(x,y)\,|\,x^2 + y^2 = 25\}$

FIGURE 4-5

It is very helpful to have geometric interpretations, when they exist, of new concepts in mathematics; geometric interpretations enhance our understanding of new ideas, aid in the "discovery" of many theorems, and often suggest an approach to the proofs of theorems. As we have seen, a relation can be interpreted as a collection of points in the coordinate plane. The *domain* of a relation is represented by the points of the graph on the x-axis actually plotted there, plus points orthogonally projected there from other points of the graph. The *range* of the relation is represented by the points of the graph on the y-axis actually plotted there, plus points orthogonally projected there from other points of the graph. In other words, the set of all horizontal components for a graph is called the domain of that graph and the set of all vertical components is called the range.

examples

1. If $f = \{(x, y)\,|\,x$ and y are integers and $x^2 + y^2 = 25\}$, then f is a relation. $D_f = R_f = \{-5, -4, -3, 0, 3, 4, 5\}$. For the graph of f, see Figure 4-6.

2. If $g = \{(x, y)\,|\,x$ is an integer and y a real number satisfying $x^2 + y^2 = 25\}$, then g is a relation. $D_g = \{-5, -4, -3, -2, -1, 0, 1, 2, 3, 4, 5\}$; $R_g = \{-5, -2\sqrt{6}, -\sqrt{21}, -4, -3, 0, 3, 4, \sqrt{21}, 2\sqrt{6}, 5\}$; graph: see Figure 4-6.

3. If $s = \{(x,y)\,|\,x$ a real number, y a non-negative real number, and $x^2 + y^2 = 25\}$, then s is a relation. $D_s = \{x\,|\,-5 \leq x \leq 5\}$; $R_s = \{y\,|\,0 \leq y \leq 5\}$; graph: see Figure 4-7.

4. If $h = \{(x, y)\,|\,y = 2x + 7$ where x is a real number on the closed interval $-5 \leq x \leq 5\}$, then h is a relation. $D_h = \{x\,|\,-5 \leq x \leq 5\}$; $R_h = \{y\,|\,-3 \leq y \leq 17\}$; graph: see Figure 4-7.

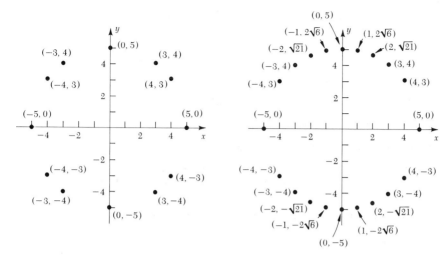

$f = \{(x, y) \mid x \text{ and } y \text{ integers and } x^2 + y^2 = 25\}$

$g = \{(x, y) \mid x \text{ an integer, } y \text{ a real number, and} \quad x^2 + y^2 = 25\}$

FIGURE 4–6

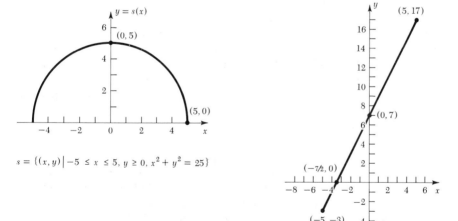

$s = \{(x, y) \mid -5 \le x \le 5,\ y \ge 0,\ x^2 + y^2 = 25\}$

$k = \{(x, y) \mid y = 2x + 7,\ -5 \le x \le 5\}$

FIGURE 4–7

exercises

Graph each of the following relations in Exercises 1 through 8 and state the domain and range of each.

1. $f = \{(3, 5), (-2, 7), (5, -5), (3, -4), (-1, -1)\}$.

2. $g = \{(x, 1) \mid x$ is a real number$\}$.

3. $h = \{(3, y) \mid y$ is a real number$\}$.

4. $F = \{(x,y) \mid x$ is a real number and y is an integer such that $x \leqslant y < x+1\}$.

5. $G = \{(x, x) \mid x$ is a real number$\}$.

6. $H = \{(x, y) \mid x$ is an integer and $x^2 + y^2 = 64\}$.

7. $v = \{(x, |x|) \mid x$ is a real number $\}$.

8. $w = \{(x, y) \mid -3 \leqslant x \leqslant 11$ and $y = x - 2\}$.

9. $z = \{(x, y) \mid$ the point (x, y) is equidistant from $(2, 3)$ and $(5, 7)\}$. Find an equation using the distance formula that can be used to define this relation.

10. Using the distance formula and the Pythagorean Theorem, prove that the points $(3, 0)$, $(5, 6)$, and $(6, -1)$ are vertices of a right triangle. Find the area of the triangle.

11. Prove that the point $(-3, 10)$ is on the perpendicular bisector of the line segment whose endpoints are $(1, -3)$ and $(8, 2)$.

12. If the coordinates (x, y) of point P satisfy the equation $x^2 + y^2 = a^2$, prove that the sum of the squares of the distances of P from $(-a, 0)$ and $(a, 0)$ is $4a^2$. Interpret geometrically.

13. Find the perimeter of a triangle whose vertices are $(7, 1)$, $(-2, 7)$, and $(-4, -3)$. Give a two-place decimal approximation.

14. Let A, B, and C be points with coordinates $(-3, 4)$, $(3, 0)$, and $(12, -6)$, respectively. Prove that the sum of the distances from A to B and B to C is the distance from A to C. Interpret geometrically.

15. Find the coordinates of the midpoint of each line segment obtained by joining each of the following pairs of points:
    (a) $(3, 8)$ and $(7, 12)$
    (b) $(2, 6)$ and $(8, 15)$
    (c) $(-4, -11)$ and $(8, 17)$

16. If (a, b) and (c, d) are the coordinates of two distinct points, find the coordinates of the midpoint of the line segment joining these two points.

17. If $(3, 4)$, $(9, 6)$, and $(5, 11)$ are three points in the plane, find the area of the triangle formed by joining these points. (Hint: Construct perpendiculars to the x-axis from each point and consider the three trapezoids formed.)

18. If (a, b), (c, d), and (e, f) are three non-collinear points in the plane, find the area of the triangle formed.

19. If P and Q have coordinates (x_1, y_1) and (x_2, y_2), respectively, find the coordinates of the point on the line segment joining P and Q which is $2/3$ of the distance $|PQ|$ from P. See Exercise 5, Section 2–3.

20. Graph the points $A(1, 1)$, $B(9, 3)$, and $C(5, 11)$. Let P, Q, and R be midpoints of the segments AB, BC, and AC. Find the coordinates of the points $2/3$ the distance from A to Q and B to R. Interpret your answer geometrically.

21. If set A has m elements and set B has n elements, how many elements in $A \times B$?

22. If $A = \{1, 2, 3\}$ and $B = \{2, 3\}$, list the elements in $A \times B$ and in $B \times A$. Is $A \times B = B \times A$?

23. If A and B are sets, under what conditions is $A \times B = B \times A$? Justify your answer.

4–2 functions

Throughout this text, we focus our attention on a very special class of relations called *real functions.*

definition: A *function F* is a relation such that no two pairs in the relation have the same first elements; that is, if F is a function and if (x, y) and (x, z) are elements of F, then $y = z$. Functions whose domains and ranges are subsets of the set of real numbers are called *real functions.*

The reader should re-examine the two lists of examples of relations in Section 4–1, page 000, and notice that relations F, H, s, and h are the only examples of functions. As a consequence of the agreement to discuss only real functions, we observe the common practice of using "function" for "real function" in what follows.

We have only discussed functions where the first element in each ordered pair is a real number. A function could be a set of ordered pairs where the first elements are themselves ordered pairs of real numbers. For example,

$$f = \{((x, y), t) \mid t = x^2 + 3y^2 \text{ where } x \text{ and } y \text{ are real numbers}\}$$

is a function; the domain of f is a set of ordered pairs of real numbers and the range of f is the set of non-negative real numbers. This is an example of what is called a *function of two variables.* Unless otherwise stated, the term *function* will refer only to a set of ordered pairs whose first and second elements are real numbers; such functions are called real functions of *one variable.*

There is a simple geometric way to determine if a relation is a function. A set of points in the rectangular coordinate plane such that no two points are on a line parallel to the y-axis is the graph of a function; in other words, any line parallel to the y-axis intersects the graph of a function in *at most* one point. From this interpretation, it is easy to see by looking at the graphs of the relations in the two sets of examples in Section 4–1 that F, H, s, and h are the only examples of functions.

A function associates with each real number in the domain one and only one number in the range. However, since it is not necessary for two ordered pairs in a function to have different second elements, we cannot assert the converse—that is, that every function associates with each number in the range one and *only* one number in the domain. Geometrically, although lines parallel to the y-axis intersect the graph of a function in at most one point, lines parallel to the x-axis may intersect the graph of a function in more than one point.

If f is a function, the number in the range associated with the number x in the domain is denoted by $f(x)$ (read "f of x", or "the value of f at x"). This notation is quite useful since we are able to abbreviate a statement such as "if f is a function, find the number in the range of f associated with 2 in the domain" by "if f is a function, find $f(2)$."

examples

1. If $F = \{(1, -3), (-4, 1/2), (0, \sqrt{3})\}$, then $F(1) = -3$, $F(-4) = 1/2$, and $F(0) = \sqrt{3}$.

2. If $g = \{(x, y)\,|\,y = x^2$ and x a real number$\}$, then $g(0) = 0$, $g(3) = 9$, $g(-1/2) = 1/4$, $g(\sqrt{5}) = 5$, etc.

3. If $f = \{(x, f(x))\,|\,f(x) = x^2 - 4\}$, then $f(1) = -3$, $f(3) = 5$, $f(\sqrt{7}) = 3$, etc.

The notation $f(x)$ is also used to simplify the definition of many functions. For example, if $F = \{(x, y)\,|\,x \geqslant 1$ and $y = \sqrt{x-1}\}$, we usually write "let F be defined by $F(x) = \sqrt{x-1}$" and *agree that the domain of F is the set of all real numbers x such that F(x) is a real number*. In general, unless some contrary statement is made, a function F will always be considered to be a subset of $R \times R$.

If $g = \{(x, y)\,|\,y = 1$ when x is an integer and $y = 2$ when x is not an integer$\}$ (see Figure 4–8), then the function g is also defined in the following manner:

Let g be the function such that $g(x) = \begin{cases} 1 \text{ when } x \text{ is an integer.} \\ 2 \text{ when } x \text{ is not an integer.} \end{cases}$

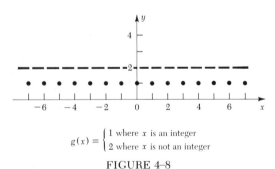

$$g(x) = \begin{cases} 1 \text{ where } x \text{ is an integer} \\ 2 \text{ where } x \text{ is not an integer} \end{cases}$$

FIGURE 4–8

Consider the function I defined by $I = \{(x, x)\,|\,x$ is any real number$\}$. This very special function associating with each x in the domain the number x in the range is called the *identity function*. The graph of the identity function is the straight line containing the origin of the rectangular coordinate system and the point (1, 1).

Let Q and R be the points with coordinates (1, 4) and (4, 1), respectively. If P is any point on the graph of the identity function, its coordinates are (x, x) for some x, and the distances between P and Q and P and R are given by the distances formula as follows:

$$PQ = \sqrt{(x-1)^2 + (x-4)^2}$$
$$PR = \sqrt{(x-4)^2 + (x-1)^2}.$$

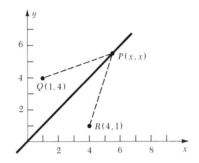

$$|PQ| = |PR|$$
$$\sqrt{(x-1)^2 + (x-4)^2} = \sqrt{(x-4)^2 + (x-1)^2}$$

FIGURE 4–9

Hence, $|PQ| = |PR|$. Since the graph of the identity function contains all points equidistant from points Q and R, it is the perpendicular bisector of the line segment joining Q and R. Hence, Q and R are symmetric to the graph of the identity function.

definition: Two points are *symmetric* to a line if and only if the line is the perpendicular bisector of the line segment joining the two points.

Two distinct points in the plane with coordinates (a, b) and (b, a) are symmetric to the graph of the identity function. The graphs of two sets of points (for example, two curves in the coordinate plane) are said to be symmetric to the graph of the identity function if and only if for each point in either set there is a point in the other set such that the pair of points are symmetric to the line.

Consider the function F defined by $F = \{(2, 3), (4, 7), (5, 3)\}$. The set of ordered pairs G obtained by interchanging the first and second coordinates in each of the ordered pairs of F is called the *inverse relation of* F; that is $G = \{(3, 2), (7, 4), (3, 5)\}$ is the inverse relation of F. Since F contains two ordered pairs with the same second coordinate, G contains two ordered pairs with the same first coordinate;

thus, although F is a function, G is not a function. It should be noted that G could be defined by $G=\{(y, x)|(x, y)$ is in $F\}$; furthermore, the graphs of F and G are symmetric to the graph of the identity function. See Figure 4–10.

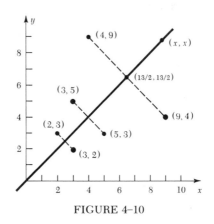

FIGURE 4–10

If $f=\{(2, 7), (3, 8), (4, 11)\}$ and if $g=\{(7, 2), (8, 3), (11, 4)\}$, then $g=\{(b, a)|(a, b)$ is in $f\}$. Since the second coordinates of the function f are distinct, the first coordinates of the relation g are distinct; thus, g is a function. The function g is called the *inverse function of f*.

definition: Let f be a function such that no *two* ordered pairs have the same second coordinate. The function $\{(b, a)|(a, b)$ is in $f\}$ is called the *inverse function of f*. The inverse of f is usually denoted by f^{-1}. (Note: "−1" is not an exponent.)

examples

1. If $f=\{(1, 3), (2, 7), (3, 8)\}$, then $f^{-1}=\{(3, 1), (7, 2), (8, 3)\}$.
2. If $f=\{(0, 1), (1/4, 1/4), (1, 0)\}$, then $f^{-1}=\{(1, 0), (1/4, 1/4), (0, 1)\}$. Since f and f^{-1} contain the same elements, $f=f^{-1}$. In other words, this is an example of a function equal to its own inverse.

It should be clear that the letters used to define a function are immaterial. The function f defined by $f(x)=3x+5$ could also be defined by $f(s)=3s+5$. Furthermore, if g is defined by $g(u)=3u+5$, then $g=f$.

If f is defined by $f(s)=3s+5$, it is evident since $s_1 \neq s_2$ implies $3s_1+5 \neq 3s_2+5$ that different numbers in the domain of f are associated with different values $f(s)$ in the range. Hence, the function f has an inverse f^{-1}. In fact, the inverse function could be defined by $f^{-1}=\{(3s+5, s)\}$. However, it is usually desirable to exhibit a formula, if one exists, to associate with each real number t in the domain of f^{-1} the corresponding number $f^{-1}(t)$ in the range. For the given function, it is quite simple to find such a formula. If t is an element in the domain of f^{-1}, then $t=3s+5$ and we seek a method to find the second element s for a given number t; this can be done by solving the equation for s. In other words, the number associated with t in the domain of f^{-1} is $(t-5)/3$; that is,

$$f^{-1}=\{(t,\frac{t-5}{3})\}.$$

exercises

1. Graph each of the given relations and answer the following questions. (a) Is the relation a function? (b) If it is a function, is the inverse relation a function?

$F=\{(2, 3), (1/2, 0), (2, 7), (-4, 6)\}$

$G=\{(7, 1), (8, 2), (-6, 11), (2, 0)\}$

$H=\{(4, 6), (3, 9), (-11, 6), (3, 11)\}$

$f=\{(x, x)|x$ is a real number$\}$

$g=\{(n, 1/n)|n$ is a positive integer$\}$

$h=\{(n, n^2)|n$ is a positive integer$\}$

$v=\{(x, 3)|x$ is a real number$\}$

$w=\{(x, |x|)|x$ is a real number$\}$

$u=\{(x, 5x+9)|x$ an integer$\}$

2. If $h=\{(n, n^2)|n$ is a positive integer$\}$, give the domain of h^{-1}.

3. If f is defined by $f(x)=\sqrt{2x+7}$, give the domain and range of f. Find a formula to define f^{-1}. State the domain and range of f^{-1}.

4. If h is a function defined by $h(x)=3x+11$, find a formula to define h^{-1}. Sketch the graph of h and h^{-1}.

5. If f is defined by $f(x)=(3x+6)/(2x-3)$ for $x\neq 3/2$, define the inverse function f^{-1}. Sketch the graphs of f and f^{-1}.

6. If f^{-1} is the inverse function of a function f and if $f^{-1}=f$, what can be said about the graph of f? See Exercise 5.

7. If F is a function defined by $F(x)=(x+2)/x$, state the domain and range of F and find a formula to define F^{-1}.

8. Graph all the points in the coordinate plane at distance 5 from the point (2, 6).
(a) Is this the graph of a function?
(b) Show that the set of points on the graph is the graph of $\{(x, y)| (x-2)^2+(y-6)^2=25\}$.

9. Graph all the points in the coordinate plane that are equidistant between the point (0, 4) and the x-axis.
(a) Is this the graph of a function?
(b) Show that the set of points on the graph is the set defined by $\{(x, y)|x^2-8y+16=0\}$.

10. If f and g are functions defined by $f(x) = x^2 + 7$ and $g(x) = 3x + 5$, find each of the following.

(a) $f(3) + g(-5)$ (b) $f(1/2) \times g(14)$

(c) $f(-2) + g(-1)$ (d) $f(t) - f(2)$

(e) $\dfrac{f(t) - f(5)}{t - 5}$ if $t \neq 5$

11. (a) A function f is called an *even function* if $f(x) = f(-x)$. What can be said about the graph of an even function?
(b) A function f is called an *odd function* if $f(x) = -f(-x)$. What can be said about the graph of an odd function?
(c) Give an example of an even function. An odd function. A function which is neither even nor odd.

12. Let f and g be functions defined by $f(x) = 2x + 1$ and $g(x) = 4x - 7$.
(a) For what real numbers x is $f(x) = g(x)$?
(b) For what real numbers x is $f(x) < g(x)$?
(c) List all elements in $f \cap g$.

13. If f is a function defined by $f(x) = (ax + b)/(cx + d)$ where $a \neq 0$, $b \neq 0$, $c \neq 0$, and $d \neq 0$, under what conditions is $f^{-1} = f$?

14. Explain the following statement: "Addition can be interpreted as a function of two variables."

15. Let $\sigma = \{(n, \sigma(n)) \mid n$ is a positive integer and $\sigma(n)$ is the sum of the factors of $n\}$.
(a) Is σ a function? Is σ^{-1} a function?
(b) State the following function values: $\sigma(3)$, $\sigma(6)$, $\sigma(5)$, $\sigma(17)$, $\sigma(28)$, $\sigma(496)$, $\sigma(m)$ if m is a prime number.
(c) If m and n are primes and $m \neq n$, prove that $\sigma(m) \times \sigma(n) = \sigma(mn)$.

4-3   constant functions and linear functions

If c is a real number, then the function f defined by $f(x) = c$ is called a *constant function*. For example, if $f(x) = 2$, then f is the constant function whose graph is the collection of all points in the plane with 2 as its second coordinate. (See Figure 4–11). The graph of a constant

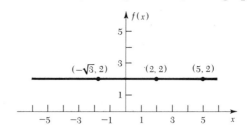

Graph of $f = \left\{(x, f(x)) \mid f(x) = 2\right\}$

FIGURE 4–11

function is continous in the sense that there are no "gaps" in the graph. A precise nongeometric definition of continuity of functions is beyond the scope of this text; for our purposes the geometric and intuitive idea of continuity will suffice.

Consider the line determined by the two points Q and R with co-ordinates $(1, 4)$ and $(5, 7)$, respectively. (See Figure 4–12.) If P is any

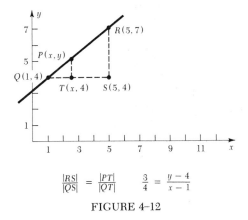

$$\frac{|RS|}{|QS|} = \frac{|PT|}{|QT|} \qquad \frac{3}{4} = \frac{y-4}{x-1}$$

FIGURE 4–12

point on this line distinct from Q and R and having (x, y) as coordi-nates, then similar right triangles PQT and RQS are formed by draw-ing lines through P, Q, and R parallel to the coordinate axes. The lengths of the sides of the triangles are thus proportional, and $|RS|/|QS| = |PT|/|QT|$. Now, $|RS| = 7-4 = 3$, $|QS| = 5-1 = 4$, $|PT| = y-4$, and $|QT| = x-1$; hence, $3/4 = (y-4)/(x-1)$.

Simplifying,

$$4(y-4) = 3(x-1)$$
$$4y - 16 = 3x - 3$$
$$4y = 3x + 13$$
$$y = \frac{3x}{4} + \frac{13}{4}.$$

Since the ordered pairs $(1, 4)$ and $(5, 7)$ satisfy the equation $y = 3x/4 + 13/4$, we conclude that if (a, b) is any point on the line containing the two given points then (a, b) is an element of the set (function) defined by $f = \{(x, y) | y = 3x/4 + 13/4\}$. We leave as an exercise for the student to prove that if (a, b) is not on the line then (a, b) is not in f. Hence, f is the function which has the given straight line as its graph.

definition: If L is any nonvertical line in the coordinate plane and if P and Q are any two points on the line with coordinates (x_1, y_1) and (x_2, y_2), then the ratio $(y_2 - y_1)/(x_2 - x_1)$ is called the *slope* of the line; it is usually denoted by m.

Although any given nonvertical line determines a unique slope, it is not true that a given slope determines a unique line. Parallel lines have the same slope—a fact left for the student to verify—so the slope determines only the orientation of a line. If the slope is zero the line is parallel to the x-axis; if the slope is positive the line "leans to the right"; and if the slope is negative the line "leans to the left." If (x_1, y_1) and (x_2, y_2) are two points on a vertical line, $x_1 = x_2$ and the slope is not defined.

The point where a nonvertical line crosses the y-axis is called the *y-intercept*. Since the coordinates of this point is the ordered pair $(0, b)$ for some real number b, we often say that the y-intercept is b. If we know that a line has a certain y-intercept and slope, the line is completely determined. For example, if a line has y-intercept 5 and slope 2/3, it is easy to graph. Since two points determine a line, we need only to find one point on the line different from $(0, 5)$. If (u, v) is to be a point on the line, then

$$\frac{v-5}{u-0} = \frac{2}{3} \text{ by the formula for slope.}$$

Hence, if we let $u = 3$ then $v = 7$ and the point $(3, 7)$ is on the line. (If we let $u = 6$, then $v - 5 = 8$ and $v = 13$.) See Figure 4–13.

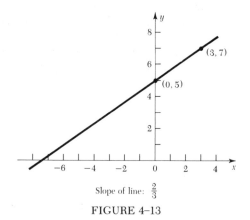

Slope of line: $\frac{2}{3}$

FIGURE 4–13

Consider the function f defined by $f(x) = mx + b$ where m and b are given real numbers and $m \neq 0$. It is obvious since $f(0) = b$ that $(0, b)$ is a point on the graph of f. For $s \neq 0$ since $f(s) = ms + b$ we know that $(s, ms + b)$ is also a point different from $(0, b)$ on the graph of f. Now, the slope of the line containing these two distinct points on the graph of f is

$$\frac{(ms + b) - b}{s - 0} = \frac{ms}{s} = m.$$

Thus, the slope of the line through the point $(0, b)$ and any other point on the graph of f is the real number m. Since the slope does not depend on the ordered pairs selected from f, the graph of f is the straight line through $(0, b)$ with slope m.

The function f defined by $f(x) = mx + b$ where $m \neq 0$ is called a *linear function*; its graph is a straight line with slope m and y-intercept b.

example

If f is given by $f(x) = -3/2x + 4$, the graph of f is a straight line with y-intercept 4 and slope $-3/2$. If (u, v) is a point on the graph different from $(0, 4)$, then $(v-4)/(u-0) = -3/2$. Letting $u = 2$, we conclude $v = 1$; hence, $(0, 4)$ and $(2, 1)$ are two points that determine the graph of f.

Although any linear function has a line in the coordinate plane as its graph, we cannot say that *every* line in the coordinate plane is the graph of a linear function. A line parallel to the y-axis has the first coordinates of all its points equal, so it is not the graph of any function. Although a line parallel to the x-axis would represent a function, the slope of this line is zero; hence, it is represented by a constant function instead of a linear function.

exercises

1. Let f be the function defined by $f(x) = 5$.
   (a) Graph f.
   (b) If $(a, 5)$ and $(b, 5)$ are any two distinct points on the graph of f, what is the distance between the two points?
   (c) What is the slope of the line?
   (d) What is the y-intercept?

2. Let g be a function defined by $g(x) = 3x + 7$.
   (a) What is the slope of the graph of g?
   (b) What is the y-intercept?
   (c) Is the point $(-5, 9)$ on the graph?
   (d) If $(a, 6)$ is a point on the graph of g, what real number does a represent?
   (e) If $(-5, b)$ is a point on the graph of g, what real number does b represent?
   (f) Find a real number t such that $g(t) = 0$.

3. Define the function whose graph is the straight line containing $(0, 7)$ with slope $2/3$.

4. Define the function whose graph is the straight line containing $(2, 4)$ and $(7, -3)$.

5. Define the function whose graph is the straight line containing $(-7, 9)$ and $(4, 9)$.

6. Prove that if (a, b) is not on the line containing $(1, 4)$ and $(5, 7)$ then $b \neq 3a/4 + 13/4$.

7. Prove that nonvertical parallel lines have the same slope.

8. Define the function whose graph is the straight line containing (x_1, y_1) and (x_2, y_2) where $x_1 \neq x_2$.

9. Let f and g be two functions defined by $f(x) = 3x - 7$ and $g(x) = 5x + 11$.
   (a) Find the real number t such that $f(t) = g(t)$.
   (b) Since f and g are sets, list the elements common to both sets and interpret geometrically.

10. (a) Construct on one coordinate system the graph of each function f defined by $f(x) = mx + 3$ where $m = 1$, $m = 2$, $m = 3$, $m = 5$, $m = 15$, $m = 0$, $m = -1$, $m = -3$, $m = -5$, and $m = -15$.
    (b) What are the coordinates of the point common to the graphs of all these functions.

11. If $g = \{(x, y) | y = mx + 3$ for every real number $m\}$, describe geometrically all the points in the coordinate plane that are not elements in g. (See Exercise 10.)

12. Consider the line containing the points $(2, 1/2)$ and $(-1/4, 5)$. Define the function whose graph is the line parallel to the given line having y-intercept -4.

13. Consider the line containing the points $(3, 4)$ and $(-1, 8)$. Define the function whose graph is the line parallel to the given line containing the point $(2, -3)$.

14. Let f, g, and h be three different linear functions given by $f(x) = m_1 x + b_1$, $g(x) = m_2 x + b_2$, and $h(x) = m_3 x + b_3$. Prove that if the graphs of f, g, and h intersect at a single point, then $m_1 b_2 + m_3 b_1 + m_2 b_3 - m_2 b_1 - m_3 b_2 - m_1 b_3 = 0$.

15. Graph each of the following on the same coordinate graph:
    (a) $f = \{(x, y) | 3x - y + 5 = 0)\}$
    (b) $g = \{(x, y) | 2x + y - 1 = 0)\}$
    (c) $h = \{(x, y) | (3x - y + 5) + t(2x + y - 1) = 0)\}$ for $t = 1$, $t = -1/2$, $t = 3$, $t = -7$, and $t = 10$. Interpret geometrically.
    (d) If $h = \{(x, y) | (3x - y + 5) + t(2x + y - 1) = 0)$ for all real numbers $t\}$, what points in the coordinate plane are in h?

16. Let $S = \{(x, y) | (x, y)$ is equidistant from $(1, 3)$ and $(8, 2)\}$ and let $T = \{(x, y) | (x, y)$ is equidistant from $(8, 2)$ and $(4, 9)\}$.
    (a) List the elements in $S \cap T$.
    (b) List the elements in $S \cap \{(x, 0) | x$ a real number$\}$.

4-4   quadratic functions

A function f defined by $f(x) = ax^2 + bx + c$ where a, b, and c are real numbers and $a \neq 0$ is called a *quadratic function*. Let us discuss as many properties of quadratic functions and their graphs as is possible with the limited number of mathematical tools at our disposal.

First, consider the special quadratic function defined by $f(x) = x^2$; that is, $a = 1$, $b = 0$, and $c = 0$ where $f(x) = ax^2 + bx + c$. Since the square of every real number is non-negative, $f(t) \geqslant 0$ for every real number t; furthermore, since $f(0) = 0$ we have that 0 is the least number in the range of f. The function is said to have an *absolute minimum* of 0. In general, if q is the *least number in the range of a function* f, then q is said to be the *absolute minimum* of the function; furthermore, the function is said to have an absolute minimum at p where p is a number in the domain of f such that $f(p) = q$. Notice that p need not be unique.

If $t \neq 0$, then (t, t^2) and $(-t, t^2)$ are two distinct points on the graph

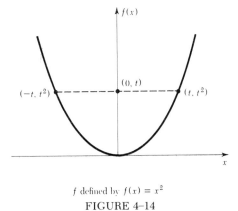

f defined by $f(x) = x^2$

FIGURE 4-14

of f. (See Figure 4-14.) The midpoint of the line segment joining (t, t^2) and $(-t, t^2)$ is $(0, t^2)$, a point on the y-axis; thus, these two points are symmetric to the y-axis and the graph of f is symmetric to the y-axis. The function is said to be *strictly increasing* on the set of non-negative numbers and *strictly decreasing* on the set of non-positive real numbers.

A function f is said to be *increasing*, or *non-decreasing*, on a subset S (containing at least two distinct elements) of its domain if $f(x) \leqslant f(y)$ for any pair of real numbers x and y in S such that $x < y$; if $f(x) < f(y)$ for $x < y$, then f is said to be *strictly increasing* on S. Similarly, a function f is said to be *decreasing*, or *non-increasing*, on a subset S of its domain if $f(x) \geqslant f(y)$ for any pair x and y in S such that $x < y$; if $f(x) > f(y)$, then f is said to be *strictly decreasing* on S. A function f is said to be *monotonic* on a set S if it is either increasing on S or decreasing on S; *strictly monotonic on S* implies that f is either strictly increasing or strictly decreasing on S.

If g is the quadratic function defined by $g(x) = 3x^2 + 6x - 7$, then

$$g(x) = 3(x^2 + 2x) - 7$$
$$= 3(x^2 + 2x + 1) - (7 + 3)$$
$$= 3(x + 1)^2 - 10.$$

Since $(x + 1)^2$ is non-negative, it is evident that the function has an absolute minimum at -1 in the domain; the absolute minimum is $g(-1) = -10$. The function is strictly increasing on the set where

$x \geqslant -1$, and is strictly decreasing on the set where $x \leqslant -1$. As the student may verify $g(-1+t) = g(-1-t)$ for any real number t; thus, the graph of g is symmetric to the line which is parallel to the y-axis and has first coordinates equal to -1. (See Figure 4-15.)

The graph of this function has the following very interesting

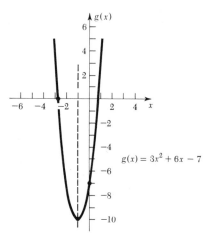

FIGURE 4-15

property. Consider the point with coordinates $(-1, -119/12)$ and the line parallel to the x-axis where $y = -121/12$. For any point (x, y) on the graph, the perpendicular distance from this point to the line $y = -121/12$ is equal to the distance between this point and $(-1, -119/12)$. The proof of this is left as an exercise for the student. Any curve which has the property that it is the collection of all points equidistant between a fixed point and a fixed line is called a *parabola*; the fixed point is called the *focus* and the fixed line the *directrix*. The graph of the function g given by $g(x) = 3x^2 + 6x - 7$ is a parabola.

4-5 algebraic and transcendental functions

The constant, linear, and quadratic functions are examples of polynomial functions. A *polynomial function* P is defined by

$$P(x) = a_0 x^n + a_1 x^{n-1} + a_2 x^{n-2} + \ldots + a_{n-1} x + a_n$$

where n is a non-negative integer and each $a_0, a_1, a_2, a_3, \ldots, a_n$ is a real number. If $a_0 \neq 0$, the number n is called the *degree* of the polynomial.

If P and Q are polynomial functions, then the function defined by $f(x) = P(x)/Q(x)$ where $Q(x) \neq 0$ is called a *rational function*. For example, the function f defined by $f(x) = (x^2 + 3x + 7)/[(x-2)^2]$ where $x \neq 2$ is a rational function. In other words, rational functions are those defined by use of one or more of the rational operations of addition, subtraction, multiplication, and division. If the algebraic operations of addition, subtraction, multiplication, division, and taking roots are employed to define a function, it is called an *algebraic function*. Since every rational operation is an algebraic operation, every rational function is also an algebraic function. The function f defined by

$$f(x) = \frac{(\sqrt{x^2+4}+3x)}{(x^2+9)}$$

is an algebraic function, but not a rational function.

It should be noted that the polynomial and rational functions are algebraic functions; the set of polynomial functions is a subset of the set of rational functions and the set of rational functions is a subset of the set of algebraic functions. The student should be somewhat familiar with several functions, such as the logarithmic and trigonometric functions that are not algebraic; that is, it is impossible to define the trigonometric functions, for example, using only the algebraic operations a finite number of times. Non-algebraic functions are called *transcendental functions*. An extensive discussion of the elementary transcendental functions is given in Chapters 5 and 6.

exercises

1. Let f be defined by $f(x) = x^2 + 6x - 9$.
   (a) Graph f.
   (b) On what set is the function strictly increasing?
   (c) On what set is the function strictly decreasing?
   (d) What is the maximum value of f? Minimum value of f?

2. Let f be defined by $f(x) = 5x^2 + 10x + 5$.
   (a) Graph f.
   (b) On what set is the function strictly increasing?
   (c) On what set is the function strictly decreasing?
   (d) What is the maximum value of f? Minimum value of f?

3. Let f be defined by $f(x) = 5x^2 - 5x + 2$.
   (a) Graph f.
   (b) On what set is the function strictly increasing?
   (c) On what set is the function strictly decreasing?
   (d) What is the maximum value of f? Minimum value of f?

4. Let f be defined by $f(x) = -5x^2 + 3x - 1$.
   (a) Graph f.
   (b) On what set is the function strictly increasing?
   (c) On what set is the function strictly decreasing?
   (d) What is the maximum value of f? Minimum value of f?

5. Let f be defined by $f(x) = ax^2 + bx + c$ where $a > 0$.
   (a) Graph f.
   (b) On what set is the function strictly increasing?
   (c) On what set is the function strictly decreasing?
   (d) What is the maximum value of f? Minimum value of f?

6. Let f be defined by $f(x) = ax^2 + bx + c$ where $a < 0$.
   (a) Graph f.
   (b) On what set is the function strictly increasing?
   (c) On what set is the function strictly decreasing?
   (d) What is the maximum value of f? Minimum value of f?

7. Let g be defined by $g(x) = (x^2 + 2x - 63)/8$. Prove that if (x, y) is any point on the graph of g, then the distance from the point (x, y) to the line $y = -10$ is equal to the distance from the point (x, y) to $(-1, -6)$.

8. Let g be defined by $g(x) = (-x^2 + 4x)/4$. Prove if (x, y) is any point on the graph of g then the distance from the point (x, y) to the line $y = 2$ is equal to the distance from the point (x, y) to $(2, 0)$.

9. Prove that every point on the graph of $g(x) = 3x^2 + 6x - 7$ is equidistant between the point $(-1, -119/12)$ and the line $y = -121/12$.

4-6   algebra of functions

We are familiar with how the rational operations of addition, subtraction, multiplication, and division are performed on pairs of real numbers; we now define these operations on pairs of functions.

If f and g are functions defined by $f(x) = 3x + 2$ and $g(x) = x^2 + 7x - 5$, we define the *sum function h of f and g*, denoted by $h = f + g$, by

$$h(x) = f(x) + g(x) = x^2 + 10x - 3.$$

We have assumed the domains of both f and g to be the set of all real numbers; thus, the domain of h is also the set of all real numbers.

Consider the following two functions with different domains:

$$f = \{(2, 4), (5, 6), (8, -1), (10, -3)\}$$

and

$$g = \{(2, 5), (7, 1), (8, 4), (10, 13), (11, -5)\}.$$

For these two functions, $D_f = \{2, 5, 8, 10\}$ and $D_g = \{2, 7, 8, 10, 11\}$. Although the domains of f and g are not equal, they do have the numbers 2, 8, and 10 common to their domains; thus, $D_f \cap D_g = \{2, 8, 10\}$. The intersection of D_f and D_g is the domain of the sum function h; hence, h is defined by

$$h = \{(x, f(x) + g(x)) | x \in D_f \cap D_g\}.$$

In our example, $h = \{(2, 9), (8, 3), (10, 10)\}$.

If f and g are defined by $f(x) = x^2 + 6$ and $g(x) = \sqrt{x - 1}$ where $D_f = \{x | x \text{ is a real number}\}$ and $D_g = \{x | x \text{ is a real number and } x \geq 1\}$, then the sum function h is defined by

$$h(x) = x^2 + 6 + \sqrt{x - 1}$$

where

$$D_h = \{x | x \text{ is a real number and } x \geq 1\}.$$

The difference, product, and quotient of two functions f and g, denoted by $f-g$, $f\times g$, and f/g, respectively, are defined by

$$f-g=\{(x,f(x)-g(x))|x\in D_f\cap D_g\},$$
$$f\times g=\{(x,f(x)\cdot g(x))|x\in D_f\cap D_g\},$$
$$f/g=\{(x,f(x)/g(x))|x\in D_f\cap D_g \text{ and } g(x)\neq 0\}.$$

examples

1. Let f and g be defined by $f(x)=2x+1$ and $g(x)=3x-6$.
   (a) The difference function $h=f-g$ is defined by $h(x)=-x+7$; the domain is the set of all real numbers.
   (b) The product function $h=f\times g$ is defined by $h(x)=(2x+1)(3x-6)=6x^2-9x-6$; the domain is the set of all real numbers.
   (c) The quotient function $h=f/g$ is defined by $h(x)=(2x+1)/(3x-6)$; the domain is the set of all real numbers except $x=2$.

2. If $f=\{(2, 4), (5, 6), (8, -1), (10, -3)\}$ and $g=\{(2, 5), (7, 1), (8, 4), (10, 13), (11, -5)\}$, then

$$f-g=\{(2,-1),(8,-5),(10,-16)\},$$
$$f\times g=\{(2,20),(8,-4),(10,-39)\},$$

and

$$f/g=\{(2,4/5),(8,-1/4),(10,-3/13)\}.$$

It can be proved that if f and g are continuous, then $f+g$, $f-g$, $f\times g$, and f/g are continuous on their respective domains. Thus, since linear functions are continuous, the functions in the first three preceding examples are continuous on their respective domains. The quotient function in Example 1(c) is said to be discontinuous at $x=2$; 2 is not in the domain of f/g.

We now define an operation on pairs of functions, which is quite different from the rational operations. Let f and g be functions defined by $f(x)=3x+5$ and $g(x)=2x-3$. Notice that $g(4)=5$ and $f(5)=20$; we write $f(g(4))$ to represent the number in the range of f associated with the number $g(4)$ in its domain. In general, for $f(g(x))$ to be defined, x must be in the domain of g so that $g(x)$ exists, and $g(x)$ must be in the domain of f. For the given function,

$$f(g(x))=f(2x-3)=3(2x-3)+5=6x-4$$

for every real number x. We have defined a new function h such that $h(x)=f(g(x))$, called the *composition of f by g*.

For any two functions f and g, the composition of f by g is denoted by $f\circ g$ and is defined as follows.

$$f\circ g=\{(x,f(g(x)))|x\in D_g \text{ and } g(x)\in D_f\}.$$

Thus,

$$g\circ f=\{(x,g(f(x)))|x\in D_f \text{ and } f(x)\in D_g\}.$$

If f and g are functions defined by $f(x) = x^2 + 6$ and $g(x) = 2x + 5$, then $f \circ g$ is defined by

$$f(g(x)) = (2x + 5)^2 + 6 = 4x^2 + 20x + 31$$

and $g \circ f$ is defined by

$$g(f(x)) = 2(x^2 + 6) + 5 = 2x^2 + 17.$$

As seen by this example, in general $f \circ g \neq g \circ f$.

examples

1. If f and g are defined by $f(x) = 7x + 2$ and $g(x) = x^2 - 5$, then $f \circ g$ is defined by $f(g(x)) = 7(x^2 - 5) + 2 = 7x^2 - 33$ and $g \circ f$ is defined by $g(f(x)) = (7x + 2)^2 - 5 = 49x^2 + 28x - 1$. The domains of both $f \circ g$ and $g \circ f$ are the set of all real numbers.

2. If $f = \{(2, 4), (3, 5), (4, -1), (5, 2)\}$ and $g = \{(2, -3), (3, 3), (4, 2), (5, 4), (-1, 1)\}$, then

$$f \circ g = \{(3, 5), (4, 4), (5, -1)\}$$

and

$$g \circ f = \{(2, 2), (3, 4), (4, 1), (5, -3)\}.$$

It should be noted that the domains of f and $g \circ f$ are the same; this is because every number in the range of f is in the domain of g.

3. If f and g are defined by $f(x) = x^2 + 1$ and $g(x) = \sqrt{x - 4}$, then $f \circ g$ is defined by

$$f(g(x)) = (\sqrt{x - 4})^2 + 1 = x - 3$$

and $g \circ f$ is defined by

$$g(f(x)) = \sqrt{(x^2 + 1) - 4} = \sqrt{x^2 - 3}.$$

The domain of $f \circ g$ is all real numbers greater than or equal to 4; the domain of $g \circ f$ is all real numbers greater than or equal to $\sqrt{3}$.

4. If f and g are defined by $f(x) = 3x + 5$ and $g(x) = (x - 5)/3$, then $f(g(x)) = x$ and $g(f(x)) = x$.

We notice in Example 4 that not only is $f \circ g = g \circ f$ but the composition of f by g and the composition of g by f is the identity function. This means that an ordered pair (a, b) is an element of f if and only if (b, a) is an element of g; in other words, f and g are the inverse functions of each other. This suggests another routine method to define the inverse of a given function. For example, if f is defined by $f(x) = (2x + 7)/(x - 3)$ and if the inverse function g exists, then $f(g(x)) = x$; hence, $(2g(x) + 7)/(g(x) - 3) = x$ and solving for $g(x)$ we get

$$
\begin{aligned}
2g(x) + 7 &= xg(x) - 3x, \\
2g(x) - xg(x) &= -3x - 7, \\
(2 - x)g(x) &= -3x - 7.
\end{aligned}
$$

Thus, the inverse function g is defined by $g(x) = (3x + 7)/(x - 2)$.

1. Let f be defined by $f(x) = 3 + \sqrt{x-4}$.
   (a) What is the minimum value of this function?
   (b) Does the function have a maximum value?
   (c) On what set is the function increasing?
   (d) On what set is the function decreasing?

2. Let f and g be defined by $f(x) = 3x + 5$ and $g(x) = 2x - 5$.
   (a) Define $f + g$. State the domain.
   (b) Define $f \times g$. State the domain.
   (c) Define f/g. State the domain.
   (d) Define $f \circ g$. State the domain.
   (e) Define $g \circ f$. State the domain.

3. Let f and g be defined by $f(x) = 5x + 7$ and $g(x) = x + 3$.
   (a) Define $f \circ g$. State the domain.
   (b) Define $g \circ f$. State the domain.

4. Let f and g be defined by $f(x) = 3x^2 + 5x - 6$ and $g(x) = x + 7$.
   (a) Define $f \circ g$. State the domain.
   (b) Define $g \circ f$. State the domain.

5. Let $f = \{(0, 1), (2, 0), (3, -4), (4, 2), (5, 1)\}$ and $g = \{(1, 0), (2, 2), (3, -1), (4, 4), (5, 3)\}$.
   (a) Define f/g. State the domain.
   (b) Define g/f. State the domain.
   (c) Define $f \circ g$. State the domain.
   (d) Define $g \circ f$. State the domain.

6. If f, g, and h are defined by $f(x) = x^2$, $g(x) = 2x + 3$, and $h(x) = x^3 - 7$, verify that $(f \circ g) \circ h = f \circ (g \circ h)$.

7. Let f be a function with domain all real numbers except 0. If $f(xy) = f(x) + f(y)$ for all real numbers in the domain of f, do each of the following.
   (a) Find $f(1)$.
   (b) Find $f(-1)$.
   (c) Prove $f(x) = f(-x)$ for all x in the domain of f.

8. Let $f = \{(2, 1), (3, 2), (4, 5), (5, 1)\}$,
   $g = \{(1, 1), (2, 2), (3, 4), (4, 3)\}$, and
   $h = \{(1, 5), (2, 3), (3, 3), (5, 1)\}$.

   List the elements in each function:

   (a) $f + g$ (b) $f \circ g$ (c) $f \circ (g + h)$
   (d) $(g + h) \circ f$ (e) $g \circ f$ (f) $(f + g) \circ (f + h)$

9. Let f be a function defined by $f(x) = 3x + 7$. Find a function g such that if $h = f \circ g$ then $h(x) = 8x^2 + 15x - 19$.

10. Let f be a function defined by $f(x) = 5x - 2$. Find a function g such that if $h = f \circ g$ then $h(x) = 3x^2 + 11x - 12$.

11. Let f, g, and h be defined by $f(x) = (3x + 5)/(x + 1)$, $g(x) = 2x - 5$, and $h(x) = x^2 + 4$. Verify that $f \circ (g \circ h) = (f \circ g) \circ h$.

12. Let f, g, and h be defined by $f(x) = (3x - 1)/x$, $g(x) = 1/x$, and $h(x) = 2x + 7$. Verify that $f \circ (g \circ h) = (f \circ g) \circ h$.

exponential and logarithm functions

5

5-1   exponential functions

Let b be any real number. The student should be familiar with the fact that b^n where n is a positive integer greater than 1 is the product of n numbers, each of which is b; furthermore, $b^1 = b$. (See Chapter 7 for an inductive definition of positive integral exponents.) If $b \neq 0$, negative integral exponents are defined by $b^{-n} = 1/b^n$. We complete the definition of b^t where t is an integer by defining $b^0 = 1$, if $b \neq 0$.

The following basic properties of exponents are a consequence of these definitions. For all integers m and n,

$$\begin{aligned}
&1. \quad b^m b^n = b^{m+n}; \\
&2. \quad b^m/b^n = b^{m-n}, \text{ provided } b \neq 0; \\
&3. \quad (b^m)^n = b^{mn}.
\end{aligned}$$

These properties can be proved for positive integers by mathematical induction. Then, the definitions for non-positive integral exponents are used to prove that each property is valid for the set of all integers.

If $b > 0$, we define $b^{1/2} = \sqrt{b}$ where $\sqrt{b}$ is the positive real number x such that $x^2 = b$. In general, if $b > 0$ we define $b^{1/n}$ by $\sqrt[n]{b}$ where $\sqrt[n]{b}$ is the positive real number x such that $x^n = b$. Also, we define $b^{m/n}$

by $(b^{1/n})^m$, or $(\sqrt[n]{b})^m$. Using these definitions, the basic properties of exponents can be proved valid for the set of all rational numbers. We shall assume the student is familiar with rational exponents and the proofs of the basic theorems for rational exponents.

We now consider the problem of defining b^x where $b > 0$ and x is any real number. In attempting to define such an expression as $5^{\sqrt{2}}$, we seek affirmative answers to two questions: (1) Can irrational exponents be useful either in the further development of mathematics or in the application of mathematics to other fields? and (2) Can irrational exponents be defined so that the basic properties of exponents which have been proved for rational numbers will remain valid for irrational numbers? In fact, the answer to each of these questions is "yes." It is not an easy task to give a precise definition of irrational exponents with the limited mathematical tools at our disposal, and without a precise definition of irrational exponents it is impossible for us to prove that the exponent properties for irrational numbers are valid, although this is the case.

There are various ways of defining irrational exponents. One of the ways that $5^{\sqrt{2}}$ can be defined is as follows:†

definition: Let $S = \{x \mid x$ is a positive rational number and $x^2 < 2\}$. The set S is not empty since, for example, 1/2, 1, and 7/5 are numbers in the set. Next, let $T = \{y \mid y = 5^x$ for every rational number x in $S\}$; thus, T contains such elements as $5^{1/2} = \sqrt{5}$, $5^1 = 5$, and $5^{7/5} = (\sqrt[5]{5})^7$. It can easily be proved that the set of real numbers T has an upper bound; thus, by the completeness property, T has a least upper bound. We then define $5^{\sqrt{2}}$ to be the least upper bound of the set T.

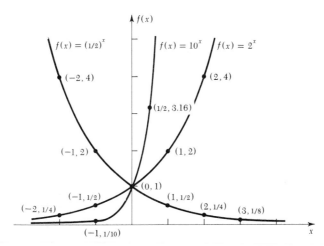

Exponential function

FIGURE 5–1

† Another method to define $5^{\sqrt{2}}$ is by using infinite sequences.

The student should look forward to "filling in the gaps" in our discussion of exponents in his future mathematical studies. At present, we must content ourselves with the fact that if $b > 0$ then b^t can be defined precisely for any real number t and the ususal properties of exponents can be proved valid for the set of real numbers.

Let f be defined by $f(x) = b^x$. If $b > 1$, the function f is continuous and strictly increasing, and if $0 < b < 1$, f is continuous and strictly decreasing. In Figure 5–1, we give a sketch of the graphs of each of the functions defined by $f(x) = b^x$ where $b = 1/2$, $b = 2$, and $b = 10$. We call f an *exponential function with base b*; the exponential function with base 10 is defined by $f(x) = 10^x$.

5–2   logarithm functions

If f is defined by $f(x) = 10^x$, then some of the ordered pairs in f are $(-1, 1/10)$, $(0, 1)$, $(1, 10)$, and $(2, 100)$. Since f is strictly increasing, it has an inverse function f^{-1} which is also strictly increasing, as indicated in Figure 5–2. Some of the ordered pairs in f^{-1} are $(1/10, -1)$,

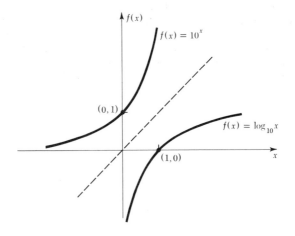

Exponential and logarithm function—base 10

FIGURE 5–2

$(0, 1)$, $(10, 1)$, and $(100, 2)$. The standard notation for the inverse function f^{-1} is $\log_{10}$ and $f^{-1}(x) = \log_{10} x$ (read "log x base 10"): The inverse function of the exponential function is called the *logarithm function*. As we have seen $\log_{10} 10 = 1$, $\log_{10} 100 = 2$, $\log_{10} 1/10 = -1$, and $\log_{10} 1 = 0$.

Since the logarithm function is strictly increasing and since $\log_{10} 1 = 0$ and $\log_{10} 10 = 1$, it follows that if $1 \leqslant x \leqslant 10$ then $0 \leqslant \log_{10} x \leqslant 1$.

If x is any number between 1 and 10, such as 2.718, the function value $\log_{10} x$ can be found in Table I, page 283. We shall discuss in the next section how $\log_{10} x$ can be approximated for any positive real number x using the function values for numbers between 1 and 10 in the domain of the logarithm function.

In general, if $y = b^x$ where $b > 0$ and $b \neq 1$, then $x = \log_b y$. Since the range of the exponential function is the set of positive real numbers, $\log_b y$ is defined only for positive real numbers y. As a consequence of the definition of the logarithm function, it follows that $\log_b b = 1$ and $\log_b 1 = 0$.

We now state three basic logarithm theorems. Let $b > 0$ and $b \neq 1$, then

theorem 5–1: $\log_b xy = \log_b x + \log_b y$ for positive real numbers x and y,

theorem 5–2: $\log_b x/y = \log_b x - \log_b y$ for positive real numbers x and y, and

theorem 5–3: $\log_b x^r = r \log_b x$ for a positive real number x and any real number r.

proof of theorem 5–1: Let $\log_b x = u$ and $\log_b y = v$. Then, $b^u = x$ and $b^v = y$ by definition.
Thus,

$$b^u \, b^v \ = xy.$$

Hence,

$$b^{u+v} \ = xy,$$

and from the definition of the logarithm function

$$\log_b xy = u + v.$$

Consequently,

$$\log_b xy = \log_b x + \log_b y.$$

proof of theorem 5–2: Left as an exercise for the student.

proof of theorem 5–3: Left as an exercise for the student.

exercises

1. Prove that $\log_b x/y = \log_b x - \log_b y$.
2. Prove that $\log_b x^r = r \log_b x$.
3. Find the number the variable represents in order to make each of the following a true statement.
   (a) $\log_{10} 1000 = y$ (b) $\log_2 8 = y$
   (c) $\log_{10} x = -2$ (d) $\log_{10} x = 2$
   (e) $\log_b 16 = 4$ (f) $\log_b 64 = 3$
   (g) $\log_{10} 10^r = 7$ (h) $\log_9 3^r = 2.5$
   (i) $\log_{10} 0.01 = x$ (j) $\log_{10} 0.0001 = t$

4. Find the number the variable represents in order to make each of the following a true statement.
(a) $\log_{10} 0.001 = x$
(b) $\log_3 81 = y$
(c) $\log_{10} x = -4$
(d) $\log_{10} x = -1$
(e) $\log_b 25 = 2$
(f) $\log_b 1/8 = 3$
(g) $\log_b 0.0625 = -4$

5. Given: $\log_{10} 2 = 0.3010$. Find each of the following. Do not use tables. (Hints: $200 = 10^2 \times 2$ and $5 = 10/2$.)
(a) $\log_{10} 20$
(b) $\log_{10} 200$
(c) $\log_{10} 0.2$
(d) $\log_{10} 0.02$
(e) $\log_{10} 5$
(f) $\log_{10} 25$
(g) $\log_{10} 4$
(h) $\log_{10} 80$
(i) $\log_{10} 6.4$
(j) $\log_{10} \sqrt{2}$
(k) $\log_{10} \sqrt{5}$
(l) $\log_{10} \sqrt{10}$

6. Given: $\log_{10} 3 = 0.4771$. Find each of the following. Do not use tables.
(a) $\log_{10} 30$
(b) $\log_{10} 300$
(c) $\log_{10} 0.3$
(d) $\log_{10} 0.03$
(e) $\log_{10} 27$
(f) $\log_{10} 8.1$
(g) $\log_{10} 0.27$
(h) $\log_{10} \sqrt{3}$
(i) $\log_{10} \sqrt[5]{3}$

7. Solve for x: $\log_{10} x^2 + \log_{10} x^3 = 10$.

8. Solve for x: $\log_{10} x^{5/2} - \log_{10} x^{1/2} = 6$.

9. If f is defined by $f(x) = b^x$ where $b = 1$, does f have an inverse function?

10. (a) If $\log_b x = y$, what is $\log_{1/b} x$?
(b) If $\log_b x = y$, what is $\log_b 1/x$?

11. State the number each letter represents.
(a) $\log_{11} 11^5 = t$
(b) $\log_3 9^{(\log_{10} x)} = 6$
(c) $\log_y 6^3 = 3$
(d) $\log_{11} x^2 = \log_{11} 100$

12. Prove that $\log_y x = 1/\log_x y$ provided x, y are positive real numbers and neither is equal to 1.

13. What is the domain of f if $f(x) = \log_b x$? What is the range of f?

5-3   computations with logarithms

From Table I, we find that $\log_{10} 4.02 = 0.6042$. (Note: log 4.02 is approximately equal to 0.6042, so it would be more proper to write $\log_{10} 4.02 \approx 0.6042$. However, we allow ourselves the latitude of using the equals sign when computing with logarithms.) Since $402 = 4.02 \times 10^2$ and since

$$\begin{aligned}
\log_{10} xy &= \log_{10} x + \log_{10} y, \\
\log_{10} 402 &= \log_{10} (4.02)(10^2) \\
&= \log_{10} 4.02 + \log_{10} 10^2 \\
&= 0.6042 + 2 \\
&= 2.6042.
\end{aligned}$$

Similarly, $\log_{10} 40,200 = 4.6042$ and $\log_{10} 0.00402 = 0.6042 + (-3)$. Since 0.00402 is less than 1, the logarithm is negative; however, for computational reasons $\log_{10} 0.00402$ is generally written $0.6042 + (-3)$, or $0.6042 - 3$, instead of -2.3958.

The logarithm of any positive number is the sum of an integer called the *characteristic* and a number x called the *mantissa* where $0 \leqslant x < 1$. For $\log_{10} 402 = 2.6042$, 2 is the characteristic and 0.6042 is the mantissa. If y is a positive number and $y = 10^n x$ where $1 \leqslant x < 10$ and n is an integer, then $\log_{10} x$ is the mantissa of $\log_{10} y$ and n is the characteristic. Only the mantissas of the logarithms of numbers between 1 and 10 are listed in Table 1; the characteristic of the logarithm of any positive number expressed in decimal notation can be determined by the following simple rules. If the number is greater than 1, the characteristic is one less than the number of digits to the left of the decimal. If the number is positive and less than 1, the characteristic is the negative of one more than the number of significant zeros to the right of the decimal, as shown in the following table.

N	*Characteristic* of $\log_{10} N$
368.21	2
7,005.07	3
0.981	-1
0.00386	-3
3.14	0

The following examples exhibit the use of logarithms in arithmetical computations. (Since all logarithms are in base 10, the base is not written.)

examples

1. Find $(684)^{1/3}(0.00261)$. Let $N = (684)^{1/3}(0.00261)$.

$$\log N = \log 684^{1/3} + \log 0.00261$$
$$= \frac{1}{3}(2.8351) + [0.4166 + (-3)]$$
$$= 0.9450 + 0.4166 - 3$$
$$= 1.3616 - 3$$
$$= 0.3616 - 2$$

Hence,

$$N = 0.02299.$$

From $\log_{10} N = 0.3616 - 2$, we conclude $N = 10^{0.3616 - 2} = 10^{0.3616} \times 10^{-2} = 2.299 \times 10^{-2}$. The number 0.3616 is the mantissa and -2 is the characteristic. Furthermore, N is called the *anti-logarithm* of $0.3616 - 2$.

2. Find $\sqrt[7]{0.00314}$. Let $N = \sqrt[7]{0.00314}$.

$$\log N = \log (0.00314)^{1/7}$$
$$\log N = \frac{1}{7} (0.4969 - 3)$$

Since 7 is not a factor of 3, we substitute $4.4969 - 7$ for $0.4969 - 3$ to facilitate the division of the logarithm by 7 and to simplify successive computations. Of course, since $11 - 14 = 0 - 3$ the number $11.4969 - 14$ could be substituted for $0.4969 - 3$ with the same results.

$$\log N = \frac{1}{7} (4.4969 - 7)$$
$$= 0.6424 - 1$$

Thus,

$$N = 0.4389.$$

3. Find $7.294/84.67$. Let $N = 7.294/84.67$.

$$\log N = \log 7.294 - \log 84.67$$
$$= 0.8630 - 1.9278$$
$$= 2.8630 - 1.9278 - 2$$
$$= 0.9352 - 2$$

Thus,

$$N = 0.08613.$$

4. Find $\dfrac{(321)^3 \sqrt[5]{0.00461}}{\sqrt[3]{136}}$. Let $N = \dfrac{(321)^3 \sqrt[5]{0.00461}}{\sqrt[3]{136}}$.

$$\log N = \log(321)^3 + \log (0.00461)^{1/5} - \log (136)^{1/3}$$
$$= 3(2.5065) + \frac{1}{5} (2.6637 - 5) - \frac{1}{3} (2.1335)$$
$$= 7.5195 + 0.5327 - 1 - 0.7112$$
$$= 8.0522 - 1.7112$$
$$= 6.3410$$

Thus,

$$N = 2{,}193{,}000.$$

5. Solve $3^{2x+1} = 15$. A standard procedure for solving exponential equations such as this is to use the fact that if $f(x) = g(x)$ then $\log f(x) = \log g(x)$ for all x where $f(x) > 0$. We exhibit two different solutions.

Solution 1
$$\log 3^{(2x+1)} = \log 15$$
$$(2x + 1)\log 3 = \log 15$$
$$(2x + 1)0.4771 = 1.1761$$
$$0.9542x + 0.4771 = 1.1761$$
$$0.9542x = 0.6990$$
$$x = \frac{0.6990}{0.9542}$$
$$x = 0.7327.$$

The quotient $0.6990/0.9542$ can be found by the long division process or by logarithms.

Solution 2
$$\log 3^{(2x+1)} = \log 15$$
$$(2x+1)\log 3 = \log 15$$
$$2x\log 3 + \log 3 = \log 15$$
$$x\log 3^2 = \log 15 - \log 3$$
$$x\log 9 = \log 5$$
$$x = \log 5/\log 9$$
$$\log x = \log(\log 5) - \log(\log 9)$$
$$= \log 0.6990 - \log 0.9542$$
$$= (0.8445 - 1) - (0.9796 - 1)$$
$$= 1.8445 - 0.9796 - 1$$
$$= 0.8649 - 1.$$

Thus,

$$x = 0.7327.$$

exercises

Perform the indicated operations.

1. $(0.00137)^5(268)^3$

2. $\sqrt[3]{0.00369}$

3. $\sqrt[5]{0.0217}$

4. $\sqrt{128} \cdot \sqrt[3]{361}$

5. $\dfrac{\sqrt[3]{684}}{\sqrt{721}}$

6. $\dfrac{(876)(38.23)^2(425)^{1/2}}{(9.12)^5(7{,}628)^{1/3}}$

Solve the following equations.

7. $2^x = 23$

8. $3^{5x+2} = 627$

9. $6(3^x) = 17$

10. $11(5^{3x-7}) = 16(3^{2x+1})$

trigonometric functions

6

6-1   introduction

We now define six functions important to the development of mathematical analysis and to many physical applications of mathematics. These are called the *trigonometric* or *circular functions.* The word "trigonometry" means *triangle measurement*; originally, the trigonometric functions were defined in terms of right triangles and were used to find unknown sides and angles of given triangles when other parts of the triangle were given. We shall take a somewhat more sophisticated geometric approach than the right triangle definitions and define the trigonometric functions in terms of the rectangular coordinate system. This approach enlarges the number of physical and mathematical applications of the trigonometric functions and, with certain restrictions, includes the right triangle definitions as special cases.

It is possible to give nongeometric definitions of the trigonometric functions, one of which is in terms of "infinite series." This approach is beyond the scope of our study, but the student should look forward to studying nongeometric definitions of the trigonometric functions and to giving nongeometric proofs of the theorems for which we give geometric proofs.

6-2 angles and angular measure

In the study of plane geometry, we learn that two different rays with a common origin divide the plane into two regions; the set of points on both rays is called an *angle*. The rays are called *sides* of the angle and the origin is called the *vertex* of the angle.

Let A be an angle with vertex V. (See Figure 6–1.) If we construct a circle with V as center and radius *one unit*, it intersects the sides of the angle points denoted by P and Q. The length of the circular arc PQ subtending angle A is denoted by $|PQ|$ and is a *measure of the angle A*. This measure for angles in terms of arc length is called *radian measure*. For example, if $|PQ|$ is of unit length, angle A is called a *radian*. If $|PQ|$ is $2\frac{1}{2}$ units in length, the measure of angle A is $2\frac{1}{2}$ radians.

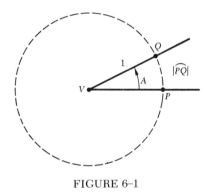

FIGURE 6–1

Consider the angle A as described above. Draw two circles with V as center, one having radius 1 and the other radius $r \neq 1$. A geometry theorem states that the ratio of the arc lengths subtending a fixed central angle is equal to the ratio of the corresponding radii; thus,

$$\frac{|SR|}{|PQ|} = \frac{r}{1}.$$

Hence, $|SR| = r|PQ|$. Consequently, if s is the length of arc subtending a central angle with θ as radian measure of a circle of radius r, then $s = r\,\theta$ and $\theta = s/r$. For $r = 1$, $\theta = s$.

The student should be familiar with *degree measure* for angles: the circumference of a circle is divided into 360 arcs of equal length and the angle subtended at the center by one of these arcs is defined to have a measure of *one degree*. Since the circumference of a circle is $2\pi r$ where r is the radius, the circumference of the unit circle is 2π. Hence, the angle with 180 degrees as measure also has π radians as measure.

The following table lists corresponding radians measure and degree measure for special angles.

Degree Measure	Radian Measure
180 degrees	π radians
90 degrees	$\pi/2$ radians
60 degrees	$\pi/3$ radians
$180/\pi$ degrees	1 radian
45 degrees	$\pi/4$ radians
30 degrees	$\pi/6$ radians
1 degree	$\pi/180$ radians

Note: $\pi/180$ radians is approximately 0.017 radians and $180/\pi$ degrees is approximately 57.3°.

6–3 angles in standard position

Consider the rectangular coordinate system and the graph of the circle with center at the origin and radius r. If T is the point of intersection of the circle and the positive x-axis, then T has coordinates $(r, 0)$. If the circle is rotated a given amount in either direction from the original position, then the point T moves to some point R with coordinates (x, y). In this case, we say an angle A is *generated* which has the positive x-axis as *initial side* and the ray from the origin through the point T as its *terminal side*. If the circle is rotated one-fourth of a revolution counterclockwise, T moves to the point with coordinates $(0, r)$ and the radian measure of the angle generated is $\pi/2$ radians. If either $x=0$ or $y=0$, then T is on one of the coordinate axes and the angle generated is called a *quadrantal angle*. If neither x nor y is zero, then one of the following is true: $x > 0$ and $y > 0$, $x < 0$ and $y > 0$, $x < 0$ and $y < 0$, or $x > 0$ and $y < 0$.

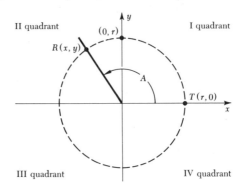

A is second quadrant angle

FIGURE 6–2

In these cases the angle is called a *first-*, *second-*, *third-*, or *fourth-quadrant* angle, respectively. The corresponding portions of the co-ordinate plane are called first, second, third, and fourth quadrants; they are generally denoted by the Roman numerals I, II, III, and IV.

There is no restriction on the amount of rotation or the direction of rotation in generating angles. If the circle is rotated counter-clockwise one and a quarter revolutions, the point T has coordinates $(0, r)$ and the measure of the angle generated is $5\pi/2$ radians. This angle has the same terminal side as the angle with measure $\pi/2$ radians; such angles are called *coterminal angles*.

An angle generated by rotating the circle clockwise is called a negative angle; the measure of such an angle is negative. For example, a clockwise revolution of one and one-half turns would describe an angle with -3π radians as measure; the equivalent degree measure is -540 degrees. The angle described by two-thirds of a revolution clockwise has measure of -240 degrees, or $-4\pi/3$ radians. Assigning

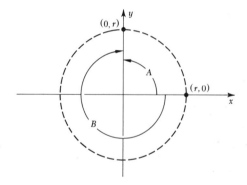

A and B are coterminal angles

Measure of A: $\pi/2$ radians or $90°$

Measure of B: $-3\pi/2$ radians or $-270°$

FIGURE 6–3

positive measure to angles generated counterclockwise and negative measure to angles generated clockwise is analogous to assigning positive numbers to points to the right of the origin and negative numbers to points to the left of the origin on the number line. In fact, if we think of the number line with its origin at the point $(1, 0)$ on the unit circle as being wrapped around the circle with positive direction counterclockwise and negative direction clockwise, the coordinates on the line could be used to find the radian measure of any angle generated having the positive x-axis as its initial side.

For convenience, we agree that no rotation describes an "angle" of $0°$ measure or 0 radians. We also agree that a rotation of one counter-clockwise revolution describes an "angle" whose measure is $360°$ or 2π radians; etc.

definition: An angle with vertex at the origin and initial side on the positive x-axis is called an angle in *standard position.*

The trigonometric functions are defined in terms of angles in
standard position in the next section.

exercises

1. Find the length of a circular arc subtending a central angle with measure
   3 radians and a radius of 5 inches.

2. Find the length of a circular arc subtending a central angle with measure
   37° and a radius of 7 inches.

3. Find the length of a circular arc subtending a central angle with measure
   129° and a radius of 20 inches.

4. What is the radian measure of an angle at the center of a circle with
   radius 2 feet subtended by an arc 3 feet in length? What is the degree
   measure of the angle?

5. A central angle with 5 radians as measure subtends an arc of 7 inches
   length on the circumference.
   (a) Find the circumference of the circle.
   (b) Find the area of the circle.

6. A central angle with 2 radians as measure subtends an arc of 3 inches on
   the circumference. Find the radius of the circle.

7. State whether the angle in standard position is a quadrantal angle, or a
   first-, second-, third-, or fourth-quadrant angle if the terminal side contains the given point.
   (a) $(1, 3)$ (b) $(-7, 2)$ (c) $(\sqrt{3}, -5)$
   (d) $(1, 0)$ (e) $(-5, 0)$ (f) $(-\sqrt{2}, 7/3)$

8. State whether the angle in standard position is a quadrantal angle, or a
   first-, second-, third-, or fourth-quadrant angle if it has the following
   measure.
   (a) 2π radians   (b) -540 degrees   (c) $-7\pi/4$ radians
   (d) 135 degrees   (e) -1137π radians   (f) 1024 degrees
   (g) -225 degrees   (h) $3\pi/4$ radians   (i) $7\pi/6$ radians
   (j) -315 degrees

9. Let A be an angle in standard position. Find the coordinates of the point
   of intersection of the terminal side of angle A and the unit circle with
   center at the origin if the measure of A is
   (a) 0 degrees   (b) $\pi/2$ radians   (c) $-3\pi/2$ radians
   (d) 180 degrees   (e) -270 degrees   (f) $\pi/4$ radians
   (g) $-3\pi/4$ radians   (h) $3\pi/2$ radians   (i) $5\pi/4$ radians
   (j) 225 degrees

10. Let A be an angle in standard position. Find the coordinates of the point
    of intersection of the terminal side of A and the unit circle with center at
    at the origin if the measure of A is

(a) 30 degrees   (b) 60 degrees   (c) $-5\pi/6$ radians
(d) 150 degrees   (e) 300 degrees   (f) $4\pi/3$ radians
(g) $-\pi/6$ radians

11. Assume the terminal side of a positive acute angle in standard position intersects a circle with center at the origin in the point $(8, 8\sqrt{3})$. Find the arc length subtended on the circumference by this angle.

12. Let the terminal side of an angle in standard position with measure 30° intersect the unit circle (center at origin with radius 1) in a point P with coordinates (x, y).
    (a) What is x?   (b) What is y?

6–4   definitions of the trigonometric functions

Consider an angle A in standard position with measure θ. Let P be any point other than the origin on the terminal side of the angle. Three numbers are associated with P: the x coordinate of P, the y coordinate of P, and the distance r of P from the origin. Although x and y may be positive, negative, or zero, r *is positive*.

definition: If A is not a quadrantal angle, then neither x nor y is zero; in this case, the three numbers associated with P determine the six ratios y/r, x/r, y/x, r/y, r/x, x/y called *trigonometric ratios*.

If $P'(x', y')$ is another point on the terminal side of angle A at

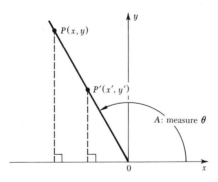

r is distance of P from the origin

r' is distance of P' from the origin

Trigonometric ratios: $y/r = y'/r'$, $x/r = x'/r'$, $y/x = y'/x'$,
$$r/y = r'/y', \quad r/x = r'/x', \quad x/y = x'/y'$$
FIGURE 6–4

distance $r' \neq r$ from the origin, the right triangles formed by dropping perpendiculars from P and P' to the x-axis are similar. Thus, the corresponding sides of the triangles are proportional and

$$y/r = y'/r',$$
$$x/r = x'/r',$$
$$y/x = y'/x',$$
$$r/y = r'/y',$$
$$r/x = r'/x',$$
and
$$x/y = x'/y'.$$

In other words, the trigonometric ratios are independent of the point chosen on the terminal side of angle A. (We leave as an exercise for the student to prove that for quadrantal angles the trigonometric ratios, if defined, are independent of the point chosen on the terminal side of the angle.)

We now define one of the six trigonometric functions. Consider any angle A with measure θ. If P is any point with coordinates (x, y) on the terminal side of an angle A at distance r from the origin, then the trigonometric ratio y/r is uniquely determined. The set s of ordered pairs $\{(\theta, y/r)\}$ is called the *sine function*; that is, the sine function is defined by

$s = \{(\theta, y/r) \mid \theta$ is the measure of any angle in standard position$\}$.

Using our familiar notation for functions, s could be defined by $s(\theta) = y/r$. Since $|y| \leq r$, $-r \leq y \leq r$ and $-1 \leq y/r \leq 1$; thus, the range of the sine function is the set of real numbers on the closed interval $[-1, 1]$. If θ is the radian measure of an angle A and if $0 < \theta < \pi$, then $y > 0$ and $s(\theta) > 0$. If $\pi < \theta < 2\pi$, then $y < 0$ and $s(\theta) < 0$.

Instead of $s(\theta)$ to denote the function value of the sine function at θ in the domain, the notation $\sin \theta$ is generally used; thus, the sine function is defined by

$$\sin \theta = y/r.$$

Since y is positive in the first and second quadrants, $\sin \theta$ is positive if θ is the measure of a first- or second-quadrant angle. Similarly, since $y < 0$ in the third and fourth quadrants, $\sin \theta$ is negative where θ is the measure of a third- or fourth-quadrant angle. If θ is the measure of a quadrantal angle with terminal side on the positive y-axis, then $y = r$ for any point $P(x, y)$ on the terminal side at distance r from the origin and $\sin \theta = 1$; if the terminal side is on the positive or negative x-axis, then $y = 0$ and $\sin \theta = 0$; and if the terminal side is on the negative y-axis, then $y = -r$ and $\sin \theta = -1$.

Let A be any angle and let θ be its measure. We define all six trigonometric functions called sine, cosine, tangent, cosecant, secant, and cotangent in terms of the trigonometric ratios.

definitions:

1. The *sine function* is $\{(\theta, y/r)\}$. The value of the sine function at θ is denoted by $\sin \theta$; thus, $\sin \theta = y/r$.

2. The *cosine function* is $\{(\theta, x/r)\}$. The value of the cosine function at θ is denoted by cos θ; thus, cos $\theta = x/r$.

3. The *tangent function* is $\{(\theta, y/x)|x \neq 0\}$. The value of the tangent function at θ is denoted by tan θ; thus, tan $\theta = y/x$.

4. The *cosecant function* is $\{(\theta, r/y)|y \neq 0\}$. The value of the cosecant function at θ is denoted by csc θ; thus, csc $\theta = r/y$.

5. The *secant function* is $\{(\theta, r/x)|x \neq 0\}$. The value of the secant function at θ is denoted by sec θ; thus, sec $\theta = r/x$.

6. The *cotangent function* is $\{(\theta, x/y)|y \neq 0\}$. The value of the cotangent function at θ is denoted by cot θ; thus, cot $\theta = x/y$.

Although the sine and cosine functions are defined for every θ, it is obvious that there are some values for which the tangent, cosecant, secant, and cotangent functions are not defined. Let us consider the tangent function; it is not defined where $x = 0$. Since $x = 0$ on the y-axis, tan θ is undefined when θ is the measure of quadrantal angles whose terminal sides are on the positive or negative y-axis. Thus, the tangent function is undefined for $\theta = \pm \pi/2, \pm 3\pi/2, \pm 5\pi/2$, etc.

Since x/y is the reciprocal of y/x, the cotangent function is called the *reciprocal function* of the tangent function. Similarly, the cosecant function is the reciprocal of the sine function and the secant function is the reciprocal of the cosine function. For any real number t, since $t = 0$ if and only if $1/t$ is undefined, it follows, for example, that csc π is undefined since sin $\pi = 0$. Furthermore, cot $\pi/2 = 0$ since tan $\pi/2$ is undefined, etc. If θ is the measure of other than a quadrantal angle,

$$\sin \theta = \frac{1}{\csc \theta}, \qquad \cos \theta = \frac{1}{\sec \theta}, \qquad \tan \theta = \frac{1}{\cot \theta}.$$

exercises

1. Consider a quadrantal angle with terminal side on the positive y-axis. Prove that the trigonometric ratios, if defined, are independent of the point chosen on the terminal side.

2. Consider a quadrantal angle with terminal side on the negative x-axis. Prove that the trigonometric ratios, if defined, are independent of the point chosen on the terminal side.

3. Consider a quadrantal angle with terminal side on the negative y-axis. Prove that the trigonometric ratios, if defined, are independent of the point chosen on the terminal side.

4. Consider a quadrantal angle with terminal side on the positive x-axis. Prove that the trigonometric ratios, if defined, are independent of the point chosen on the terminal side.

5. (a) State the range of the cosine function.
   (b) State the range of the secant function.

   (c) State the range of the tangent function.
   (d) State the range of the cotangent function.
   (e) State the range of the cosecant function.

6. State each of the following function values.
   (a) $\sin \pi/2$ (b) $\cos \pi/2$ (c) $\cot \pi/2$ (d) $\csc \pi/2$
   (e) $\sin -\pi/2$ (f) $\cos -\pi$ (g) $\tan -3\pi$ (h) $\cos -3\pi/2$

7. State each of the following function values.
   (a) $\cos \pi$ (b) $\tan \pi$ (c) $\sec \pi$ (d) $\sin \pi$
   (e) $\sin -\pi$ (f) $\cos -\pi/2$ (g) $\csc -\pi/2$ (h) $\cot -3\pi/2$

8. If the point $(3, 4)$ is on the terminal side of an angle in standard position with measure θ, find
   (a) $\sin \theta$ (b) $\cos \theta$ (c) $\tan \theta$ (d) $\csc \theta$
   (e) $\sec \theta$ (f) $\cot \theta$ (g) $(\sin \theta)^2 + (\cos \theta)^2$

9. If the point $(-2, \sqrt{3})$ is on the terminal side of an angle in standard position with measure θ, find
   (a) $\sin \theta$ (b) $\cos \theta$ (c) $\tan \theta$ (d) $\csc \theta$
   (e) $\sec \theta$ (f) $\cot \theta$ (g) $(\sin \theta)^2 + (\cos \theta)^2$

10. Prove for any θ that $(\sin \theta)^2 + (\cos \theta)^2 = 1$.

11. Prove $(\tan \theta)^2 < (\sec \theta)^2$ for any angle with measure θ for which the functions are defined.

12. If θ is the measure of a first- or third-quadrant angle and if $\tan \theta < 1$, prove that $\cot \theta > 1$.

13. Complete the following table.

SIGNS OF TRIGONOMETRIC FUNCTION VALUES FOR QUADRANT ANGLES

Function	I quadrant	II quadrant	III quadrant	IV quadrant
sin	+	+	−	−
cos	+			
tan	+			
csc	+			
sec	+			
cot	+			

14. Let θ be the measure of an angle in standard position and let P be a point with coordinates (x, y) on the terminal side at distance r from the origin. If P' is the point at distance r from the origin on the terminal side of an angle with $-\theta$ as measure, what are the coordinates of P'?

6–5   trigonometric function values of special angles

We have no simple analytic technique for finding sin 20°. In calculus, we learn how such function values can be approximated, but at present we must resort to the tables provided in the Appendix to find a decimal approximation of sin 20°. Many of the trigonometric function values, however, can be found by using the definitions of the trigonometric functions and elementary geometry theorems. The two main theorems used are the Pythagorean Theorem and the theorem stating that in a 30°—60° right triangle the side opposite the 30° angle is half the length of the hypotenuse.

To find the trigonometric function values of two angles with measures of 225 degrees and 180 degrees, respectively, we draw the

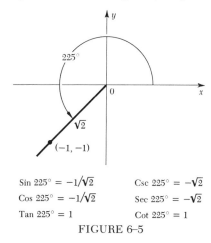

$$\text{Sin } 225° = -1/\sqrt{2} \qquad \text{Csc } 225° = -\sqrt{2}$$
$$\text{Cos } 225° = -1/\sqrt{2} \qquad \text{Sec } 225° = -\sqrt{2}$$
$$\text{Tan } 225° = 1 \qquad \text{Cot } 225° = 1$$

FIGURE 6–5

angles in standard position as in Figure 6–5, locate points on the terminal sides of the angles, and use the definitions of the trigonometric functions. Since the terminal side of the angle with 225° ($5\pi/4$ radians) as measure contains points with coordinates such that $x = y$, we can choose P with $(-1, -1)$ as coordinates. The distance of P from the origin is $\sqrt{2}$; thus,

$$\sin 225° = -1/\sqrt{2} \qquad \csc 225° = -\sqrt{2}$$
$$\cos 225° = -1/\sqrt{2} \qquad \sec 225° = -\sqrt{2}$$
$$\tan 225° = 1 \qquad \cot 225° = 1.$$

Since the terminal side of the angle with 180° (π radians) as measure is on the negative x-axis, we can choose P with $(-1, 0)$ as coordinates. The distance r of P from the origin is 1; thus,

$$\sin 180° = 0 \qquad \csc 180° \text{ is not defined,}$$
$$\cos 180° = -1 \qquad \sec 180° = -1,$$
$$\tan 180° = 0 \qquad \cot 180° \text{ is not defined.}$$

exercise

Complete the following table.

RADIAN MEASURE

Function	0	$\pi/6$	$\pi/4$	$\pi/3$	$\pi/2$	$2\pi/3$	$3\pi/4$	$5\pi/6$	π	$7\pi/6$	$5\pi/4$	$4\pi/3$	$3\pi/2$	$5\pi/3$	$7\pi/4$	$11\pi/6$	2π
$\sin\theta$									0	$-\dfrac{\sqrt{2}}{2}$							
$\cos\theta$									-1	$-\dfrac{\sqrt{2}}{2}$							
$\tan\theta$									0	1							
$\csc\theta$									$\sim$	$-\sqrt{2}$							
$\sec\theta$									-1	$-\sqrt{2}$							
$\cot\theta$									$\sim$	1							

The trigonometric functions are examples of what are called *periodic functions.*

definition: For any function f, if there is a real number $p \neq 0$ such that $f(x) = f(x + p)$ for all x in the domain of f, then f is called a *periodic function with period* p.

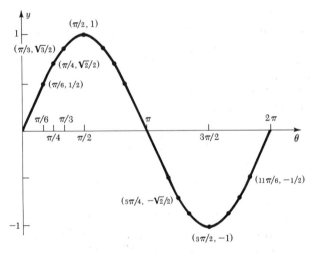

Graph: $y = \sin\theta$ Domain: $[0, 2\pi]$

FIGURE 6–6

Often, more than one number p exists for a given periodic function f such that $f(x)=f(x+p)$. If the set of periods of a periodic function contains a least *positive* number t, then t is called the *primitive period* of f.

From the definition of the sine function, we conclude that

$$\sin \theta = \sin (\theta + 2k\pi)$$

where k is any integer. The sine function is periodic with periods $\pm 2\pi$, $\pm 4\pi$, $\pm 6\pi$, etc. The primitive period of the sine function is 2π. Geometrically, this means that the graph of the sine function on the closed interval $[0, 2\pi]$ determines the entire graph of the function; the graph on the intervals $[2\pi, 4\pi]$, $[-2\pi, 0]$, etc. is the same as on the interval $[0, 2\pi]$. (See Figure 6–6.) By using the values of the sine function determined in the previous exercise, we can graph the sine function on the interval $[0, 2\pi]$.

Following are the graphs of the other five trigonometric functions. The student should be able to sketch these by plotting the points from the table in the exercise on page 84.

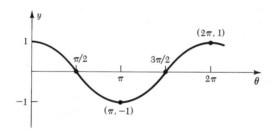

Graph of cosine function: $y = \cos \theta$

FIGURE 6–7 (a)

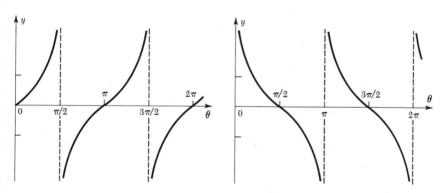

Graph of tangent function: $y = \tan \theta$ Graph of cotangent function: $y = \cot \theta$

FIGURE 6–7 (b)

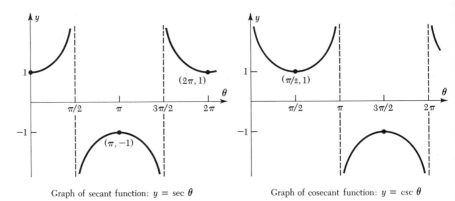

Graph of secant function: $y = \sec \theta$ Graph of cosecant function: $y = \csc \theta$

FIGURE 6-7 (c)

exercises

1. What is the primitive period of the (a) cosine function? (b) secant function? (c) cosecant function? (d) tangent function? (e) cotangent function?

2. Using the values obtained in the exercise on page 84 and the fact that the cosine and secant functions are periodic, sketch the graphs of the two functions on the closed interval $[-2\pi, 2\pi]$ on the same coordinate system.

3. Using the values obtained in the exercise on page 84 and the fact that the tangent and cotangent functions are periodic, sketch the graphs of the two functions on the closed interval $[-2\pi, 2\pi]$ on the same coordinate system.

4. For what intervals in the domain of the sine function is the function increasing? Decreasing?

5. For what intervals in the domain of the cosine function is the function increasing? Decreasing?

6. For what intervals in the domain of the tangent function is the function increasing? Decreasing?

7. For what intervals in the domain of the cotangent function is the function increasing? Decreasing?

8. Which of the trigonometric functions are odd functions?

9. Which of the trigonometric functions are even functions?

10. (a) If $f(x) = \sin 3x$, what is the primitive period of f?
    (b) If $g(x) = \sin x/5$, what is the primitive period of g?
    (c) If f is a periodic function with p as its primitive period, what is the primitive period of $f \circ g$ where $g(x) = ax$ and a is a positive real number?

11. (a) Graph f defined by $f(x) = 3 \sin 2x$.
    (b) Graph f defined by $f(x) = \frac{1}{2} \sin x/3$.

12. (a) Graph f defined by $f(x) = 3 \cos 2x$.
    (b) Graph f defined by $f(x) = 5 \cos x/4$.

6–6 basic trigonometric identities

definition: Let f be a function with domain D_f and let g be a function with domain D_g. If $f(x) = g(x)$ for all $x \in D_f \cap D_g$, then the equality is called an *identity* on $D_f \cap D_g$.

For example, if f and g are defined by $f(x) = x^2 - 4$ and $g(x) = (x - 2)(x + 2)$, then since $x^2 - 4 = (x - 2)(x + 2)$ for every real number x the equality is an *identity* on the set of real numbers. If F is defined by

$$F(x) = x + 2$$

and G is defined by

$$G(x) = \frac{x^2 - 4}{x - 2},$$

then

$$x + 2 = \frac{x^2 - 4}{x - 2}$$

is an identity on $\{x | x \text{ is a real number and } x \neq 2\}$. It should be noted that F and G are not equal as functions since 2 is in the domain of F but not in the domain of G. However, $F = G$ on $D_f \cap D_g$.

Let f and g be functions and assume $D_f \cap D_g \neq \emptyset$. It might be that $f(x) \neq g(x)$ for every $x \in D_f \cap D_g$. In this case "$f(x) = g(x)$" is called a *null equation*. If S is a non-empty set, if $S = \{x | f(x) = g(x)\}$, and if $S \subset D_f \cap D_g$, then "$f(x) = g(x)$" is called a *conditional equation*.

From the definition of the trigonometric functions and the identity concept, we conclude that the following are identities.

$$(1) \qquad \sin \theta = \frac{1}{\csc \theta}$$

$$(2) \qquad \cos \theta = \frac{1}{\sec \theta}$$

$$(3) \qquad \tan \theta = \frac{1}{\cot \theta}$$

Such identities involving the trigonometric functions are called *trigonometric identities*.

If $P(x, y)$ is any point at distance r from the origin on the terminal side of an angle in standard position with measure θ, then

$$\tan \theta = \frac{y}{x}.$$

Thus,

$$\tan \theta = \frac{y/r}{x/r},$$

and we conclude that

(4)
$$\tan \theta = \frac{\sin \theta}{\cos \theta}$$

for any θ in the domain of the tangent function. Furthermore, since the cotangent function is the reciprocal of the tangent function,

(5)
$$\cot \theta = \frac{\cos \theta}{\sin \theta}$$

for any θ in the domain of the cotangent function.

Since $x^2 + y^2 = r^2$ for any point $P(x, y)$ at the distance r from the origin on the terminal side of an angle with measure θ,

$$\frac{x^2}{r^2} + \frac{y^2}{r^2} = 1$$

and

(6)
$$\cos^2 \theta + \sin^2 \theta = 1. \quad [\text{Note: } \cos^2 \theta = (\cos \theta)^2.]$$

Also,

$$\frac{x^2}{y^2} + \frac{y^2}{y^2} = \frac{r^2}{y^2}$$

for $y \neq 0$ and

$$\frac{x^2}{x^2} + \frac{y^2}{x^2} = \frac{r^2}{x^2}$$

for $x \neq 0$; thus,

(7)
$$\cot^2 \theta + 1 = \csc^2 \theta$$

and

(8)
$$1 + \tan^2 \theta = \sec^2 \theta.$$

Six more important trigonometric identities follow immediately from the definitions of the trigonometric functions. If $P(x, y)$ is any point at distance r from the origin on the terminal side of an angle in standard position with measure θ, then the point P' at distance r from the origin on the terminal side of the angle with measure $(-\theta)$ has coordinates $(x, -y)$. Thus, by definition of the trigonometric functions, $\sin \theta = y/r$ and $\sin (-\theta) = -y/r$; consequently,

(9)
$$\sin (-\theta) = -\sin \theta;$$

that is, the sine function is an odd function. Similarly, it follows that

(10)
$$\cos (-\theta) = \cos \theta,$$

(11) $$\tan(-\theta) = -\tan\theta,$$

(12) $$\csc(-\theta) = -\csc\theta,$$

(13) $$\sec(-\theta) = \sec\theta,$$

(14) $$\cot(-\theta) = -\cot\theta.$$

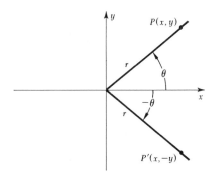

$$\text{Sin } \theta = \frac{y}{r} = -\left(\frac{-y}{r}\right) = -\sin(-\theta) \qquad \text{Cos } \theta = \frac{x}{r} = \cos(-\theta)$$

$$\text{Tan } \theta = \frac{y}{x} = -\left(\frac{-y}{x}\right) = -\tan(-\theta)$$

FIGURE 6–8

The preceding fourteen trigonometric identities are basic identities. Other important trigonometric identities can be derived from these and the following identity.

(15) $$\cos(\alpha - \beta) = (\cos\alpha)(\cos\beta) + (\sin\alpha)(\sin\beta)$$

To prove this identity geometrically, we draw the unit circle with center at the origin of the coordinate system and let it intersect the terminal sides of angles in standard position having measures θ and ϕ.

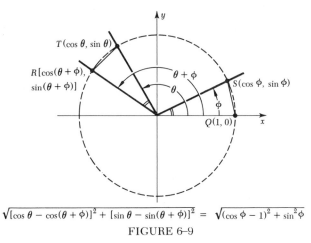

$$\sqrt{[\cos\theta - \cos(\theta + \phi)]^2 + [\sin\theta - \sin(\theta + \phi)]^2} = \sqrt{(\cos\phi - 1)^2 + \sin^2\phi}$$

FIGURE 6–9

It is obvious from observing Figure 6–9 that triangles OQS and ORT are congruent; thus,

$$|TR| = |SQ|.$$

(If $\theta + \phi = 180°$, or if the angle with measure $\theta + \phi$ is coterminal with one of the other angles, the triangles mentioned are not determined. We leave as an exercise for the student to derive the identity in these cases.)

Since $|TR| = |SQ|$, we conclude by the distance formula that

$$[\cos \theta - \cos (\theta + \phi)]^2 + [\sin \theta - \sin (\theta + \phi)]^2 = (\cos \phi - 1)^2 + (\sin \phi)^2.$$

Hence,

$$\cos^2 \theta - 2 \cos \theta \cos (\theta + \phi) + \cos^2 (\theta + \phi) + \sin^2 \theta - 2 \sin \theta \sin (\theta + \phi)$$
$$+ \sin^2 (\theta + \phi) = \cos^2 \phi - 2 \cos \phi + 1 + \sin^2 \phi.$$

Since

$$\cos^2 \alpha + \sin^2 \alpha = 1,$$
$$-2 \cos \theta \cos (\theta + \phi) - 2 \sin \theta \sin (\theta + \phi) = -2 \cos \phi.$$

Dividing by -2 and letting $\beta = \theta$ and $\alpha = \theta + \phi$,

(15) $\cos (\alpha - \beta) = (\cos \alpha) (\cos \beta) + (\sin \alpha) (\sin \beta).$

We now prove that $\cos (\alpha + \beta) = (\cos \alpha) (\cos \beta) - (\sin \alpha) (\sin \beta)$ is an identity.

Since

$$\cos (\alpha + \beta) = \cos (\alpha - (-\beta)),$$
$$\cos (\alpha + \beta) = \cos \alpha \cos (-\beta) + \sin \alpha \sin (-\beta) \qquad \text{by (15)}$$
$$= \cos \alpha \cos \beta - \sin \alpha \sin \beta \qquad \text{by (9) and (10).}$$

Thus,

(16) $\cos (\alpha + \beta) = \cos \alpha \cos \beta - \sin \alpha \sin \beta.$

Let us consider more carefully what constitutes a *proof* that an equality is an identity. For example, let us prove that

$$\frac{\sec^2 \theta - \tan^2 \theta - 2 \sin^2 \theta}{\cos \theta + \sin \theta} = \cos \theta - \sin \theta$$

is an identity.

$$\frac{\sec^2 \theta - \tan^2 \theta - 2 \sin^2 \theta}{\cos \theta + \sin \theta} = \frac{(1 + \tan^2 \theta) - \tan^2 \theta - 2 \sin^2 \theta}{\cos \theta + \sin \theta} \qquad (8)$$

$$= \frac{1 - 2 \sin^2 \theta}{\cos \theta + \sin \theta} \qquad \text{(addition)}$$

$$= \frac{(\cos^2 \theta + \sin^2 \theta) - 2 \sin^2 \theta}{\cos \theta + \sin \theta} \qquad (6)$$

$$= \frac{\cos^2 \theta - \sin^2 \theta}{\cos \theta + \sin \theta} \qquad \text{(addition)}$$

$$= \frac{(\cos \theta - \sin \theta)(\cos \theta + \sin \theta)}{\cos \theta + \sin \theta} \qquad \text{(factoring)}$$

$$= (\cos \theta - \sin \theta)$$

This shows that

$$\frac{\sec^2 \theta - \tan^2 \theta - 2 \sin^2 \theta}{\cos \theta + \sin \theta} = \cos \theta - \sin \theta$$

for all θ where $\cos \theta + \sin \theta \neq 0$.

Suppose we are not able to find a direct proof, as in the preceding example, that an equality is an identity. It is often easier to give an indirect proof. That is, assume for *some* θ that

$$\frac{\sec^2 \theta - \tan^2 \theta - 2 \sin^2 \theta}{(\cos \theta + \sin \theta)} \neq (\cos \theta - \sin \theta). \qquad \text{(A)}$$

Since we are not interested in numbers θ where $(\cos \theta + \sin \theta) = 0$, if (A) is true then $\sec^2 \theta - \tan^2 \theta - 2 \sin^2 \theta \neq (\cos \theta - \sin \theta)(\cos \theta + \sin \theta)$. This follows from the fact that if a, b, c are numbers such that $a \neq b$ and $c \neq 0$, then $ac \neq bc$. Furthermore, it follows that

$$\sec^2 \theta - \tan^2 \theta - 2 \sin^2 \theta \neq \cos^2 \theta - \sin^2 \theta$$

$$\sec^2 \theta - \tan^2 \theta \neq \cos^2 \theta + \sin^2 \theta$$

$$(1 + \tan^2 \theta) - \tan^2 \theta \neq 1$$

$$1 \neq 1.$$

Since the conclusion is false, the assumption is false and

$$\frac{\sec^2 \theta - \tan^2 \theta - 2 \sin^2 \theta}{\cos \theta + \sin \theta} = \cos \theta - \sin \theta$$

for *all* θ except where $\cos \theta + \sin \theta = 0$.

Consider the equality

$$\frac{\cot \theta - 1}{\cot \theta + 1} = \frac{1 - \tan \theta}{1 + \tan \theta}.$$

For all θ for which this is true, we conclude

$$(\cot \theta - 1)(1 + \tan \theta) = (\cot \theta + 1)(1 - \tan \theta).$$

Thus,

$$\cot \theta - 1 + 1 - \tan \theta = \cot \theta - 1 + 1 - \tan \theta,$$

and this implies $0 = 0$. What conclusions can we reach? Essentially, we have proved if $a = b$ then $0 = 0$; this tells us nothing about the equality of a and b. (If $a=b$ implied, say, $0=1$, then we could assert that since the conclusion is false the assumption is false; that is, $a \neq b$). Of course, if all the "steps" in the above proof are reversible, we can assert that $a=b$ is a true statement since $0=0$ is a true statement. (A true hypothesis cannot imply a false conclusion.) In other words, the sequence of logical steps from

$$\frac{\cot \theta - 1}{\cot \theta + 1} = \frac{1 - \tan \theta}{1 + \tan \theta}$$

to $0=0$ is no proof that equality is an identity; the steps in reverse order form a valid proof.

exercises

1. If $\theta + \phi = 180°$, $\beta = \theta$ and $\alpha = \theta + \phi$, prove that $\cos(\alpha - \beta) = (\cos \alpha)(\cos \beta) + (\sin \alpha)(\sin \beta)$.

2. If the angle with $\theta + \phi$ as measure is coterminal with the angle with ϕ as measure and if $\alpha = \theta + \phi$ and $\beta = \theta$, prove that $\cos(\alpha - \beta) = (\cos \alpha)(\cos \beta) + (\sin \alpha)(\sin \beta)$.

3. Which of the following are algebraic identities? Give the solution set for conditional equations.
   (a) $x^3 - 8 = (x - 2)(x^2 + 2x + 4)$
   (b) $\dfrac{x^2 - 9}{x + 3} = x - 3$
   (c) $x^3 + 2x^2 + 6x = x^3 + 3x$
   (d) $\dfrac{x - 6}{\sqrt{x + 30} - 6} = \sqrt{x + 30} + 6$
   (e) $\dfrac{x + 6}{x + 2} = \dfrac{x + 3}{x + 5}$
   (f) $\dfrac{x^5 - 32}{x - 2} = x^4 + 2x^3 + 4x^2 + 8x + 16$
   (g) $|x + 1| + |2x + 1| = x - 12$

Prove that each of the following eight exercises is a trigonometric identity.

4. $\cos 2\theta = \cos^2 \theta - \sin^2 \theta$. [Hint: $\cos 2\theta = \cos(\theta + \theta)$.]

5. $\cos 2\theta = 2 \cos^2 \theta - 1$. [See Exercise 4 and identity (6).]

6. $\cos 2\theta = 1 - 2 \sin^2 \theta$. [See Exercise 4 and identity (6).]

7. $1 - \tan^4 \theta = \dfrac{\cos 2\theta}{\cos^4 \theta}$

8. $\sin^3 \theta + \sin \theta \cos^2 \theta = \sin \theta$

9. $\cos(90° - \theta) = \sin \theta$

10. $\cos(180° - \theta) = -\cos \theta$

11. $\dfrac{1}{\csc \theta + \cot \theta} = \csc \theta - \cot \theta$

12. Find $\cos 15°$ without the use of tables. [Hint: $15° = 45° - 30°$.]

13. Find cos 75° without the use of tables.

14. Find cos 225° without the use of tables.

15. (a) Find sin 15° by using Exercise 12 and identity (6).
    (b) Check your result by using Exercise 6.

16. Is $\dfrac{\sin\theta}{1+\cos\theta}+\dfrac{1+\cos\theta}{\sin\theta}=2\csc\theta$ an identity? Justify your answer.

17. Is $\dfrac{\cos^2\theta}{1-\sin\theta}+\dfrac{\cos^2\theta}{1+\sin\theta}=2$ an identity? Justify your answer.

18. If $\sin\theta=5/13$ and $0<\theta<\pi/2$, find $\cos\theta$, $\tan\theta$, and $\csc\theta$.

19. Prove that $\cos\theta-\cos\phi=-2\sin\dfrac{\theta+\phi}{2}\sin\dfrac{\theta-\phi}{2}$ is an identity. [Hint: Let $\alpha+\beta=\theta$ and $\alpha-\beta=\phi$; then, use the fact that $\alpha=\dfrac{\theta+\phi}{2}$ and $\beta=\dfrac{\theta-\phi}{2}$.]

20. Prove that $\cos\theta+\cos\phi=2\cos\dfrac{\theta+\phi}{2}\cos\dfrac{\theta-\phi}{2}$ is an identity. [Hint: See Exercise 19.]

21. If $\sin\theta=2/7$ and $\pi/2<\theta<\pi$, find $\cos\theta$, $\tan\theta$, and $\csc\theta$.

6-7   other trigonometric identities

In Section 6–6, we derived a trigonometric identity for cos $(\alpha+\beta)$. From this we obtain what are called the *double angle identities* for the cosine function:

$$\cos 2\theta=\cos(\theta+\theta)=\cos^2\theta-\sin^2\theta.$$

Since

$$\sin^2\theta+\cos^2\theta=1,$$

(17) $$\cos 2\theta=2\cos^2\theta-1$$

and

(18) $$\cos 2\theta=1-2\sin^2\theta.$$

From (17), $\cos^2\theta=(1+\cos 2\theta)/2$ and $\cos\theta=\pm\sqrt{(1+\cos 2\theta)/2}$. Similarly, from (18) we conclude that $\sin\theta=\pm\sqrt{(1-\cos 2\theta)/2}$. If we let $\phi=2\theta$, we obtain what are often called the *half-angle identities*. That is,

(19) $$\cos\frac{\phi}{2}=\pm\sqrt{\frac{1+\cos\phi}{2}}$$

and

(20) $$\sin\frac{\phi}{2}=\pm\sqrt{\frac{1-\cos\phi}{2}}.$$

We now derive the trigonometric identity involving $\sin (\alpha + \beta)$. Since $\cos (\pi/2 - \theta) = \cos \pi/2 \cos \theta + \sin \pi/2 \sin \theta$, $\cos (\pi/2 - \theta) = \sin \theta$. If we let $\theta = \pi/2 - \phi$, then $\cos \phi = \sin (\pi/2 - \phi)$.

$$\sin (\alpha + \beta) = \cos (\pi/2 - (\alpha + \beta))$$
$$= \cos ((\pi/2 - \alpha) - \beta)$$
$$= \cos (\pi/2 - \alpha) \cos \beta + \sin (\pi/2 - \alpha) \sin \beta$$
$$= \sin \alpha \cos \beta + \cos \alpha \sin \beta$$

(21) $\quad \sin (\alpha + \beta) = \sin \alpha \cos \beta + \cos \alpha \sin \beta$

Since $\sin (\alpha - \beta) = \sin (\alpha + (-\beta)) = \sin \alpha \cos (-\beta) + \cos \alpha \sin (-\beta)$,

(22) $\qquad \sin (\alpha - \beta) = \sin \alpha \cos \beta - \cos \alpha \sin \beta$.

exercises

Prove that each of the following is an identity.

1. $\sin 2\theta = 2 \sin \theta \cos \theta$

2. $\sin \theta + \sin \phi = 2 \sin \dfrac{\theta + \phi}{2} \cos \dfrac{\theta - \phi}{2}$. [Hint: Add (21) and (22), letting $\theta = \alpha + \beta$ and $\phi = \alpha - \beta$.]

3. $\sin \theta - \sin \phi = 2 \cos \dfrac{\theta + \phi}{2} \sin \dfrac{\theta - \phi}{2}$. [Hint: See Exercise 2.]

4. $\tan (\theta + \phi) = \dfrac{\tan \theta + \tan \phi}{1 - \tan \theta \tan \phi}$. $\left[\text{Hint: } \tan (\theta + \phi) = \dfrac{\sin (\theta + \phi)}{\cos (\theta + \phi)}. \right]$

5. $\tan (\theta - \phi) = \dfrac{\tan \theta - \tan \phi}{1 + \tan \theta \tan \phi}$. [Hint: See Exercise 4.]

6. $\tan 2\theta = \dfrac{2 \tan \theta}{1 - \tan^2 \theta}$. [Hint: See Exercise 4.]

7. $\sin (\theta + \phi) \sin (\theta - \phi) = \sin^2 \theta - \sin^2 \phi$.

8. $\dfrac{\sin (\theta + \phi) + \sin (\theta - \phi)}{\cos (\theta + \phi) + \cos (\theta - \phi)} = \tan \theta$

9. $\dfrac{\sin \theta + \sin 2\theta}{1 + \cos \theta + \cos 2\theta} = \tan \theta$

10. $\tan \dfrac{\theta}{2} = \pm \sqrt{\dfrac{1 - \cos \theta}{1 + \cos \theta}}$

11. $\dfrac{\cos 3\theta}{\sin \theta} + \dfrac{\sin 3\theta}{\cos \theta} = 2 \cot 2\theta$

12. $\dfrac{2 \tan \dfrac{\theta}{2}}{1 + \tan^2 \dfrac{\theta}{2}} = \sin \theta$

13. $\sec 2\theta - \tan 2\theta = \dfrac{1 - 2 \sin \theta \cos \theta}{1 - 2 \sin^2 \theta}$

14. $\dfrac{\sin 3\theta}{\sin \theta} - \dfrac{\cos 3\theta}{\cos \theta} = 2$

15. $\sin 3\theta = 3 \sin \theta - 4 \sin^3 \theta$

16. $\dfrac{\cos 6\theta + \cos 2\theta}{\sin 6\theta - \sin 2\theta} = \cot 2\theta$

17. $\dfrac{\tan^2 \theta}{1 + \sec \theta} + 1 = \sec \theta$

18. $\dfrac{\sin 5\theta + \sin 3\theta}{\sin 2\theta \cos 2\theta} = 4 \cos \theta$

19. $\dfrac{\sin 3\theta}{1 - \cos 3\theta} = \dfrac{\tan 3\theta}{\sec 3\theta - 1}$

20. $\cos \theta + \cos 2\theta + \cos 3\theta = \dfrac{\cos 2\theta \sin \dfrac{3\theta}{2}}{\sin \dfrac{\theta}{2}}$ (Hint: $\sin A \cos B = $ $1/2 \left[\sin (A+B) + \sin (A-B) \right].$)

summary of important trigonometric identities

(1) $$\sin \theta = \frac{1}{\csc \theta}$$

(2) $$\cos \theta = \frac{1}{\sec \theta}$$

(3) $$\tan \theta = \frac{1}{\cot \theta}$$

(4) $$\tan \theta = \frac{\sin \theta}{\cos \theta}$$

(5) $$\cot \theta = \frac{\cos \theta}{\sin \theta}$$

(6) $$\cos^2 \theta + \sin^2 \theta = 1$$

(7) $$\cot^2 \theta + 1 = \csc^2 \theta$$

(8) $$1 + \tan^2 \theta = \sec^2 \theta$$

(9) $$\sin (-\theta) = -\sin \theta$$

(10) $$\cos (-\theta) = \cos \theta$$

(11) $$\tan (-\theta) = -\tan \theta$$

(12) $$\csc (-\theta) = -\csc \theta$$

(13) $$\sec (-\theta) = \sec \theta$$

(14) $$\cot (-\theta) = -\cot \theta$$

(15) $$\cos (\theta - \phi) = (\cos \theta)(\cos \phi) + (\sin \theta)(\sin \phi)$$

(16) $$\cos (\theta + \phi) = \cos \theta \cos \phi - \sin \theta \sin \phi$$

(17) $$\cos 2\theta = 2 \cos^2 \theta - 1$$

(18) $$\cos 2\theta = 1 - 2 \sin^2 \theta = \cos^2 \theta - \sin^2 \theta$$

(19) $$\cos \frac{\phi}{2} = \pm \sqrt{\frac{1 + \cos \phi}{2}}$$

(20) $$\sin \frac{\theta}{2} = \pm \sqrt{\frac{1 - \cos \theta}{2}}$$

(21) $$\sin (\theta + \phi) = \sin \theta \cos \phi + \cos \theta \sin \phi$$

(22) $$\sin (\theta - \phi) = \sin \theta \cos \phi - \cos \theta \sin \phi$$

(23) $$\sin 2\theta = 2 \sin \theta \cos \theta$$

(24) $$\tan (\theta + \phi) = \frac{\tan \theta + \tan \phi}{1 - \tan \theta \tan \phi}$$

(25) $$\tan (\theta - \phi) = \frac{\tan \theta - \tan \phi}{1 + \tan \theta \tan \phi}$$

(26) $$\tan 2\theta = \frac{2 \tan \theta}{1 - \tan^2 \theta}$$

6–8   right triangles

Suppose A is an acute angle in standard position as in Figure 6–10. Let B be a point at distance r from the origin on the terminal side of

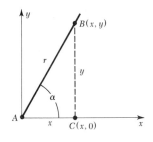

FIGURE 6–10

A with coordinates (x,y). If C is the foot of the perpendicular drawn from B to the positive x-axis, triangle ABC is a right triangle where $|AC| = x$, $|BC| = y$, and $|AB| = r$. Thus, x is the length of the side adjacent to angle A, y is the length of the side opposite angle A, and r is the length of the hypotenuse. If α is the measure of an *acute* angle A, the trigonometric functions can be defined in terms of a right triangle as follows.

I.
$$\sin \alpha = \frac{\text{length of opposite side}}{\text{length of hypotenuse}}$$

II.
$$\cos \alpha = \frac{\text{length of adjacent side}}{\text{length of hypotenuse}}$$

III.
$$\tan \alpha = \frac{\text{length of opposite side}}{\text{length of adjacent side}}$$

IV.
$$\csc \alpha = \frac{\text{length of hypotenuse}}{\text{length of opposite side}}$$

V.
$$\sec \alpha = \frac{\text{length of hypotenuse}}{\text{length of adjacent side}}$$

VI.
$$\cot \alpha = \frac{\text{length of adjacent side}}{\text{length of opposite side}}$$

Suppose a ship is 4 miles from a straight north-south shoreline and is sailing north, parallel to the shore. If a lighthouse is sighted at a bearing 65° north of east (see Figure 6–11), let us use the trigonometric functions to find the distance s of the ship from the lighthouse. Since the legs of the right triangle involved are the adjacent sides and the hypotenuse, choose either the definition of the cosine or the secant.

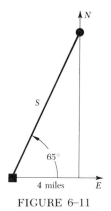

FIGURE 6-11

$$\cos 65° = \frac{\text{distance from shore}}{\text{distance from lighthouse}} \qquad \sec 65° = \frac{\text{distance from lighthouse}}{\text{distance from shore}}$$

$$\cos 65° = \frac{4}{s} \qquad\qquad\qquad \sec 65° = \frac{s}{4}$$

$$s = \frac{4}{\cos 65°} \qquad\qquad\qquad s = 4 \sec 65°$$

In Table 2, we find that $\cos 65° = 0.4226$ and $\sec 65° = 2.366$. Hence,

$$s = \frac{4}{0.4226}, \qquad\qquad s = 4(2.366),$$

$$s = 9.465 \text{ miles}, \qquad\qquad s = 9.464 \text{ miles}.$$

The difference in the answers is a consequence of error introduced by the four-place approximation of the values of the trigonometric functions as given in Table 2. Since it is easier to find the product $4(2.336)$ than the quotient $4/0.4226$, the secant function would usually be used to work this problem.

If the length of two sides of a right triangle are given, the length of the remaining side and the measures of the two acute angles can be found using the above definitions. Also, if one side and the measure of an acute angle of a right triangle are given, the lengths of the remaining sides and the measure of the other acute angle can be found using the preceding definitions. Finding the remaining unknown parts is often called "solving the right triangle." It is standard notation to label a right triangle ABC with right angle C, a the length of side opposite angle A, b the length of side opposite angle B, c the length of hypotenuse, and α, β, γ, the measures of angles A, B, C, respectively.

examples

1. If $a = 15$, $\beta = 37°$, and $\gamma = 90°$, find b, c, and α.

Solution: $\alpha = 180° - (90° + 37°) = 53°$.

$$\tan \beta = \frac{b}{a} \qquad\qquad \sec \beta = \frac{c}{a}$$

$$\tan 37° = \frac{b}{15} \qquad\qquad \sec 37° = \frac{c}{15}$$

$$\begin{aligned} b &= 15(\tan 37°) & c &= 15(\sec 37°)\\ &= 15(0.7536) & &= 15(1.252)\\ &= 11.304 & &= 18.78 \end{aligned}$$

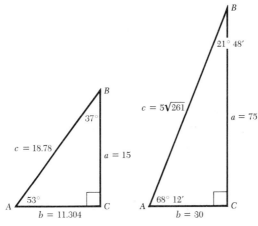

FIGURE 6–12

2. If $\gamma = 90°$, $a = 75$, and $b = 30$, find c, α, and β.

Solution: $c = \sqrt{a^2 + b^2} = \sqrt{75^2 + 30^2} = \sqrt{6{,}525} = 5\sqrt{261} = 5(16.16) = 80.80$.
$\tan \alpha = 75/30 = 2.5$. In Table 2 , we find that $\tan 68°10' = 2.496$ and $\tan 68°20' = 2.517$. If we assume that the graph of the tangent function throughout this $10'$ interval is a straight line, we can approximate α with a reasonable degree of accuracy. The tangent function increases 0.021 in the $10'$ interval and 2.5 is 0.004 greater than 2.496.

$$\frac{t}{0.004} = \frac{10}{0.021}$$

$$t = \frac{40}{21}$$

$$t = +2'$$

$$\alpha = 68°12' \quad \text{and} \quad \beta = 90° - 68°12' = 21°48'$$

In a right triangle ABC, $\sin \alpha = a/c$ and $\cos \beta = a/c$. Thus, for the complementary angles α and β ($\alpha + \beta = 90°$), $\sin \alpha = \cos \beta$. The sine and cosine functions are often called *co-functions.* Similarly, tangent and cotangent, secant and cosecant functions are called co-functions. Since the value for the function of any acute angle is the value of the co-function of the complementary angle, it is necessary only to have function values for each of the trigonometric functions for angles with measures between 0° and 45°.

exercises

Solve the following right triangles. ($\gamma = 90°$)

1. $\alpha = 28°$, $b = 20$

2. $\beta = 36°$, $c = 25$

3. $\alpha = 39°$, $c = 36$

4. $\beta = 58°$, $a = 18$

5. $\beta = 68°$, $b = 40$

6. $\alpha = 34°$, $17'$, $c = 27.8$

7. $\alpha = 28°48'$, $b = 2.37$

8. $a = 30$, $b = 40$

9. $a = 23$, $c = 56$

10. $b = 18.4$, $c = 37.2$

6–9 oblique triangles

Consider a triangle ABC with sides of length a, b, c and with angle measures α, β, γ. (See Figure 6–13.) At least three values among

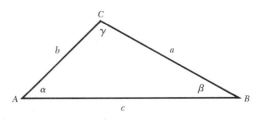

FIGURE 6–13

a, b, c, α, β, and γ must be given to determine a triangle. Let us consider combinations of given sides and angles and the conditions under which they determine a triangle. Obviously, α, β, γ do not determine a unique triangle; thus, we have essentially four different combinations of three given values that determine a triangle:

    I. The measure of any two angles and the length of any side. This combination always determines a unique triangle provided the sum of the measures of the two angles is less than 180°.

   II. The lengths of all three sides. This given combination always determines a unique triangle, provided the sum of the lengths of two sides is greater than the third.

  III. The lengths of two sides and the measure of the angle included between the sides. A unique triangle is determined if the measure of the angle is less than 180°.

IV. The lengths of two sides and the measure of an angle opposite one of the sides. This case is more complicated than the others so we consider the method for constructing a triangle with the given information. Suppose we are given a, b, and α. Construct the side with length b first. (See Figure 6–14.) Then, construct angle A with

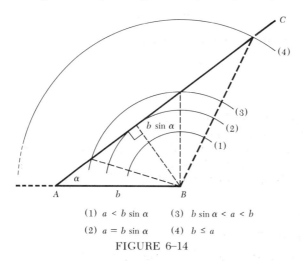

(1) $a < b \sin \alpha$ (3) $b \sin \alpha < a < b$

(2) $a = b \sin \alpha$ (4) $b \leq a$

FIGURE 6–14

measure α at one endpoint of this side. From the other end, construct an arc with radius of length a. Four things can happen: (1) The arc will not intersect the other side and a triangle is not determined ($a < b \sin \alpha$). (2) The arc has the other side as tangent. In this case, a right triangle is determined and $a = b \sin \alpha$. (3) If $b \sin \alpha < a < b$, two triangles are determined. (4) If $a \geq b$, one triangle is determined.

We now turn our attention to deriving what are called the law of sines and the law of cosines; these laws can be used to find the lengths of the sides and the measure of the angles of an oblique triangle.

In a given oblique triangle, construct a perpendicular from C to side AB. It will intersect AB or AB extended. (See Figure 6–15.) Let h

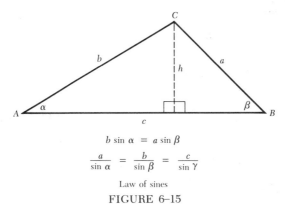

$b \sin \alpha = a \sin \beta$

$$\frac{a}{\sin \alpha} = \frac{b}{\sin \beta} = \frac{c}{\sin \gamma}$$

Law of sines

FIGURE 6–15

be the length of the perpendicular. Since $\sin\alpha=\sin(180°-\alpha)$, $h=b\sin\alpha$, and $h=a\sin\beta$ in either of the constructed right triangles. Consequently, $b\sin\alpha=a\sin\beta$ and

$$\frac{a}{\sin\alpha}=\frac{b}{\sin\beta}.$$

Similarly, we can prove that $b/\sin\beta=c/\sin\gamma$. Thus,

$$\frac{a}{\sin\alpha}=\frac{b}{\sin\beta}=\frac{c}{\sin\gamma}.$$

We have proved that the lengths of the sides of a triangle are proportional to the sines of the measures of the opposite angles; this is called the *law of sines*. It should be clear from the following examples that the law of sines can be used to find the unknown parts of a triangle determined under Case I or Case IV.

examples

1. If $\alpha=40°$, $\beta=75°$, and $c=20$, find a, b, and γ.

Solution: $\gamma=180°-(40°+75°)=180°-115°=65°$.

Since

$$\frac{a}{\sin 40°}=\frac{20}{\sin 65°}, a=\frac{20\sin 40°}{\sin 65°}=\frac{20(0.6428)}{0.9063}=14.185.$$

Since

$$\frac{b}{\sin 75°}=\frac{20}{\sin 65°}, b=\frac{20\sin 75°}{\sin 65°}=\frac{20(0.9659)}{0.9063}=21.315.$$

2. If $a=15$, $b=12$, and $\alpha=80°$, find c and β.

Since

$$\frac{b}{\sin\beta}=\frac{a}{\sin\alpha}, \sin\beta=\frac{b\sin\alpha}{a}=\frac{12\sin 80°}{15}=\frac{12(0.9848)}{15}=0.7878.$$

Thus, $\beta=51°59'$ and $\gamma=48°1'$.

Since $$\frac{c}{\sin\gamma}=\frac{b}{\sin\beta}, c=\frac{b\sin\gamma}{\sin\beta}=\frac{12(0.7432)}{0.7878}=11.3.$$

In a given oblique triangle, construct a perpendicular from C to side AB, or AB extended. (See Figure 6–16.) Let h be the length of this altitude.

$$h^2=b^2-x^2 \quad\text{and}\quad h^2=a^2-(c-x)^2.$$

Thus, $b^2-x^2=a^2-c^2+2cx-x^2$ and $a^2=b^2+c^2-2cx$. Since $x=b\cos\alpha$,

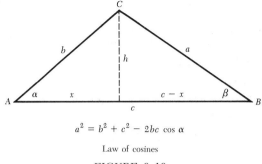

$$a^2 = b^2 + c^2 - 2bc \cos \alpha$$

Law of cosines

FIGURE 6–16

(1) $$a^2 = b^2 + c^2 - 2bc \cos \alpha.$$

(We leave as an exercise for the student to prove that (1) is valid if the constructed altitude intersects AB extended. Notice that if $\alpha = 90°$, then $a^2 = b^2 + c^2$—the Pythagorean Theorem.)

As a consequence of (1) and the symmetry in lettering of the triangle, we can conclude that

(2) $$b^2 = a^2 + c^2 - 2ac \cos \beta$$

and

(3) $$c^2 = a^2 + b^2 - 2ab \cos \gamma.$$

The three formulas (1), (2), and (3) are called the cosine laws. The *law of cosines* states: The square of the length of any side in a triangle is equal to the sum of the squares of the lengths of the other two sides, less twice the product of the lengths of these two sides and the cosine of the measure of the included angle. The law of cosines can be used to find the unknown parts of a triangle determined under Case II and Case III.

examples

1. If $a = 20$, $b = 15$, and $c = 18$, find α.

Solution:
$$a^2 = b^2 + c^2 - 2bc \cos \alpha$$
$$400 = 225 + 324 - 540 \cos \alpha$$
$$540 \cos \alpha = 149$$
$$\cos \alpha = 0.2759$$
$$\alpha = 73°59'.$$

2. If $a = 30$, $b = 18$, and $\gamma = 46°$, find c.

Solution:
$$c^2 = a^2 + b^2 - 2ab \cos \gamma$$
$$c^2 = 900 + 324 - 1080 \cos 46°$$
$$= 1224 - 1080(0.6947)$$
$$= 1224 - 750.276$$
$$= 473.724$$
$$c = 21.8$$

exercises

1. Derive the law of cosines when the altitude from one vertex intersects the extended opposite side at a point exterior to the triangle.
2. If $a = 26$, $b = 34$, $c = 41$, find α.
3. If $a = 76.1$, $b = 38.5$, $c = 49$, find β.
4. If $\alpha = 37°$, $\beta = 103°$, $a = 36$, find b.
5. If $\beta = 64°10'$, $\gamma = 63°$, $b = 50$, find a.
6. If $a = 30$, $b = 28$, $\gamma = 40°$, find c and α.
7. If $b = 29$, $c = 17.4$, $\alpha = 37°23'$, find a and β.
8. If $c = 16$, $a = 30$, $\alpha = 71°$, find b and β.
9. If $c = 30$, $a = 24$, $\alpha = 62°$, find b and β.
10. If $a = 52$, $\beta = 30°$, $b = 26$, find c and γ.

6-10 trigonometric equations and inequalities

definition: If f and g are functions and if there is a non-empty proper subset S of $D_f \cap D_g$ such that $f(x) = g(x)$ for all $x \in S$, the equality is called a *conditional equation*, or *equation*. The proper subset S of $D_f \cap D_g$ for which $f(x) = g(x)$ is called the *solution set* of the equation.

For example, if f and g are defined by $f(x) = 3x - 2$ and $g(x) = x^2$, $\{1,2\}$ is the solution set of $x^2 = 3x - 2$. If f and g are trigonometric functions, a conditional equation $f(x) = g(x)$ is called a *trigonometric equation*.

Let f and g be functions defined by $f(x) = \sin x$ and $g(x) = \cos x$. The set $f \cap g$ is the set of ordered pairs in both f and g; geometrically, $f \cap g$ is the set of points of intersection of the graphs of f and g. (See Figure 6–17.) The number of points common to the two graphs is

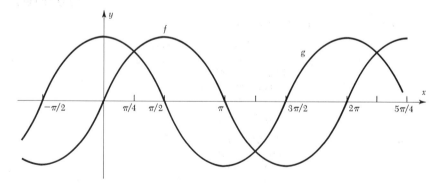

FIGURE 6–17

infinite. Algebraically, to find the coordinates of the points of intersection of the graph of f and g, we find the values for x such that $f(x) = g(x)$; in other words, we find the solution set of the trigonometric equation $\sin x = \cos x$.

One method to solve the equation $\sin x = \cos x$ is the following. Since $\sin x = \pm 1$ for any x such that $\cos x = 0$, there is no x in the solution set such that $\cos x = 0$. Hence, x is a solution of $\sin x = \cos x$ if and only if

$$\frac{\sin x}{\cos x} = 1,$$

or

$$\tan x = 1.$$

Since $\tan x = 1$ if and only if $x = \pi/4 + k\pi$ where k is an integer, the solution set is

$$\{x | x = \pi/4 + k\pi, \ k \text{ an integer}\}.$$

Furthermore,

$$f \cap g = \{(\pi/4 + k\pi), \sin(\pi/4 + k\pi)\}.$$

A standard technique used in solving trigonometric equations (and trigonometric inequalities) is to begin by expressing the equation (or inequality) in terms of only one of the trigonometric functions. This procedure is exhibited in the following examples.

examples

1. Solve: $2 \sin^2 x + 3 \cos x = 0$.

   Solution:
   $$2(1 - \cos^2 x) + 3 \cos x = 0$$
   $$2 \cos^2 x - 3 \cos x - 2 = 0$$
   $$(2 \cos x + 1)(\cos x - 2) = 0.$$

   Thus, x is a solution of $2 \sin^2 x + 3 \cos x = 0$ if and only if

   $$2 \cos x + 1 = 0 \qquad \text{or} \qquad \cos x - 2 = 0,$$
   $$\cos x = -1/2 \qquad \text{or} \qquad \cos x = 2.$$

   Since $-1 \leqslant \cos x \leqslant 1$ *for all* x, $\cos x \neq 2$ for any x. Consequently, the only solutions are those such that $\cos x = -1/2$. Thus, $x = 2\pi/3 + 2k\pi$ or $x = 4\pi/3 + 2k\pi$ (where k is an integer) are the only solutions.

2. Solve: $\tan x + \sec x = 1$.

   Solution:
   $$\sec x = 1 - \tan x$$
   $$\pm\sqrt{1 + \tan^2 x} = 1 - \tan x$$
   $$1 + \tan^2 x = 1 - 2 \tan x + \tan^2 x$$
   $$\tan x = 0$$
   $$x = k\pi, \text{ where } k \text{ is an integer.}$$

We have shown that the equation can have no solutions other than $x = k\pi$. We have not proved that if $x = k\pi$ then $\sec x = 1 - \tan x$. Since $(a)^2 = (b)^2$ does not necessarily imply that $a = b$, the steps are not reversible and we should check our "candidates" for solution. A simple check proves that $x = k\pi$ where k is an odd integer is not a solution; hence, $x = k\pi$, where k is an even integer, is the solution.

3. Solve: $\sin 3x + \sin x = 0$.

Solution: Since

$$\sin \alpha + \sin \beta = 2 \sin \frac{\alpha + \beta}{2} \cos \frac{\alpha - \beta}{2},$$
$$\sin 3x + \sin x = 2 \sin 2x \cos x.$$

Hence,

$$2 \sin 2x \cos x = 0$$
$$\sin 2x = 0 \quad \text{or} \quad \cos x = 0$$
$$2x = k\pi \quad \text{or} \quad x = \pi/2 + k\pi, \ k \text{ an integer.}$$

Thus, $x = k\pi/2$ or $x = \pi/2 + k\pi = k'\pi/2$ where $k' = 2k + 1$. Consequently, $x = k\pi/2$ where k is an integer are the only solutions.

4. Solve: $\cos x/3 + \sin x = 0$.

Solution: Recall that $\sin x = \cos(\pi/2 - x)$ and

$$\cos \alpha + \cos \beta = 2 \cos \frac{\alpha + \beta}{2} \cos \frac{\alpha - \beta}{2}.$$

Thus,

$$\cos x/3 + \cos(\pi/2 - x) = 0$$
$$2 \cos \frac{x/3 + \pi/2 - x}{2} \cos \frac{x/3 - \pi/2 + x}{2} = 0$$
$$\cos(\pi/4 - x/3) \cos(2x/3 - \pi/4) = 0$$
$$\cos(\pi/4 - x/3) = 0 \quad \text{or} \quad \cos(2x/3 - \pi/4) = 0.$$

Since $\cos(-\theta) = \cos \theta$, we conclude that

$$\cos(x/3 - \pi/4) = 0 \qquad \text{or} \qquad \cos(2x/3 - \pi/4) = 0$$
$$x/3 - \pi/4 = \pi/2 + k\pi \qquad \text{or} \qquad 2x/3 - \pi/4 = \pi/2 + k\pi,$$
$$k \text{ an integer;}$$
$$x = 9\pi/4 + 3k\pi \qquad \text{or} \qquad x = 9\pi/8 + 3k\pi/2.$$

5. Solve: $3 - 3 \sin x - 2 \cos^2 x > 0$.

Solution:
$$3 - 3 \sin x - 2(1 - \sin^2 x) > 0$$
$$2 \sin^2 x - 3 \sin x + 1 > 0$$
$$(2 \sin x - 1)(\sin x - 1) > 0.$$

I. $2 \sin x - 1 > 0$
and $\sin x - 1 > 0$
$\sin x > 1/2$
and $\sin x > 1$.
Since $\sin x \leq 1$ for all x, no x exists such that $\sin x > 1$. This possibility for the product yields no solution.

or II. $2 \sin x - 1 < 0$ and $\sin x - 1 < 0$
$\sin x < 1/2$ and $\sin x < 1$.
Since $\sin x < 1$ for all x except $x = \pi/2 + 2k\pi$ where k is an integer, the inequality is satisfied by any x such that $\sin x < 1/2$. That is, $\{x \mid -7\pi/6 + 2k\pi < x < \pi/6 + 2k\pi, \ k \text{ an integer}\}$.

exercises

Find the solution set of each of the following where $0 \leqslant x \leqslant 2\pi$.

1. $\sin^2 x + \sin x - 2 = 0$
2. $2 \sin^2 x + \sin x = 0$
3. $\sin x + \cos x = 1$
4. $2 \cos^2 x + \sin x = 2$
5. $\tan x + \sec^2 x = 3$
6. $\sin^2 x + \cos x = 3$
7. $\cos 3x - \cos x = 0$
8. $\cos 2x + \cos 4x = 0$
9. $\cos x + \sin x/3 = 0$
10. $\cos x + \sin x/2 = 0$
11. $\sin 2x + \cos x = 0$
12. $\sin x < \cos x$
13. $\tan^2 x - \tan x < 0$

6–11   inverse trigonometric functions

Let us consider the sine function. Some of the ordered pairs of the sine function are $(0, 0)$, $(\pi/6, 1/2)$, $(\pi/2, 1)$, $(\pi, 0)$, and $(-\pi, 0)$. It is obvious that the three ordered pairs $(0, 0)$, $(\pi, 0)$, and $(-\pi, 0)$ have the same second coordinate and $\{(a, b)\,|\,(b, a)$ is an element of the sine function$\}$ is not a function. However, if we restrict the domain of the sine function to $\{x\,|-\pi/2 \leqslant x \leqslant \pi/2\}$, the function with this domain is strictly increasing so for $x_1 \neq x_2$ in the domain, $\sin x_1 \neq \sin x_2$. Consequently, the function has an inverse; it is called the *inverse sine function*. The inverse sine function has $[-1, 1]$ as its domain and $[-\pi/2, \pi/2]$ as its range. The inverse sine function is not only strictly increasing but it is also a continuous function. (See Figure 6–18.)

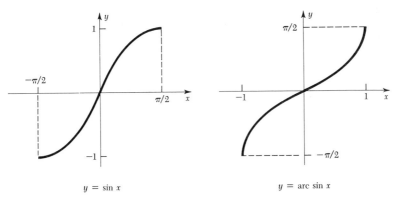

$y = \sin x$ $y = \text{arc sin } x$

FIGURE 6–18

We use $\sin^{-1} x$, or arc $\sin x$, to denote the function value of the inverse sine function at x in its domain. For example, since $\sin \pi/6 = 1/2$, $\sin^{-1} 1/2 = \pi/6$; similarly, arc $\sin 1 = \pi/2$. We have already discussed the fact that if f and f^{-1} are inverse functions, then $f(f^{-1}(x)) = x$; thus $\sin(\sin^{-1} x) = \sin^{-1}(\sin x) = x$. Notice that $\sin(\sin^{-1} 1/2) = \sin \pi/6 = 1/2$, but that $\sin^{-1}(\sin 3\pi/2) = \sin^{-1}(-1) = -(\pi/2)$. Why is

$\sin^{-1}(\sin x) \neq x$ in this second equality? We have agreed that the inverse sine function is the inverse of the function obtained by restricting the domain of the sine function to $[-\pi/2, \pi/2]$; therefore, $\sin^{-1}(\sin x) = x$ if and only if $x \in [-\pi/2, \pi/2]$.

The cosine function increases strictly on the closed intervals $[(2n-1)\pi, 2n\pi]$, n an integer, and decreases on the intervals $[2n\pi, (2n+1)\pi]$. The function defined by $f(x) = \cos x$ with domain $[0, \pi]$ has an inverse function called the inverse cosine function. We use $\cos^{-1} x$, or arc $\cos x$, to denote the value of the inverse cosine

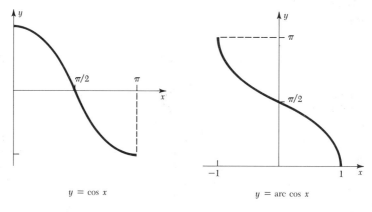

$y = \cos x$ $y = \text{arc } \cos x$

FIGURE 6–19

function at x in its domain. For example, arc $\cos 0 = \pi/2$, $\cos^{-1} 1/2 = \pi/3$, $\cos^{-1}(-1/2) = 2\pi/3$, arc $\cos(-1) = \pi$, and arc $\cos \sqrt{3}/2 = \pi/6$. It should be noted that choosing to restrict the domain of the cosine function to $[0, \pi]$ in order to define the inverse cosine function was an arbitrary choice; we could restrict the domain to, say, $[\pi, 2\pi]$. However, by agreement the inverse cosine is a (single-valued) function with $[-1, 1]$ as its domain and $[0, \pi]$ as its range.

Defining the inverse tangent function presents an interesting problem not confronted in defining the inverse sine and inverse cosine functions. The tangent function is strictly increasing on every interval in its domain but it is not a continuous function. (See Figure 6–20.) We could restrict the domain of the tangent function to $(-\pi/2, \pi/2)$ or $(0, \pi)$ to define the inverse tangent function; of course, we could restrict the domain to $(-\pi/4, 3\pi/4)$, but it is reasonable to assume that there is some advantage to restricting the domain so that the range of inverse tangent will coincide with that of the inverse sine, or inverse cosine. We choose to restrict the domain of the tangent function to $(-\pi/2, \pi/2)$ in defining the inverse tangent function; this makes the tangent and inverse tangent continuous functions. (The student will learn in calculus that continuity is a most desirable property.)

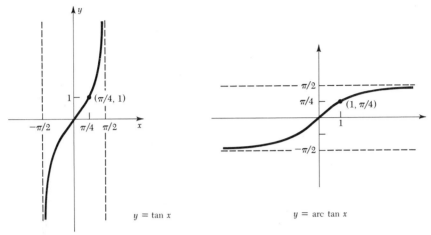

FIGURE 6–20

Not all of the inverse trigonometric functions are continuous. For example, the cosecant function is strictly decreasing on $(-\pi/2, 0) \cup (0, \pi/2)$, but it is not defined at 0 and is discontinuous there. (See

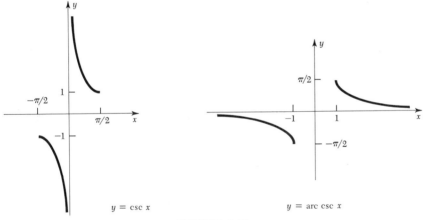

FIGURE 6–21

Figure 6–21.) Thus, the inverse cosecant function which is defined so that $-\pi/2 \leqq \text{arc csc } x \leqq \pi/2$ is also a discontinuous function. The inverse secant is defined so that $0 \leq \text{arc sec } x \leq \pi$ and the inverse cotangent is defined so that $-\pi/2 < \text{arc cot } x < \pi/2$.

exercises

1. Graph the inverse secant function.
2. Graph the inverse cotangent function.

3. Find each of the following function values.
   (a) arc sin 1/2   (b) arc tan 1   (c) arc tan −1
   (d) $\cot^{-1}$ −1   (e) $\cos^{-1}$ $\sqrt{3}/2$ (f) arc csc 2

4. Find each of the following function values.
   (a) arc cos 1/2   (b) arc sin −1/2   (c) arc cot −1
   (d) $\sec^{-1}$ 1   (e) $\csc^{-1}$ −1   (f) arc tan 0

5. Find each of the following function values.
   (a) sin (arc sin 1/2)   (b) tan (arc sin 1/2)
   (c) sin (arc cos 1/2)   (d) $\tan^{-1}$ (sin $\pi/2$)

6. Find each of the following function values.
   (a) tan (arc sec −2)   (b) cot (arc csc −2)
   (c) $\cos^{-1}$ (tan $\pi/4$)   (d) $\csc^{-1}$ (sin −$\pi/2$)

7. Prove each of the following.
   (a) arc sin (−x) = −arc sin x
   (b) arc cos (−x) = π − arc cos x

8. Prove each of the following.
   (a) arc tan (−x) = −arc tan x
   (b) arc sec (−x) = π − arc sec x

9. Solve for x.
   (a) arc sin 12/13 − arc cos 3/5 = arc cos x.   [Hint: Use cos (A − B)
       = cos A cos B + sin A sin B.]
   (b) arc tan 3/4 + arc cos −4/5 = arc sin x.

10. Solve for x.
   (a) arc tan −4/3 − arc sin x = arc cos 3/5
   (b) tan (arc sin 3/5) = cot x

mathematical induction

7

Many statements, or propositions, in mathematics are concerned with the set of positive integers. For example, consider the following statements.

1. For every positive integer n, $x - y$ is a factor of $x^n - y^n$.

2. For every positive integer n, a set with n elements has 2^n subsets.

3. For every positive integer n, $4^{n+1} + 5^{2n-1}$ has 21 as a factor.

4. For every positive integer n, a segment of length $\sqrt{n}$ can be constructed with straightedge and compass.

5. For every positive integer n,

$$(\cos \theta)(\cos 2\theta)(\cos 4\theta) \ldots (\cos 2^{n-1} \theta) = \frac{\sin 2^n \theta}{2^n \sin \theta}.$$

Each of these propositions may take the form "For every positive integer n, $P(n)$," where $P(n)$ is an open sentence such as "$x - y$ is a factor of $x^n - y^n$." For each statement, we want to prove that if $S = \{n \mid P(n) \text{ is a true statement}\}$ then S is the set all positive integers.

111

Such proofs can be based on the well-ordering property: Every non-empty set of positive integers contains a least integer. (See Chapter 2.)

To prove that $x - y$ is a factor of $x^n - y^n$ for every positive integer n, let $S = \{n | x - y$ is a factor of $x^n - y^n\}$. Since $x - y$ is a factor of $x^1 - y^1$, the integer 1 is obviously in S. If $x - y$ is not a factor of $x^n - y^n$ for some positive integer, then the complement of S relative to the set N of positive integers is not empty; that is, $S_N' \neq \emptyset$. By the well-ordering property, S_N' has a least integer in it. Let t be the least integer in S_N'; that is, t is the least positive integer for which $x - y$ is *not* a factor of $x^n - y^n$ if $n = t$. Since 1 is in S, $t \neq 1$ and $t - 1 > 0$. Furthermore, since t is the least postive integer for which $x - y$ is not a factor of $x^n - y^n$, we conclude that although $x - y$ is not a factor of $x^t - y^t$ it is a factor of $x^{t-1} - y^{t-1}$. But,

$$x^t - y^t = x^t - xy^{t-1} + xy^{t-1} - y^t$$
$$= x(x^{t-1} - y^{t-1}) + y^{t-1}(x - y).$$

Since $x - y$ is a factor of each term of the sum on the right side of the equality, $x - y$ is a factor of the sum; that is, $(x - y)$ is a factor of $x^t - y^t$. This is a contradiction. Hence, $S_N' = \emptyset$ and S is the set of all positive integers. The theorem is proved.

This example will serve as a pattern to prove what is called the *first principle of mathematical induction*. This method of proof is discussed in the next section.

7–2   induction principles

theorem 7–1: *first principle of mathematical induction.* Let $P(n)$ be an open sentence. Assume $P(1)$ is a true statement and assume for any integer $k \geq 1$ that $P(k+1)$ is true whenever $P(k)$ is true. Then $P(n)$ is true for every positive integer n.

proof: Let $S = \{n | n$ is a positive integer and $P(n)$ is true$\}$. (We prove that S_N' is empty by assuming it is not empty and arriving at a contradiction.)

If there is some positive integer for which $P(n)$ is false, then S_N' is non-empty where N is the set of positive integers. By the well-ordering property, S_N' contains a least positive integer t for which $P(t)$ is false. Since $P(1)$ is given to be true, $t \neq 1$ and $t - 1 > 0$. Since t is the least positive integer for which $P(t)$ is false, we conclude that $P(t-1)$ is true.

By the hypothesis of the theorem, $P(k+1)$ is true whenever $P(k)$ is true for any integer $k \geq 1$. Since $(t-1) + 1 = t$, it follows that $P(t)$ is true if $P(t-1)$ is true. This is a contradiction.

Hence, S_N' is empty and $S = N$. Consequently, $P(n)$ is true for every positive integer n.

As a consequence of the first principle of induction, to prove an open sentence $P(n)$ is true for every positive integer n we need to prove two things: (1) Prove $P(1)$ is true. (2) Prove $P(k+1)$ is true on the assumption that $P(k)$ is true for any positive integer k.

examples

1. Prove that for every positive integer n, $(n^3 + 2n)/3$ is a positive integer.

proof: *Part 1.* For the positive integer $n = 1$, $(1^3 + 2(1))/3 = 1$; hence, $(n^3 + 2n)/3$ is a positive integer for $n = 1$.

Part 2. Assume $(k^3 + 2k)/3$ is a positive integer for some positive integer k. (We need to prove that

$$\frac{(k+1)^3 + 2(k+1)}{3}$$

is a positive integer.)

$$\frac{(k+1)^3 + 2(k+1)}{3} = \frac{k^3 + 3k^2 + 3k + 1 + 2k + 2}{3}$$
$$= \frac{(k^3 + 2k) + (3k^2 + 3k + 3)}{3}$$
$$= \frac{k^3 + 2k}{3} + (k^2 + k + 1)$$

Since $(k^3 + 2k)/3$ is a positive integer by assumption, the sum $(k^3 + 2k)/3 + (k^2 + k + 1)$ is a positive integer. The theorem is proved.

2. Let a line segment AB of unit length be given. Prove for every positive integer n that a line segment of length $\sqrt{n}$ can be constructed by straightedge and compass.

proof: *Part 1.* Let $P(n)$ denote the open sentence, "A line segment of length $\sqrt{n}$ can be constructed by straightedge and compass." Since $\sqrt{1} = 1$ and since the given unit segment can be duplicated, $P(1)$ is true.

Part 2. Assume $P(k)$ is true. That is, assume a line segment of length $\sqrt{k}$ can be constructed by straightedge and compass for a positive integer k. On the segment AB of unit length, construct a line segment BC per-

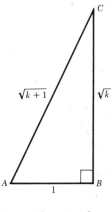

$$\left(\sqrt{k+1}\right)^2 = \left(\sqrt{k}\right)^2 + 1^2$$

FIGURE 7–1

pendicular to AB at B with length $\sqrt{k}$. This is possible since a line perpendicular to a given line at a given point can be constructed with straightedge and compass and since it was assumed a segment of length $\sqrt{k}$ is constructable.

By the Pythagorean Theorem, we conclude that the hypotenuse AC of the right triangle ABC has length $\sqrt{k+1}$. Thus, $P(k+1)$ is true on the assumption that $P(k)$ is true.

Parts 1 and 2 prove the theorem.

Let $P(n)$ denote the open sentence $2^n < n!$ Since $2^1 > 1!$, $2^2 > 2!$, and $2^3 > 3!$, we see that $P(1)$, $P(2)$, and $P(3)$ are false. However, it is true that $2^n < n!$ for every positive integer $n \geq 4$. In order to prove this, let $Q(m)$ denote the open sentence

$$2^{m+3} < (m+3)!$$

For any positive integer $m \geq 1$, $m+3 \geq 4$; hence, if $Q(m)$ is true for every integer $m \geq 1$, then $P(n)$ is true for every integer $n \geq 4$.

Since $2^4 < 4!$, $Q(m)$ is true for $m = 1$. Assume $Q(k)$ is true for some positive integer k; that is, assume that $2^{k+3} < (k+3)!$ is a true statement.

Multiplying by 2,

$$2^{k+4} < 2[(k+3)!].$$

Since $2 < k+4$ for any positive integer k,

$$2^{k+4} < 2[(k+3)!] < (k+4)[(k+3)!] = (k+4)!$$

Thus,

$$2^{(k+1)+3} < [(k+1)+3]!$$

and $Q(k+1)$ is true. Consequently, $Q(m)$ is true for every positive integer by the first principle of mathematical induction and $P(n)$ is true for every integer $n \geq 4$.

theorem 7-2:   Let $P(n)$ be an open sentence. Assume $P(a)$ is true for some positive integer a and assume for any integer $k \geq a$ that $P(k+1)$ is true whenever $P(k)$ is true. Then, $P(n)$ is true for every integer $n \geq a$.

proof: Let $Q(m)$ be the open sentence $P(m-1+a)$. Now, if m is any positive integer, then $m-1+a \geq a$. Therefore, if we can prove that $Q(m)$ is true for every positive integer m, then $P(n)$ is true for every integer $n \geq a$, since every integer $n \geq a$ can be expressed as $n = m-1+a$ for some $m \geq 1$. Thus, we use the first principle of induction to show that $Q(m)$ is true for every positive integer. By the definition of $Q(m)$, $Q(1)$ is the statement

$$P(1-1+a) = P(a).$$

By hypothesis, $P(a)$ is true so it follows that $Q(1)$ is true.

Assume that $Q(k)$ is true for some integer $k \geq 1$. Again, by definition of $Q(m)$, this means that

$$P(k-1+a)$$

is true.

By hypothesis, $P[(k+1)-1+a]$ is true since $P(k-1+a)$ is true; that is,

$$P(k+a) = Q(k+1)$$

is true. Therefore, by the first principle of induction, we conclude that $Q(m)$ is true for every positive integer and $P(n)$ is true for every positive integer $n \geq a$.

Certain concepts depend on what is called an *inductive definition* for their precise definitions. To illustrate what is called an inductive definition, let us consider the inductive definition of positive integral exponents. The idea is to give a meaning to the symbol a^n, where a is a real number, for every positive integer n. With this in mind, we propose the following definition of a^n.

definition: For any real number a, we define
  (1) $a^1 = a$, and
  (2) $a^{k+1} = (a^k) \cdot a$, where k is a positive integer.

This definition permits us to prove that a^n is defined for every positive integer n by using Theorem 7–1 or in the following manner. If a^n is not defined for some positive integer n, then the set S of positive integers for which a^n is not defined is not empty. Let t be the least positive integer in S. By (1), we have that $t \neq 1$, and, thus, $(t-1)$ is a positive integer. Furthermore, a^{t-1} is defined, since $t-1 < t$. By (2), $a^{(t-1)+1} = (a^{t-1}) \cdot a$; that is, $a^t = (a^{t-1}) \cdot a$. Since a^t is defined, we have a contradiction. We conclude that S is empty and a^n is defined for every positive integer.

It should be clear from this example of an inductive definition that if a concept involving the positive integers is defined for 1 and is also defined for the integer $(k+1)$ whenever it is defined for k, then it is defined for every positive integer.†

exercises

Prove each of the following.

  1. For every positive integer n, $n^5 - n$ has 5 as a factor.
  2. For every positive integer n, $2^{2n+1} + 1$ has 3 as a factor.

† For a more comprehensive discussion of mathematical induction, see Youse, *Mathematical Induction*, Emory University Series, Prentice-Hall, Inc., 1964.

3. For every positive integer n,

$$(\cos\theta)(\cos 2\theta)(\cos 4\theta)\ldots(\cos 2^{n-1}\theta) = \frac{\sin 2^n\theta}{2^n\sin\theta}.$$

4. For every positive integer n, $4^{n+1}+5^{2n-1}$ has 21 as a factor.

5. For every positive integer n, $x^{2n}-y^{2n}$ has $(x+y)$ as a factor.

6. For every positive integer n, $x^{2n-1}+y^{2n-1}$ has $(x+y)$ as a factor.

7. For every positive integer n, $\cos n\pi = (-1)^n$.

8. For every positive integer n, a set with n elements has 2^n subsets.

9. For every positive integer n, $n^5/5 + n^3/3 + 7n/15$ is an integer.

10. For every positive integer n, $n^7/7 + n^3/3 + 11n/21$ is an integer.

11. For every positive integer n, $6^{n+2}+7^{2n+1}$ has 43 as a factor.

12. Let A and B be two sets with n elements in each. Prove that $n!$ is the number of one-to-one correspondences between the two sets.

13. Let $P(n)$ be an open sentence. Assume $P(1)$ is a true statement and assume for any positive integer k that if $P(t)$ is true for every positive integer $t < k$, then $P(k)$ is true. Prove that $P(n)$ is true for every positive integer n.

°14. Let $P(n)$ be an open sentence. Assume $P(2^k)$ is true for every positive integer k and assume for any positive integer u that if $P(u)$ is true then $P(u-1)$ is true. Prove that $P(n)$ is true for every positive integer.

sequences and sigma notation

8

When we discuss the set of prime numbers, the set of positive even integers, or the set of positive multiples of 5, each set is often exhibited by a partial list of the elements. For example, the primes are listed "sequentially" as 2, 3, 5, 7, 11, 13, 17, 19, 23, ... , the even positive integers as 2, 4, 6, 8, 10, 12, ... , and the multiples of 5 as 5, 10, 15, 20, 25, 30, ... Each set is *ordered* by listing the smallest number in the set first, the next smallest second, the next smallest third, etc. Thus, we speak of the first, second, and third prime numbers. Any method for putting a given set into one-to-one correspondence with the set of positive integers defines what is called a *sequence*.

definition: A function s with the set of positive integers as its domain is called an *infinite sequence*.

If the range of a sequence is a subset of the set of real numbers, it is called a *real sequence*. If $s = \{(n, 2n) \mid n$ is a positive integer$\}$, then s is the real sequence of even integers.

If s is a sequence, the function value of s at n, which we have previously denoted by $s(n)$, is called the nth *term of the sequence*. Generally, the notation s_n is used instead of $s(n)$ to denote the nth term of a sequence. Instead of defining the sequence of even integers by $s(n) = 2n$, we usually write $s_n = 2n$. In this example, $s_1 = 2$, $s_2 = 4$, $s_3 = 6$, $s_4 = 8$, $s_5 = 10$, etc. Since a sequence s is completely determined by the value of s for each n, we often denote s by $\{s_n\}$, or $\{s(n)\}$.

examples

1. If $s = \{(n, 1/n)$ where n is a positive integer$\}$, then s is a sequence. Other notations for this sequence are $\{1/n\}$ and $\{1, 1/2, 1/3, 1/4, 1/5, \ldots, 1/n, \ldots\}$.

2. If a sequence s is defined by $s_n = 2^{n-1}$, then $s_1 = 1$, $s_2 = 2$, $s_3 = 4$, $s_4 = 8$, $s_5 = 16$, etc.

3. If $s = \{(n, (-1)^{n-1})$ where n is a positive integer$\}$, then $s_1 = 1$, $s_2 = -1$, $s_3 = 1$, $s_4 = -1$, $s_5 = 1$, etc. This sequence can also be defined in the following manner.

$$s_n = \begin{cases} 1 \text{ where } n \text{ is odd.} \\ -1 \text{ where } n \text{ is even.} \end{cases}$$

Often a sequence is defined by an inductive definition. An inductive definition of a sequence $\{s_n\}$ defines s_1 and then defines each term thereafter in terms of its immediate predecessor. For example, let

$$s_n = \begin{cases} 1 \text{ where } n = 1. \\ n(s_{n-1}) \text{ where } n > 1. \end{cases}$$

Since s_n is defined for $n = 1$ and is defined for $k + 1$ whenever it is defined for k, we conclude that s_n is defined for every positive integer. (See Chapter 7.) For this sequence, $s_1 = 1$, $s_2 = 2 \cdot 1$, $s_3 = 3 \cdot 2 \cdot 1$, $s_4 = 4 \cdot 3 \cdot 2 \cdot 1$, etc. This sequence is called the factorial sequence; its nth term is denoted by $s_n = n!$.

If we define a function s with domain the set of integers n such that $1 \leq n \leq t$ where t is a given positive integer, this function is called a finite sequence. For example, if $s = \{(n, n+2) | 1 \leq n \leq 5\}$, then $s_1 = 3$, $s_2 = 4$, $s_3 = 5$, $s_4 = 6$, and $s_5 = 7$. The function consists only of the ordered pairs $(1, 3)$, $(2, 4)$, $(3, 5)$, $(4, 6)$, $(5, 7)$, and it is a finite sequence with five terms.

For convenience, we agree that n is a variable on the set of positive integers unless stated otherwise.

exercises

1. Let $s = \{(n, 4n - 1)\}$. What are s_1, s_2, s_3, s_4, s_5, s_6, and s_7?

2. Let s be defined by $s_n = (-1)^{n-1}n^n$. What are s_1, s_2, s_3, s_4, and s_5?

3. Let t be the sequence defined by

$$t_n = \frac{(-1)^n - 1}{2}.$$

List the first ten terms of this sequence. What is t_{99}?

4. (a) If 2, 5, 8, 11, 14, 17, 20, ... are consecutive members of a sequence t, what conjecture would you make concerning t_8? t_n?
   (b) Let k be any real number. Consider the sequence defined by

$$s_n = \frac{(k-23)}{7!}(n-7)(n-6)(n-5)(n-4)(n-3)(n-2)(n-1) + (3n-1).$$

   What are s_1, s_2, s_3, s_4, s_5, s_6, s_7, and s_8?
   (c) Discuss the significance of (a) and (b).

5. If $a_n = 2n - 1$, find the sum of the first two terms of this sequence. The sum of the first three terms. Four terms. Five terms. Twenty terms.

6. Let $\{s_n\}$ be defined inductively by $s_1 = 1$, $s_2 = 3$, and $s_{k+1} = 3s_k - 2s_{k-1}$ for $k \geq 2$.
   (a) What are s_3, s_4, s_5, s_6, s_7, s_8?
   (b) Conjecture the value of s at n.
   (c) Use mathematical induction to prove your conjecture.

7. Let $\{t_n\}$ be defined inductively by $t_1 = 1$, $t_2 = 2$, and $t_{k+2} = t_{k+1} + t_k$ for $k \geq 1$.
   (a) What are t_3, t_4, t_5, t_6, t_7, t_8?
   (b) Let $\{s_n\}$ be defined by $s_n = t^2_{n+1} - t_n t_{n+2}$. What are s_1, s_2, s_3, s_4, s_5, s_6, s_7?
   (c) What conjecture would you make concerning s_n?
   (d) Prove your conjecture.

*8. (a) Let $\{s_n\}$ be defined by $s_1 = 1$ and $s_k = \sqrt{5s_{k-1} + 1}$ for $k > 1$. What are s_2, s_3, s_4?
    (b) Prove that

$$s_n < \frac{5 + \sqrt{29}}{2}$$

for every positive integer n. [Hint: Prove

$$s_n \leq \frac{5 + \sqrt{29}}{2}$$

for all n by mathematical induction. Then prove for any n that

$$s_n \neq \frac{5 + \sqrt{29}}{2}.]$$

8-2 sigma notation

Let $\{s_n\}$ be the sequence defined by $s_n = 2n$. If we want to express the sum of the first seven terms of this sequence of even integers, we could write

$$2 + 4 + 6 + 8 + 10 + 12 + 14.$$

To express the sum of the first 100 terms, we could write

$$2+4+6+8+\cdots+198+200.$$

The sigma notation is used to avoid such "addition strings." The following is an inductive definition of the sigma notation.

definition: For any sequence of numbers $\{s_n\}$, let

(1) $$\sum_{n=1}^{1} s_n = s_1$$

and

(2) $$\sum_{n=1}^{k+1} s_n = \left(\sum_{n=1}^{k} s_n\right) + s_{k+1} \qquad \text{where } k \text{ is a positive integer.}$$

Since $\sum_{n=1}^{k} s_n$ is defined for $k=1$ and is defined for $k+1$ whenever it is defined for the positive integer k, $\sum_{n=1}^{k} s_n$ is defined for every positive integer k. Occasionally, we call $\sum_{n=1}^{k} s_n$ *the definite sum of s_n from 1 to k.*

As a consequence of the above definition,

$$\sum_{n=1}^{1} s_n = s_1$$

$$\sum_{n=1}^{2} s_n = \left(\sum_{n=1}^{1} s_n\right) + s_2 = s_1 + s_2$$

$$\sum_{n=1}^{3} s_n = \left(\sum_{n=1}^{2} s_n\right) + s_3 = s_1 + s_2 + s_3$$

$$\sum_{n=1}^{4} s_n = \left(\sum_{n=1}^{3} s_n\right) + s_4 = s_1 + s_2 + s_3 + s_4.$$

Thus,

$$\sum_{n=1}^{7} 2n = 2+4+6+8+10+12+14,$$

and the sum of the first 100 even positive integers can be denoted conveniently by

$$\sum_{n=1}^{100} 2n$$

Notice that $2+4+6+8+10=2(1+2+3+4+5)$. This suggests an important property of the sigma notation which we now state and prove.

theorem 8–1: Let $\{s_n\}$ be a sequence.

$$\sum_{n=1}^{k} cs_n = c \sum_{n=1}^{k} s_n$$

where c is a given real number.

proof (mathematical induction): *Part 1.* By definition of the sigma notation,

$$\sum_{n=1}^{1} cs_n = cs_1 \quad \text{and} \quad \sum_{n=1}^{1} s_n = s_1.$$

Thus,

$$c \sum_{n=1}^{1} s_n = cs_1 \quad \text{and} \quad \sum_{n=1}^{1} cs_n = c \sum_{n=1}^{1} s_n.$$

Therefore, the statement is true for $k=1$.

Part 2. Assume that

$$\sum_{n=1}^{k} cs_n = c \sum_{n=1}^{k} s_n.$$

Then,

$$\sum_{n=1}^{k+1} cs_n = \sum_{n=1}^{k} cs_n + cs_{k+1} \qquad \text{Definition of sigma notation}$$

$$= c \sum_{n=1}^{k} s_n + cs_{k+1} \qquad \text{Assumption}$$

$$= c \left(\sum_{n=1}^{k} s_n + s_{k+1} \right) \qquad \text{Distributive property}$$

$$= c \sum_{n=1}^{k+1} s_n. \qquad \text{Definition of sigma notation}$$

Parts 1 and 2 prove the statement for every integer k.

If $\{s_n\}$ and $\{t_n\}$ are two sequences, then

$$\sum_{n=1}^{3} (s_n + t_n) = (s_1 + t_1) + (s_2 + t_2) + (s_3 + t_3)$$

$$= (s_1 + s_2 + s_3) + (t_1 + t_2 + t_3)$$

$$= \sum_{n=1}^{3} s_n + \sum_{n=1}^{3} t_n.$$

This exhibits a second general property of the sigma notation.

theorem 8–2: Let $\{s_n\}$ and $\{t_n\}$ be sequences. Then,

$$\sum_{n=1}^{k} (s_n + t_n) = \sum_{n=1}^{k} s_n + \sum_{n=1}^{k} t_n$$

for every positive integer k.

proof: Left as an exercise for the student.

Another important property of the sigma notation is called the *telescoping property*. For the sequence $\{s_n\}$,

$$\sum_{n=1}^{3} (s_{n+1} - s_n) = (s_4 - s_3) + (s_3 - s_2) + (s_2 - s_1)$$

$$= s_4 - s_1.$$

The following theorem is a general statement of the telescoping property.

theorem 8-3 (telescoping property):   Let $\{s_n\}$ be a sequence. Then,

$$\sum_{n=1}^{k} (s_{n+1} - s_n) = s_{k+1} - s_1$$

for every positive integer k.

proof: Left as an exercise for the student.

The symbolism

$$\sum_{n=1}^{k} 5 \quad \text{or} \quad \sum_{n=1}^{k} a_n$$

where $a_n = 5$ for all n, represents the sum of k fives. Thus,

$$\sum_{n=1}^{6} 5 = 30 \quad \text{and} \quad \sum_{n=1}^{100} 1 = 100.$$

We can consider

$$\sum_{n=1}^{k} 5 \quad \text{as} \quad \sum_{n=1}^{k} 5n^0$$

so

$$\sum_{n=1}^{3} 5 = \sum_{n=1}^{3} 5n^0 = 5(1)^0 + 5(2)^0 + 5(3)^0 = 15.$$

examples

1. Since $(n+1)^2 - n^2 = 2n + 1$ for every integer n,

$$\sum_{n=1}^{k} [(n+1)^2 - n^2] = \sum_{n=1}^{k} (2n + 1)$$

by the telescoping property, where $s_n = n^2$,

$$\sum_{n=1}^{k} [(n+1)^2 - n^2] = (k+1)^2 - 1^2.$$

Furthermore,

$$\sum_{n=1}^{k} (2n+1) = \sum_{n=1}^{k} 2n + \sum_{n=1}^{k} 1$$
$$= 2 \left(\sum_{n=1}^{k} n \right) + k.$$

Hence,

$$(k+1)^2 - 1 = 2 \left(\sum_{n=1}^{k} n \right) + k$$

and

$$2 \sum_{n=1}^{k} n = k^2 + k.$$

Thus,

$$\sum_{n=1}^{k} n = \frac{k(k+1)}{2}.$$

Consequently, the sum of the first k positive integers is $[k(k+1)]/2 \cdot$ (This important fact should be remembered.)

2. To find the sum of the first k odd positive integers, we proceed as follows.

$$\sum_{n=1}^{k} (2n-1) = \sum_{n=1}^{k} 2n - \sum_{n=1}^{k} 1$$
$$= 2 \left(\sum_{n=1}^{k} n \right) - k$$
$$= k(k+1) - k$$
$$= k^2$$

3. If $\{s_n\}$ is the sequence defined by $s_n = 3n - 1$, $s_1 = 2$, $s_2 = 5$, $s_3 = 8$, $s_4 = 11$, etc. The sum of the first fifty terms of this sequence is obtained in the following manner.

$$\sum_{n=1}^{50} (3n-1) = \sum_{n=1}^{50} 3n - \sum_{n=1}^{50} 1$$
$$= 3 \left(\sum_{n=1}^{50} n \right) - 50$$
$$= \frac{3(50)(51)}{2} - 50$$
$$= 3,775$$

4. To find the sum of the first k perfect squares, we proceed as follows. Since $n^3 - (n-1)^3 = 3n^2 - 3n + 1$ for every positive integer n,

$$\sum_{n=1}^{k} [n^3 - (n-1)^3] = \sum_{n=1}^{k} 3n^2 - \sum_{n=1}^{k} 3n + \sum_{n=1}^{k} 1$$

for every positive integer k. Thus,

$$k^3 - 0^3 = 3 \left(\sum_{n=1}^{k} n^2 \right) - 3 \left(\sum_{n=1}^{k} n \right) + k,$$

and

$$3 \sum_{n=1}^{k} n^2 = k^3 + \frac{3k(k+1)}{2} - k.$$

Hence,

$$3 \sum_{n=1}^{k} n^2 = \frac{k(2k^2 + 3k + 1)}{2}$$

and

$$\sum_{n=1}^{k} n^2 = \frac{k(k+1)(2k+1)}{6}.$$

exercises

Evaluate each of the following.

1. $\sum_{n=1}^{27} 5n$

2. $\sum_{n=1}^{30} (7n + 2)$

3. $\sum_{n=1}^{100} (3n^2 + 1)$

4. $\sum_{n=1}^{20} (n^2 + n + 3)$

5. $\sum_{n=1}^{50} \frac{1}{n(n+1)}$ $\left[\text{Hint: } \frac{-1}{n(n+1)} = \frac{1}{n+1} - \frac{1}{n}. \right]$

6. $\sum_{n=1}^{15} n^3$ [Hint: $n^4 - (n-1)^4 = 4n^3 - 6n^2 + 4n - 1$.]

7. $\sum_{n=1}^{k} n^3$ [Hint: See Exercise 6.]

8. $\sum_{n=1}^{20} \frac{1}{n(n+1)(n+2)}$ $\left[\text{Hint: } \frac{-2}{n(n+1)(n+2)} = \frac{1}{(n+1)(n+2)} - \frac{1}{n(n+1)}. \right]$

9. $\sum_{n=1}^{k} (3n^3 - 3n^2 + 1)$ [Hint: See Exercise 7.]

10. $\sum_{n=1}^{k} n^4$

11. Prove that

$$\sum_{n=1}^{k} (-1)^{n-1} n^2 = (-1)^{k-1} \sum_{n=1}^{k} n$$

for every positive integer k.

12. Prove that

$$\sum_{n=k+1}^{2k} \frac{1}{n} = \sum_{n=1}^{2k} \frac{(-1)^{n-1}}{n}$$

for every positive integer k.

8-3   arithmetic and geometric series

If $\{s_n\}$ is a sequence defined by $s_n = 3n$, then

$$\sum_{n=1}^{1} 3n = 3,$$

$$\sum_{n=1}^{2} 3n = 3+6 = 9,$$

$$\sum_{n=1}^{3} 3n = 3+6+9 = 18, \text{ etc.}$$

We have defined a new sequence $\{\sigma_k\}$ called a *series* where

$$\sigma_k = \sum_{n=1}^{k} s_n.$$

If we let

$$\sigma_k = \sum_{n=1}^{k} 3n,$$

then $\sigma_1 = 3, \sigma_2 = 9, \sigma_3 = 18$, etc. The series $\{\sigma_k\}$ could also be defined by

$$\sigma = \left\{ \left(k, \sum_{n=1}^{k} 3n \right) \middle| k \text{ is a positive integer} \right\}.$$

The kth term σ_k of the series is called the kth *partial sum* of the sequence $\{s_n\}$, or more often, the sum of k terms of $\{s_n\}$.

Given a sequence $\{s_n\}$, it is not always easy to find a formula, even if one exists, that defines the kth partial sum σ_k of the sequence $\{s_n\}$. However, there are two types of sequences called arithmetic and geometric sequences for which a formula for the kth partial sum can be found without great difficulty.

definition: An *arithmetic sequence* $\{s_n\}$ is a sequence for which there exists a real number d such that $s_{n+1} - s_n = d$ for every positive integer n; the number d is called the *common difference* of the terms.

For example, if $\{s_n\}$ is defined by $s_n = 3n$, then since $3(n+1) - 3n = 3n + 3 - 3n = 3$ the sequence is an arithmetic sequence and the common difference of the terms is three. The sequence of even integers is an arithmetic sequence with two as the common difference.

One of the simplest arithmetic sequences is the sequence of positive integers; this sequence is defined by $s_n = n$ and the common difference is one. We have already proved that

$$\sum_{n=1}^{k} n = \frac{k(k+1)}{2};$$

thus, the sequence $\{\sigma_k\}$ of partial sums of the positive integers is defined by

$$\sigma_k = \frac{k(k+1)}{2}.$$

If $\{s_n\}$ is an arithmetic sequence, the sequence defined by

$$\sigma_k = \sum_{n=1}^{k} s_n$$

is called an *arithmetic series*.

If $\{s_n\}$ is an arithmetic sequence, then $s_2 = s_1 + d$ where d is the common difference of the terms. Furthermore, $s_3 = s_2 + d = (s_1 + d) + d = s_1 + 2d$, $s_4 = s_1 + 3d$, $\ldots$, $s_n = s_1 + (n-1)d$. Thus,

$$\begin{aligned}
\sigma_k &= \sum_{n=1}^{k} s_n \\
&= \sum_{n=1}^{k} [s_1 + (n-1)d] \\
&= \sum_{n=1}^{k} s_1 + \sum_{n=1}^{k} (n-1)d \\
&= ks_1 + d \sum_{n=1}^{k} (n-1) \\
&= ks_1 + \frac{d(k-1)k}{2} \\
&= \frac{k[2s_1 + (k-1)d]}{2}.
\end{aligned}$$

We have proved that

$$\frac{k[2s_1 + (k-1)d]}{2}$$

is the sum of the first k terms of an arithmetic sequence with first term s_1 and common difference d. In other words, if $\{s_n\}$ is an arithmetic sequence with common difference d, then the sequence σ_k of partial sums is defined by

$$\sigma_k = \frac{k[2s_1 + (k-1)d]}{2}.$$

If $s_n = 3n$, then

$$\sigma_k = \frac{k[(2)(3) + (k-1)3]}{2}$$

$$\sigma_k = \frac{3k(k+1)}{2}.$$

If $\{s_n\}$ is a sequence defined by $s_n = 7n - 5$, it is an arithmetic sequence with $s_1 = 2$ and common difference $d = 7$. We can find

$$\sum_{n=1}^{31} (7n - 5)$$

by the method discussed in the preceding section or by using the formula for the thirty-first partial sum of an arithmetic sequence. Using the latter,

$$\sigma_{31} = \frac{31[(2)(2) + (30)(7)]}{2}$$
$$= 3{,}317.$$

Let us consider a job with two (quite hypothetical) salary offers. One offer is \$100,000 a day for thirty days; the other is also a thirty-day offer and pays 1 cent for the first day's work, 2 cents for the second day's work, 2^2 cents for the third day's work, 2^3 cents for the fourth day's work, and 2^{n-1} cents for the nth day's work. Which is the better salary offer?

If one assumes that the greater total salary is the more attractive offer, we need to know the total amount of each offer. Under the first salary arrangement, one would make \$3,000,000 and under the second arrangement one would make

$$1 + 2 + 2^2 + 2^3 + 2^4 + \cdots + 2^{28} + 2^{29} \text{ cents.}$$

If S represents the second salary, we desire to know whether $S < \$3{,}000{,}000$ or $S > \$3{,}000{,}000$. Of course, S could be found by finding each day's payment under the second salary offer and then adding each of these thirty numbers. However, the process of finding the sum can be simplified considerably in the following manner. If

$$S = 1 + 2 + 2^2 + 2^3 + 2^4 + \cdots + 2^{28} + 2^{29},$$

then

$$2S = 2 + 2^2 + 2^3 + 2^4 + 2^5 + \cdots + 2^{29} + 2^{30}.$$

Subtracting S from $2S$, we get $S = 2^{30} - 1$. Since $2^{30} = 1{,}073{,}741{,}824$, we conclude that $2^{30} - 1$ cents is \$10,737,418.23. (2^{30} could be approximated by logarithms.) The second payments are said to increase *geometrically* and $1 + 2 + 2^2 + 2^3 + \cdots + 2^{29}$ is called a *geometric series*. More precisely,

$$\sigma_k = \sum_{n=1}^{k} 2^{n-1}$$

defines what is called a geometric series.

definition: A geometric sequence $\{s_n\}$ is a sequence for which there exists a number r such that $s_{n+1} = rs_n$ for every positive integer n; the number r is called the common ratio.

For example, if s_n is defined by $s_n = 2^{n-1}$, then since $s_{n+1} = 2s_n$ the sequence is a geometric sequence with first term $s_1 = 1$ and common ratio 2.

The sequence $\{\sigma_k\}$ defined by

$$\sigma_k = \sum_{n=1}^{k} ar^{n-1}$$

is called a *geometric series*. We now proceed to find a formula for σ_k in much the same manner that we found the salary S in our problem. If

$$\sigma_k = \sum_{n=1}^{k} ar^{n-1} \qquad \text{where } r \neq 1,$$

then

$$r\,\sigma_k = r \sum_{n=1}^{k} ar^{n-1}$$
$$= \sum_{n=1}^{k} ar^{n}.$$

Thus,

$$r\,\sigma_k - \sigma_k = \sum_{n=1}^{k} ar^{n} - \sum_{n=1}^{k} ar^{n-1}$$
$$(r-1)\,\sigma_k = \sum_{n=1}^{k} (ar^{n} - ar^{n-1})$$
$$(r-1)\,\sigma_k = a \sum_{n=1}^{k} (r^{n} - r^{n-1})$$
$$(r-1)\,\sigma_k = a(r^{k} - r^{0})$$
$$\sigma_k = \frac{a(r^{k} - 1)}{r - 1}.$$

Hence, $a(r^{k} - 1)/r - 1$ is the kth partial sum of the geometric sequence $s_n = ar^{n-1}$ where $r \neq 1$. If $r = 1$, every term is a and $\sigma_k = ka$.

exercises

Let $\{s_n\}$ be a sequence with kth partial sum $\sigma_k = \sum_{n=1}^{k} s_n$.

1. If $\{s_n\}$ is an arithmetic sequence such that $\sigma_{22} = 100$ and $s_1 = 3$, find d.

2. If $\{s_n\}$ is an arithmetic sequence such that $\sigma_{30} = 273$ and $s_1 = 2$, find d.

3. If $\{s_n\}$ is an arithmetic sequence such that $d = 3$ and $s_1 = 5$, find σ_{37}.

4. If $\{s_n\}$ is an arithmetic sequence such that $d = 2/3$ and $s_1 = 5/3$, find σ_{51}.

5. If $\{s_n\}$ is a geometric sequence such that $\sigma_8 = 100$ and $r = 2$, find a.

6. Find $\sum_{n=1}^{10} 7(3^n)$.

7. Find $\sum_{n=1}^{8} (3n + 2^n)$.

8. Suppose a town has a 100,000 population today and the population increases at a rate of 3% each year.
   (a) What will be the population at the end of twenty years? (Hint: If P is present population and r is rate of increase, prove
   $$\sum_{k=1}^{n} P(1+r)^{k-1}$$
   is the population in n years.)

9. Let $\sigma(n)$ be the sum of the factors of a positive integer n. (See Exercise 15, page 54.)
   (a) Show that $\sigma(6) = 2 \times 6$, $\sigma(28) = 2 \times 28$, $\sigma(496) = 2 \times 496$, and $\sigma(8,128) = 2 \times 8,128$.
   (b) If n is a positive integer such that $\sigma(n) = 2n$, n is called a *perfect number*. The numbers 6, 28, 496, 8,128, and 33,550,336 are the first five perfect numbers. Express each as a product of prime numbers.
   (c) Show that each of the first five perfect numbers is of the form $2^{p-1}(2^p - 1)$ where $(2^p - 1)$ is a prime number.
   (d) List all the factors of $(2^p - 1)$ if $(2^p - 1)$ is a prime number.
   (e) List all the factors of 2^{p-1}.
   (f) List all the factors of $n = 2^{p-1}(2^p - 1)$ if $(2^p - 1)$ is a prime number.
   (g) Prove that if $(2^p - 1)$ is a prime number and $n = 2^{p-1}(2^p - 1)$, then $\sigma(n) = 2n$.

10. Let $t(n)$ be the sum of the proper factors of n. (The proper factors of n are all factors except 1 and n.)
    (a) Find a number n such that $2t(n) + 1 = n$.
    (b) If $n = 3^p(3^{p+1} - 2)$ where $(3^{p+1} - 2)$ is a prime, prove that $2t(n) + 1 = n$. (See Exercise 9.)

probability

9

9-1   introduction

It is likely that each of us has, on one occasion or another, flipped a coin in order to determine which of two given alternatives should be pursued, such as who should pay for soft drinks, or whether one should walk home or ride a bus. There seems to be great faith in the flipping of a "fair" coin in the sense that we seem to "know" that it is just as likely to come up with a head as it is with a tail. People questioned about the fairness of this procedure usually justify it with something about a "50–50 chance," or that "half of the time the coin should come up one way and half the time the other way," or that of the two outcomes assumed equally likely for this experiment, one is called a head and the other a tail. We will examine this last description more fully.

The experience of flipping a coin involves many facets. First, one needs to consider all of the possible outcomes of the experiment. This is a large task and not always possible, so one replaces the actual experiment with an idealized experiment and considers only the outcomes possible for this idealized experiment. In this instance, the outcomes for the actual experiment could include: head, tail, stand on its rim, roll down an open sewer grating and disappear, and so on.

The outcomes for the *idealized* experiment are considered to be only: head, tail.

Next, one must make some kind of judgment about the outcomes of the idealized experiment. If there are many outcomes and any one is assumed to be as likely as any other, then one assigns an equal "probability," or technically, a probability measure or "weight," to each outcome. For example, one would assign the weight 1/2 to the outcome "head" and the weight 1/2 to the outcome "tail" if it is believed that these two outcomes are equally likely. As another example, in the rolling of a fair ("unloaded") six-sided die, one might assign the weight 1/6 to each of the six faces, only one of which will be uppermost when the die stops rolling.

In the two examples mentioned in the previous paragraph, note that equal weights were assigned to the outcomes assumed equally likely. Further advance knowledge of the experiment may lead one to believe that the outcomes are not equally likely. For instance, we might feel that the person flipping a coin has some magical influence or some influencing twist of the wrist while doing the flipping, and we might then believe that a head is twice as likely as a tail whenever that person flips the coin. In this latter case, one might assign the weight 2/3 to the outcome "head" and the weight 1/3 to the outcome "tail." The posting of "odds" at a race track is another form of assigning these weights when one does not believe that all horses entered have an equally likely chance of winning the race.

The student will note that the weights assigned have been proper fractions in each example so far. This choice of proper fractions can be traced to the French mathematician Pierre Simon Laplace (1749–1827) and the classic definition of probability that he gave. Paraphrased, it says:

definition: If there are n different equally likely outcomes of an idealized experiment, and s of these outcomes are to be considered a "success," then the probability of a success is the number s/n.†

In other words, for an experiment with equally likely outcomes, one assigns as a probability of success the ratio of the number of outcomes which are a success to the total number of outcomes of the experiment. For example, in the rolling of a fair six-sided die, if a success is having either the two- or the five-spotted side being uppermost at the end of the roll, then one would assign the weight 2/6 to the outcome "success." It is apparent from this classical definition that the weights

† The word "success," as used in the study of probability, does not necessarily imply a desirable outcome—simply a predicted one. A medical researcher, for example, might label a "success" every outcome of an experiment in which a drug being tested proved toxic or fatal; an actuary might call "success" any accident for which his company had a responsibility to the insured.

(or probabilities) assigned must be proper fractions—that is, numbers between zero and one—since there cannot be more successful outcomes than there are total outcomes. The special cases of assigning a weight of zero or a weight of one are quite possible and will be discussed later.

Using the ideas expressed so far, let us analyze the experiment of two persons flipping coins simultaneously. The idealized experiment for the two coins, A and B, consists of the outcomes assumed equally likely, head and tail, for each coin. Although the weights for each coin are known, this more complex experiment requires us to know the outcomes of the tosses taken together. It is convenient in these so-called "compound" experiments to use a "tree" diagram to analyze all possible outcomes of the two-coin toss. For the outcome "head" on coin A, coin B may come up either "head" or "tail," and for the outcome "tail" on coin A, again coin B can come up either "head" or "tail." There are actually four possible outcomes, listed in the order (coin A, coin B) as follows: (head, head), (head, tail), (tail, head), (tail, tail). The tree diagram is drawn in Figure 9–1.

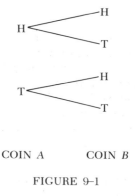

COIN A   COIN B

FIGURE 9–1

The weight 1/4 is assigned to each of the four outcomes shown since they are assumed to be equally likely. The probabilities of the various outcomes are therefore:

Outcome	Probability
Two heads	1/4
Faces match	2/4
At least one tail came up	3/4

In each experiment discussed so far, determining the total number of outcomes for a given experiment and counting the number of successful outcomes has been fairly easy and straightforward. As the complexity of the experiments increases, the usually simple matter of counting becomes increasingly more difficult. The following fairly obvious principle will be useful in these counting problems.

definition: If a first task can be completed in each of M different ways and, following this, a second task can be completed in each of N different ways, then the two tasks can be completed in the order stated in $M \cdot N$ different ways. This is known as the *fundamental principle of counting*.

For example, you will note that the experiment with the two coins could end in $2 \cdot 2 = 4$ different ways, according to this principle. The experiment of throwing a fair die and tossing a fair coin can end $6 \cdot 2 = 12$ different ways. A restaurant menu which lists seven different appetizers, ten different entrees, and eight different desserts confronts a diner with having to choose one of the $7 \cdot 10 \cdot 8 = 560$ different complete meals offered!

exercises

1. In drawing a card from a standard bridge deck of playing cards, what is the probability of drawing the ace of spades?

2. A salesmen can get from town A to town B by five different routes, and from town B to town C by six. How many different routes can he take from town A to town C?

3. There are twenty-four letters in the Greek alphabet. How many different Greek letter fraternity names using either two or three letters can be formed? (A letter can be repeated in a given name.)

4. Draw a tree diagram to illustrate the outcomes of the experiment of tossing three fair coins simultaneously. What is the probability of having exactly two of the three coins come up tails?

5. How many outcomes are there for the experiment of rolling two fair dice? In how many of these outcomes will the sum of the two sets of spots equal seven? What is the probability of rolling a seven?

6. In how many different ways can six coins, tossed simultaneously, come up?

7. A telephone survey in a given community shows that eighty-eight people would vote "Yes" on a given question, sixty-nine would vote "No" on the same question, and twenty-three people would abstain from voting. The polltaker believes that this is a representative sample. What probability weight would you assign to the probability that the next phone call will produce a "Yes" vote?

8. In how many ways can a chairman and a recorder be selected from a group of twenty-five people, if the same person cannot hold both jobs?

9. What probability would you assign to a "success" in an experiment if a success could not possibly happen? What probability would you assign

to a "success" if every outcome of the experiment was defined to be a success?

10. A digit is chosen from the set $\{1, 2, \ldots, 9\}$. After this is done, a second digit is chosen from the set $\{0, 1, \ldots, 9\}$. The two digits chosen are written as a two-digit number in this order. What is the probability that this two-digit number is divisible by seven?

11. A six-sided die is loaded so that each of the outcomes $1, 2, 3, 4, 5$ is equally likely and that the outcome 6 is twice as likely as any one of the other five outcomes. What probability would you assign to the outcome 3 in rolling this die?

9-2 arrangements

As a natural extension of the fundamental principle of counting, consider the following experiment: four chips are placed into a box. Each chip is painted a different color; red, yellow, blue, and green, for example. One chip at a time will be drawn from the box and the chip will be carefully placed on top of the numbers $1, 2,$ and 3 written on a piece of paper. How many different ways can this experiment end? A complete listing of all possible ways, with the aid of a tree diagram, is as follows, in the order: first chip, second chip, third chip:

R Y B	Y R B	B R Y	G R Y
R YG	Y RG	B RG	G RB
RB Y	YB R	B YR	G YR
RBG	YBG	B YG	G YB
RG Y	YG R	BG R	GB R
RG B	YG B	BG Y	GB Y

That the twenty-four different cases listed above are fairly obvious may be reasoned from the fundamental principle by saying: There are four different possibilities for the first chip, and then three different possibilities for the second chip, and then only two different possibilities for the third chip, for a total of $4 \cdot 3 \cdot 2 = 24$ different outcomes. If one adds a fifth different colored chip to the box and attempts again to list all outcomes of the experiment of drawing three of them, one after the other, the listing of the $5 \cdot 4 \cdot 3 = 60$ different outcomes becomes very tedious. It becomes apparent that a general formula is needed if any variations of the experiment are to be attempted.

In general, suppose one has N different colored chips in the box—one chip of each color—and wishes to draw R of these chips, one after the other, keeping track of the order in which the chips are drawn. The number of outcomes of this experiment is denoted by the symbol $(N)_R$ and is defined by the formula

$$(2.1) \qquad (N)_R = N(N-1)(N-2) \cdots (N-R+1).$$

It is understood that this definition can be used only when both N and R are positive integers and $R \leqslant N$. The symbol $(N)_R$ will denote the number of arrangements of the N different chips, taken R at a time, one after the other, with the order in which the chips are drawn carefully considered. (Some authors use the word *permutations* in place of *arrangements*.)

Of special interest is the case $R = N$—that is, the drawing of all of the chips in the box and placing them in the order drawn. The number of arrangements in this case is

$$(2.2) \qquad (N)_N = N(N-1)(N-2) \cdots (2)(1) = N!,$$

and so formula (2.1) can now be written

$$(2.3) \qquad\qquad (N)_R = \frac{N!}{(N-R)!}.$$

The student will note that formulas (2.1) and (2.3) are compatible only if we define the symbol $0! = 1$.

example

From a collection of marine signal flags containing one each of forty different flags, the number of different signals, reading from top to bottom and containing four flags only, is $(40)_4 = 40!/36!$, or more than two million different signals.

The notation $(N)_R$ has found widespread use because of its analogy with a different experiment and the number of outcomes—namely, the case where each item is replaced before the next one is drawn. In this case, the fundamental principle would tell us that there would be N^R different outcomes when we drew R chips in this manner.

example

From a club containing thirty members, in how many ways can a president, a secretary, and a treasurer be chosen, if no person has more than one post? The answer is, of course, given by $(30)_3 = 30!/27!$ or 24,360 ways.

From this example, we pose the following question. In how many ways can a three-member governing committee be chosen from the same club of thirty members, where each person chosen has equal powers and responsibilities and governs jointly at all times? The answer to this question is not as apparent as the answer in the immediately preceding example, for the order in which the three governors are chosen will make no difference to the people or to the club. We are interested only in determining the number of truly different committees of three which can be chosen from the club, where by truly different we mean that no two committees can have exactly the same three members. In brief, two committees will be truly different in this sense if one contains at least one member that is not on the other committee.

A hint to the number of committees that can be formed in this manner is given by examining the twenty-four outcomes of the experiment listed at the beginning of this section. The collection RYG, for instance, appears six times in the list. In fact, there are but four truly different collections (or committees) in the list of twenty-four outcomes, and for each of these four, there is a total of six outcomes with exactly the same three entries. The six entries in different order for each collection of three different objects could have been anticipated from the fundamental principle by reasoning that for each of the four truly different collections of three objects there are $3! = 6$ different ways of rearranging the order of the objects chosen.

If we return to the original question and the thirty-member club and denote the number of truly different committees by the symbol $\binom{30}{3}$, then for each truly different committee there are $3! = 6$ ways to rearrange the order. Then it should be readily apparent that the number of truly different committees and the number of arrangements (where order is considered) are related by $\binom{30}{3} \cdot 3! = (30)_3$, or that

$$\binom{30}{3} = (30)_3/3! = 4{,}060$$

truly different committees. At this stage one should probably be thankful for the invention of the "nominating committee" for a club!

In general, then, to determine the number of truly different collections of R items, drawn one at a time from a collection of N different items, one need only evaluate the equation

$$\binom{N}{R} = (N)_R/R! = \frac{N!}{(N-R)!R!}.$$

The symbol $\binom{N}{R}$ means: "The number of *combinations* of N different objects, taken R at a time." Each truly different collection of R objects is called a combination.

examples

1. The number of different five-card poker hands is $\binom{52}{5} \approx 2{,}600{,}000$ and the number of different bridge hands is $\binom{52}{13} \approx 635{,}000{,}000{,}000$, or 6.35×10^{11}.

2. The set $\{1,2,3\}$ has $\binom{3}{1}=3$ subsets with one element, $\binom{3}{2}=3$ subsets with two elements and $\binom{3}{3}=1$ subset with three elements. The symbol $\binom{3}{0}=1$ refers to which subset?

exercises

1. How many different one-, two-, or three-flag signals can be flown, if one has forty different flags to draw from and each flag is to be used only once in each signal?

2. How many different committees of four senators each can be formed from the U.S. Senate? How many committees can be formed if no committee has both senators from the same state?

3. How many of the five-card poker hands will have exactly two spades?

4. The following question was asked on an examination: "There are four different routes between town A and town B. How many ways can a person make the round trip?" Explain why each of the following answers should get full credit, and the reasoning behind each.

   (a) $\binom{4}{2}=6$ (b) $(4)_2=12$ (c) $4^2=16$

5. In how many ways can two juniors and three seniors be chosen from a group which contains ten juniors and twelve seniors?

6. Prove: $\binom{N}{R}=\binom{N}{N-R}$.

7. In what sense does the formula in Exercise 6 have any meaning, if $\binom{N}{R}$ refers to the number of committees of R persons each, chosen from a group of N members?

8. The symbol
$$\binom{N}{N_1,N_2,\cdots,N_k}$$
with $N_1+N_2+\cdots N_k=N$, denotes the number of different arrangements of N objects where there are N_1 identical objects of the first kind, N_2 identical objects of the second kind, etc. Show that
$$\binom{N}{N_1,N_2,\cdots,N_k}=\frac{N!}{N_1!\,N_2!\cdots N_k!}.$$

9. How many different four-letter "words" can be made from the word REED? List them and confirm your answer. How many of them are words that you know? Do the same for the word MISSISSIPPI, using all eleven letters, but do not list them if there are more than twenty-four.

10. In how many ways can exactly two tails come up when five coins are flipped simultaneously?

9-3   binomial theorem

Let us collect in an orderly fashion the values of the symbol $\binom{N}{R}$ as defined in the preceding paragraph, when N and R are positive integers and $R \leqslant N$. The definition $0! = 1$ enables us to extend the definition to include the cases $N = 0$ and $R = 0$ in this collection:

for $N = 0$ $$\binom{0}{0} = 1;$$

for $N = 1$ $$\binom{1}{0} = 1, \quad \binom{1}{1} = 1;$$

for $N = 2$ $$\binom{2}{0} = 1, \quad \binom{2}{1} = 2, \quad \binom{2}{2} = 1;$$

for $N = 3$ $$\binom{3}{0} = 1, \quad \binom{3}{1} = 3, \quad \binom{3}{2} = 3, \quad \binom{3}{3} = 1;$$

for $N = 4$ $$\binom{4}{0} = 1, \quad \binom{4}{1} = 4, \quad \binom{4}{2} = 6, \quad \binom{4}{3} = 4, \quad \binom{4}{4} = 1;$$

and so on.

In order to have a clearer view of this array (called "Pascal's Triangle"), let us remove the combinations symbols and display only their values:

$$
\begin{array}{ccccccccccccc}
 & & & & & & 1 & & & & & & \\
 & & & & & 1 & & 1 & & & & & \\
 & & & & 1 & & 2 & & 1 & & & & \\
 & & & 1 & & 3 & & 3 & & 1 & & & \\
 & & 1 & & 4 & & 6 & & 4 & & 1 & & \\
 & 1 & & 5 & & 10 & & 10 & & 5 & & 1 & \\
1 & & 6 & & 15 & & 20 & & 15 & & 6 & & 1 \\
\end{array}
$$

$\cdots \cdots$

The student no doubt will have discovered by this time that each number in a row (except the 1 at each end) is the sum of the two numbers just above it, on each side, in the preceding row. In symbols,

$$(3.1) \qquad \binom{N+1}{R} = \binom{N}{R-1} + \binom{N}{R}.$$

The relation (3.1) may be shown by two different methods — a direct method using the definitions of the symbols involved, and an indirect method using the ideas of subsets from the preceding paragraph.

proof: Consider a collection of $N+1$ different symbols, which we will call $a,b,c,d,\ldots,r,s,t,\ldots$ The symbol $\binom{N+1}{R}$ on the left of (3.1) denotes the number of different subsets of size R which can be formed from the $N+1$ symbols. In order to interpret the right-hand side of (3.1), let us fix our attention on just one of the symbols, say, b. The first term, $\binom{N}{R-1}$, is the number of subsets which can be formed, *using the symbol b* and any other $(R-1)$ of the N symbols remaining. In brief, the first term represents the number of subsets which include the symbol b. The second term, $\binom{N}{R}$, can be interpreted as follows: From the original collection of $(N+1)$ symbols, delete this same symbol, b; the second term will then represent the number of subsets of size R which can be formed from the original set, with b missing. In brief, the second term represents the number of subsets which do *not* include the symbol b.

We now seemingly digress from the above to explore another topic. Consider the various integral powers of the binomial expression, $a+b$, beginning with the integer 0:

$$(a+b)^0 = 1,$$
$$(a+b)^1 = a+b,$$
$$(a+b)^2 = a^2 + 2ab + b^2,$$
$$(a+b)^3 = a^3 + 3a^2b + 3ab^2 + b^3,$$
$$(a+b)^4 = a^4 + 4a^3b + 6a^2b^2 + 4ab^3 + b^4.$$
$$\cdots\cdots\cdots$$

which the student may verify for himself by direct methods. If one focuses his attention only on the numerical coefficient in each term and reads across each row, it becomes apparent that these coefficients are simply the various rows of Pascal's Triangle, one row at a time. This is a conjecture at this stage, of course, but it is true and a very important theorem. Called the Binomial Theorem, it is written

$$(a+b)^n = \sum_{k=0}^{n} \binom{n}{k} a^{n-k}b^k$$

for non-negative integers n.

The proof of the Binomial Theorem, using the method of mathematical induction from Chapter 7, is fairly simple:

$$(a+b)^{n+1} = (a+b)^n (a+b)$$
$$= \left[\sum_{k=0}^{n} \binom{n}{k} a^{n-k}b^k\right] (a+b),$$

assuming that the theorem is true for case n. The various terms in the expansion of the first factor above are displayed as follows:

$$(a+b)^{n+1} = \left[\binom{n}{0} a^n + \binom{n}{1} a^{n-1}b + \binom{n}{2} a^{n-2}b^2 + \cdots \right.$$
$$\left. + \binom{n}{k} a^{n-k}b^k + \cdots + \binom{n}{n} b^n \right] \cdot (a+b).$$

Applying the distributive law to the right member yields

$$(a+b)^{n+1} = \binom{n}{0} a^{n+1} + \binom{n}{1} a^n b + \binom{n}{2} a^{n-1}b^2 + \cdots$$
$$+ \binom{n}{k} a^{n-k+1}b^k + \cdots + \binom{n}{n} ab^n$$
$$+ \binom{n}{0} a^n b + \binom{n}{1} a^{n-1}b^2 + \cdots + \binom{n}{k-1} a^{n-k+1}b^2 + \cdots$$
$$+ \binom{n}{n} b^{n+1}.$$

Collect like terms from the right-hand side:

$$(a+b)^{n+1} = \binom{n}{0} a^{n+1} + \left[\binom{n}{1} + \binom{n}{0} \right] a^n b + \left[\binom{n}{2} + \binom{n}{1} \right] a^{n-1}b^2 +$$
$$\cdots + \left[\binom{n}{k} + \binom{n}{k-1} \right] a^{n-k+1}b^k + \cdots$$
$$+ \left[\binom{n}{n} + \binom{n}{n-1} \right] ab^n + \binom{n}{n} b^{n+1}.$$

The first term on the right has the coefficient $\binom{n}{0} = 1$, and may be replaced by the coefficient $\binom{n+1}{0} = 1$; similarly, the last term on the right may have its coefficient replaced by $\binom{n+1}{n+1} = \binom{n}{n} = 1$. All other terms in the expansion have coefficients which may be rewritten using Theorem (3.1), and the result is case $(n+1)$—that is, the desired result:

$$(a+b)^{n+1} = \binom{n+1}{0} a^{n+1} + \binom{n+1}{1} a^n b + \cdots + \binom{n+1}{k} a^{n-k+1}b^k + \cdots$$
$$+ \binom{n+1}{n} ab^n + \binom{n+1}{n+1} b^{n+1}.$$

Many theorems and applications follow from the Binomial Theorem, and we shall return to it in one application in Section 6. A few of the immediate consequences are listed here.

examples

1. Let $a = b = 1$ in the expansion of $(a+b)^n$.

$$2^n = \binom{n}{0} + \binom{n}{1} + \binom{n}{2} + \cdots + \binom{n}{n}.$$

This again confirms a result from Chapter 1—namely, that a given set of n distinct elements has exactly 2^n subsets. The student may wish to experiment with a few rows of Pascal's Triangle and verify a few cases for himself.

2. The twelfth term in the expansion of $(a+b)^{20}$ is $\binom{20}{11} a^9 b^{11}$, if the terms are written in descending powers of a.

3. The term involving b^6 in the expansion of $(2a+b^2)^8$ is $\binom{8}{3}(2a)^5(b^2)^3$. (This is the fourth term in descending powers of $2a$.)

4. Assuming that the Binomial Theorem also applies, we may write

$$(1+x)^{1/2} = \binom{1/2}{0} + \binom{1/2}{1}x + \binom{1/2}{2}x^2 + \cdots$$

where the symbol $\binom{1/2}{k}$ can be evaluated by using

$$\binom{1/2}{k} = \frac{(1/2)_k}{k!}.$$

The formal result is an unending series (an infinite series) and the first few terms are displayed.

$$(1+x)^{1/2} = 1 + \frac{1}{2}x - \frac{1}{8}x^2 + \frac{1}{16}x^3 - \frac{5}{128}x^4 + \cdots.$$

The first three terms in the series for $(1.02)^{1/2}$ yields 1.00995, a result accurate to five decimal places.

exercises

1. Verify that in any one row of Pascal's Triangle, the first entry minus the second plus the third minus the fourth and so on, for the entire row, always totals zero. State the theorem which says this is always so, for any positive integer n, using the combinations symbols, and then prove this theorem.

2. Find the sum of the first element, the third, the fifth, etc., in any row of Pascal's Triangle. After experimenting with several rows of the triangle, make an educated guess for all positive even integers n, about the sum formed in the described manner. Try to establish your conjecture as a theorem. (Hint: Use Example 1 and Exercise 1.)

3. Find the numerical coefficient of the term involving b^6 in the expansion of $(2a+b)^8$.

4. Find the numerical coefficient of the sixth term (with the expansion written in descending powers of a) in the expansion of $(a-2b)^8$.

5. By identifying the expansion, find the sum

$$\sum_{k=0}^{5} \binom{5}{k} 3^k 2^{5-k}$$

without evaluating each term.

6. The number $e = 2.71828 \ldots$ is a very important mathematical constant which the student will encounter later in more advanced mathematics. It is defined as the limiting value of the function $f(x) = (1+x)^{1/x}$ as the variable x approaches zero. Assuming that the binomial expansion applies (as in Example 4), display the first six terms in the expansion $f(x)$ and simplify. Evaluate the resulting simplified expansion for the value $x = 0$.

7. What does Exercise 6 in the preceding section tell you about the symmetry of Pascal's Triangle?

9–4   sample spaces

Let us return to some of the ideas expressed in Section 9–1 concerning the outcomes of idealized experiments. In that section, for a given experiment, every conceivable outcome was listed in its simplest terms — that is, a given outcome ideally cannot be further subdivided into "simpler" outcomes. For example, the outcomes of the coin-tossing experiment were listed simply as (head, tail), while the outcomes of the die-rolling experiment were listed as (1,2,3,4,5,6). This collection, or set, of outcomes will be called the "sample description space," or "sample space," in common use. The careful definition of this sample space is as follows: If every conceivable outcome of a given experiment is listed in its simplest terms in such a way that, for every outcome, there is exactly one element in the set of outcomes, then the resulting set of outcomes is called a sample space. The points in this set are simple events, and we will combine these simple events (or sample points) into compound events which are also subsets of the sample space.

The sample space, denoted by the symbol S, must be carefully formulated using the above description.

examples

1. The sample space for the experiment of throwing a die and flipping a coin consists of the set of twelve points,

$$S = \{(1,H),(1,T),(2,H),(2,T), \ldots , (6,H),(6,T)\}.$$

2. The sample space S for the experiment of drawing two balls, one after the other without replacing the first, from an urn containing four red balls and five green balls, consists of the four points:

$$S = \{(R,R),(R,G),(G,R),(G,G)\}.$$

Once the sample space S has been established for a given experiment, then we begin the task of assigning probabilities to the various simple outcomes listed in S. This can be done in a fairly arbitrary manner, as we shall see, keeping but two restrictions in mind, as noted in the following definition: To each simple outcome X of an idealized experiment, listed in the same space S, we assign a non-negative real number, called the probability of X, in such a way that the sum of all of the probabilities assigned to the points of S shall be one. In symbols, for each event X listed in S, we assign a real number $Pr(X)$ with the restriction that

(a) $Pr(X) \geqslant 0$,
(b) $Pr(S) = \sum_{\text{all } X \text{ in } S} Pr(X) = 1$.

The student will note that these numbers $Pr(X)$ are simply the weights assigned to various outcomes in Section 9–1.

Once the probabilities for the simple events have been established, then the probability assigned to a compound outcome will be simply the sum of all of the probabilities that have been assigned to its elements. With these two restrictions noted, various consequences follow almost immediately. For example, if set A is a subset of set B— that is, $A \subseteq B$—then $Pr(A) \leqslant Pr(B)$, as might be anticipated. This follows from the observation that there cannot be more points assigned to A than to B, and hence the sum of the probabilities assigned to A cannot exceed the sum of the probabilities assigned to B. As a second example, it follows then that each of the numbers $Pr(X)$ must lie in the closed interval $[0,1]$. This follows from: (a) the empty set will sensibly be assigned a probability of zero, and since the empty set is a subset of any given set, $0 \leqslant Pr(X)$; (b) since any set of outcomes X is a subset of the sample space S,

$$Pr(X) \leqslant Pr(S) = 1.$$

We have thus arrived at Laplace's classical definition of probability using the definitions and restrictions necessary for defining a sample space. Various other theorems will follow immediately from the above association of an outcome of an experiment with the element of a set. Some are listed in the exercises and others will be discussed in the next section.

We conclude this section with some examples of the definitions and resultant uses of the sample space for given experiments.

examples

1. In the experiment of rolling a die and flipping a coin, define the compound event A as "an odd number and a head came up." Having assigned the probability $1/12$ to each of the simple outcomes of this experiment, it is apparent from the listings in S that

$$Pr(A) = 3/12 = 1/4.$$

2. If one assigns the weight $1/36$ to each of the thirty-six simple outcomes of the experiment of rolling a red die and a green die simultaneously, then

$$Pr \text{ (the sum "3")} = 2/36 = 1/18$$

and

$$Pr \text{ (the sum "7")} = 6/36 = 1/6.$$

The student may wish to verify these numbers by listing the thirty-six possible outcomes—that is, defining S by the roster method.

3. In the previous example, if we denote by B the compound event "a sum of seven or at least one six was thrown," then an examination of S shows that $Pr(B) = 15/36$ is correct, and not the simple sum of $Pr(\text{sum } 7) = 6/36$ and $Pr(\text{at least one six}) = 11/36$. Why is it not possible simply to add the two probabilities?

exercises

1. A man has six pairs of socks in his dresser drawer—one pair each of red, orange, yellow, blue, indigo, and violet. He intends to draw two socks at random from the drawer, one after the other, to wear to school that day. How many elements are there in the sample space, if the order in which he draws the socks is disregarded? What is the probability he will get a matching pair?

2. What is the probability of obtaining an odd sum when two dice are thrown? What is the probability of obtaining a sum greater than nine?

3. If one throws three dice at once, how many points are there in the sample space for the experiment?

4. Urn I contains three black and two white balls; urn II contains four white and three black balls. One ball is drawn at random from urn I and transferred, color unnoted, to urn II. Then one ball is drawn at random from urn II. What is an appropriate sample space for this experiment?

5. A man has ten electric bulbs in a carton. He knows that three of them are defective, but does not know which three. He plans to draw two of the bulbs, one after the other, and test them. What is an appropriate sample space for this experiment?

6. A student has a penny, a nickel, a dime, a quarter, and a half-dollar in his pocket. With his mittens on, he draws out three of the coins. How many elements are there in the sample space for this experiment? What is the probability that the amount of money drawn is a prime number? More than 40¢? Includes the penny?

7. A campus vending machine has been tampered with so many times that 10% of the time it gives the purchaser nothing in return; when it does yield something, it dispenses bubble gum five times more often than it dispenses a toy. What is the probability that it yields either nothing or a toy when you put money in it?

8. Two digits are selected from the set $\{1,2,3,4,5\}$ one after the other, without replacement. The order in which these digits are drawn is to be considered.
   (a) Display an appropriate sample space for this experiment.
   (b) What is the probability that the second digit selected is less than the first?

(c) Repeat parts (a), (b) if the original set is 1,2,3,4,5,6.

(d) Repeat parts (a), (b) if the original set is $1,2,3,\ldots,n$.

9. A fair coin is tossed until the first head appears or until you have flipped a total of four times.

(a) Display an appropriate sample space for this experiment.

(b) By considering the elements in this sample space and the pertinent sample point in the one-toss, two-tosses, three-tosses, and four-tosses experiment, assign probabilities to the points listed in the sample space in (a).

(c) Verify that the numbers you have assigned total one.

9–5 probability theorems

Once we have established the sample space for a given experiment and have assigned the probabilities for each simple event in the sample space, we are in a position to analyze more complicated experiments. In general, the more complicated experiments are the more interesting and useful ones. The student will likely agree that it would be more interesting to know the chances of improving a five-card poker hand in draw poker than to know the chances of drawing the queen of spades from an ordinary deck. The various theorems in this section will be fairly powerful tools to assist us in the analysis of the more complex phenomena. The student may first wish to review briefly the material on sets in Chapter 1, for this section will draw freely from the ideas in that chapter and will extend some of the concepts presented there.

First, we have been considering the various simple outcomes of an idealized experiment as points in a set called the sample space. Various outcomes of the experiment will consist of a subcollection of these points of the sample space, and will accordingly be treated as subsets of the sample space. One very useful device in this treatment of sets will be the Venn diagram, named after the English logician John Venn (1834–1923). For two subsets A, B of a sample space S, the subsets are pictured as two overlapping circles, as shown in Figure 9–2. Using the notation of Chapter 1, four subsets of the

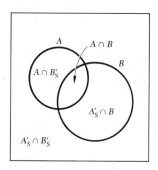

FIGURE 9–2

sample space S are depicted on the diagram. Any point which lies in both subset A and subset B will lie in the overlapping part, $A \cap B$, while any point which lies either in subset A or in subset B (or both) will lie somewhere inside the two circles, $A \cup B$. A point which lies outside A but in the sample space S will be in the subset A'_S, the complement of A with respect to S, while any point which lies outside of both circles will be in the set $(A \cup B)' = A'_S \cap B'_S$—that is, in neither of the two circles, as verified in Chapter 1. The corresponding Venn diagram for the three subsets A, B, and C of a sample space S is shown in Figure 9–3, with eight subsets located.

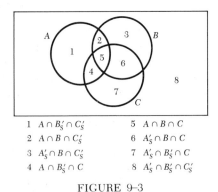

1 $A \cap B'_S \cap C'_S$	5 $A \cap B \cap C$
2 $A \cap B \cap C'_S$	6 $A'_S \cap B \cap C$
3 $A'_S \cap B \cap C'_S$	7 $A'_S \cap B'_S \cap C$
4 $A \cap B'_S \cap C$	8 $A'_S \cap B'_S \cap C'_S$

FIGURE 9–3

Next, we will look at some of the theorems which can be easily verified with the aid of these Venn diagrams.

theorem 9–1:   For any two events A and B associated with a sample space S,

$$Pr(A \cup B) = Pr(A) + Pr(B) - Pr(A \cap B).$$

reasoning: We wish to add all of the probabilities assigned to the events which lie inside the two circles shown in Figure 9–2. Since, on the right side above, we are adding the probabilities of the events in A and then the probabilities for the events in B, we are counting the events which lie in the intersection $A \cap B$ twice. Hence, we subtract the probabilities appearing in the intersection and consequently count each event and its probability once and once only.

example: In drawing one card from an ordinary bridge deck, let A be the event "a spade is drawn" and B be the event "a queen is drawn." Then the event $A \cup B$ is the event "a spade or a queen is drawn," and the event $A \cap B$ is "a spade and a queen is drawn—that is, "the queen of spades is drawn." Then,

$$Pr(A \cup B) = 13/52 + 4/52 - 1/52 = 16/52 = 4/13.$$

We next consider a very useful corollary to Theorem 9–1.

corollary: If the events A and B associated with a sample space S are mutually exclusive—that is, both events cannot happen simultaneously—then $Pr(A \cup B) = Pr(A) + Pr(B)$.

If the events A and B are mutually exclusive, then the set $A \cap B$ is empty and $Pr(A \cap B) = 0$.

In drawing one card from a bridge deck, let A be the event "a jack is drawn" and B be the event "a queen is drawn." The probability that the card drawn is either a jack or a queen is then given by $Pr(A \cup B) = 4/52 + 4/52 = 2/13$.

theorem 9–2: If A_S' is the complement of the set A with respect to the sample space S, then $Pr(A_S') = 1 - Pr(A)$.

reasoning: For any event A associated with the sample space S, $A \cup A_S' = S$. Since $A \cap A_S' = 0$, the above corollary gives us directly $Pr(A \cup A_S') = Pr(S)$

$$Pr(A \cup A_S') = Pr(S) = 1 = Pr(A) + Pr(A_S').$$

example: In throwing three fair coins simultaneously, what is the probability that at least one head appeared? If A is the event "at least one head appears," then A_S' is the event "no heads appear."

$$Pr(A) = 1 - Pr(A_S') = 1 - \frac{1}{8} = 7/8.$$

Next, suppose that 100 students on a college campus have given their opinions on a certain issue and the results are tabulated as follows.

	Men	*Women*
Yes	10	20
No	30	40

If one selects one of these students at random, what is the probability that the person selected will vote Yes? If Y is the event "the person selected votes Yes," then $Pr(Y) = .30$. Similarly, if M is the event "the person selected is a man," then $Pr(M) = .40$. Question: Suppose we know that the person selected voted Yes. What is the probability that this person is a man? The answer is, of course, 10/30, since knowing that person voted Yes restricts our original sample space to only the $10 + 20 = 30$ people who voted Yes, of which only ten were men. If we denote the event "the person selected is a man, given that the person selected voted 'Yes' " by the symbol M/Y (read "M-slash-Y"), then it should be apparent from the above that

$$Pr(M/Y) = \frac{Pr(M \cap Y)}{Pr(Y)}.$$

This formula has no meaning if $Pr(Y) = 0$, for several reasons, not the least of which is that since M/Y means "on condition that Y has already happened," it would be nonsense to have Y be the impossible event. Incidentally, if the student's intuition is upset by the fact that the probability of selecting a man was *decreased* by the *addition* of information about the person selected, recall that we are dealing with an original sample space and a restricted sample space, respectively. Also, additional information does not always decrease the probability of the event, since in this example, Pr(person selected voted Yes) $=30/100$, while Pr(the person selected voted Yes, given that the person selected is a woman)$=Pr(Y/M')=20/60>30/100$.

From the formula $Pr(M/Y)=Pr(M\cap Y)/Pr(Y)$ comes a useful formula for multiplication of probabilities:

$$Pr(M\cap Y)=Pr(Y)\cdot Pr(M/Y),$$

for any two events M and Y associated with a sample space S. Sometimes it happens that $Pr(M/Y)=Pr(M)$—that is, that the probability of event M occurring is not influenced by the fact that event Y has already happened. In this case, the events M and Y are said to be "independent events." In general, the probabilities of the form $Pr(M/Y)$ are called "conditional probabilities."

examples

1. In the earlier experiment with flipping a fair coin and rolling a fair die, we assigned the probability $1/12$ to each of the twelve outcomes. If H is the event "the coin came up heads" and S is the event "the die came up 6," then

$$Pr(H/S)=Pr(H\cap S)\div Pr(S)=1/12\div 1/6=1/2=Pr(H).$$

The events H and S in this case are independent events.

2. Consider an urn in which three red balls and four green balls have been placed. We will draw out two balls, one after the other, without replacing the first ball drawn. Let R_1, G_2, etc. be the events "a red ball was drawn the first time, a green ball was drawn the second time, etc.," respectively. If the various draws are made at random from the urn, then $Pr(R_1)=3/7$, $Pr(G_1)=4/7$, $Pr(R_2/R_1)=2/6$, and $Pr(R_2/G_1)=3/6$. The event $R_2=R_1R_2$ $\cup$ G_1R_2, and since this is the union of two mutually exclusive events, the corollary to Theorem 9–1 applies directly. Thus,

$$Pr(R_2)=Pr(R_1R_2\cup G_1R_2)=Pr(R_1)\cdot Pr(R_2/R_1)+Pr(G_1)\cdot Pr(R_2/G_1)=3/7.$$

exercises

1. In the last example of the preceding section, let A be the event "a sum of seven was thrown" and B be the event "at least one six was thrown" when two dice are thrown simultaneously. Using Theorem 1, find the probability of the event $A\cup B$.

2. In the example of the 100 college students voting on a certain issue, denote the set of men by M and the set of people who vote Yes by Y and draw the Venn diagram for the set of 100 people, putting the correct number of people in each of the four subsets.

3. In a poll, the magazine reading habits of 100 people were found to be as follows.

> 44 read magazine A 12 read magazines A and B
> 38 read magazine B 15 read magazines A and C
> 30 read magazine C 13 read magazines B and C
> 5 read all three magazines

If a person is selected at random from this group of 100 people, what is the probability that:
(a) he reads none of the three magazines?
(b) he reads exactly one of the three magazines?
(c) he reads exactly two of the magazines?

4. If the probability that your school will win any basketball game is 3/5, what is the probability that it will win at least one of the two games it will play this coming Friday and Saturday?

5. An urn contains three red balls and four green balls. One ball is drawn from the urn and replaced, along with two more balls of the same color as the one drawn. What is the probability of drawing a red ball the first time? What is the probability of drawing a red ball on the second draw? Guess the probability of drawing a red ball on the nth draw.

6. Two fair dice are rolled. What is the probability that the sum is not five?

7. A student estimates his chances of passing his mathematics course is .6 and his chances of passing his history course is .7, while his probability of passing at least one of them is .8. What is his probability of passing both of the courses?

8. An integer is selected at random from the set $\{1,2,3, \ldots ,100\}$. What is the probability that it is divisible by 3 or 7?

9. Three coins are tossed simultaneously. What is the probability that all three come up heads, given that at least two of them came up heads?

10. An old chest contains three drawers. Drawer 1 contains two gold coins, drawer 2 contains one gold coin and one silver coin, while drawer 3 contains two silver coins. A drawer is selected at random and a coin extracted. What is the probability it is a gold coin? What is the probability that the second drawer was selected, given that the coin withdrawn was silver?

11. One urn contains A red balls and B green balls; a second urn contains C red balls and D green balls.
(a) If one urn is selected at random and a ball extracted, what is the probability it is red?
(b) In a separate experiment the two urns are combined into one and a ball is selected from this combined urn. What is the probability it is red?

(c) Under what conditions, if any, are your answers in (a) and (b) the same? (Hint: There are two possibilities.)

12. Six dice are thrown simultaneously. What is the probability that at least one "1" came up?

13. A coin is thrown ten times. What is the probability that the coin comes up heads the tenth time, given that it comes up heads the first time? Let $p = Pr$(head on any one toss) on this particular coin. Does your answer depend on the number of tosses made?

14. A coin is flipped four times. What is the probability that only the fourth flip came up heads? What is the probability that exactly one of the flips came up heads? Why is there a difference between your two answers?

9-6 bernoulli trials

Let us pause to reconsider the various coin-flipping experiments from the preceding sections of this chapter. In each case, there were but two outcomes: head, tail. The probability of a head with a given coin did not change as we continued to flip the coin. In general, if we have a sequence of independent trials in which the only outcomes are "success" or "failure" and the probability of a success does not change from one trial to the next, then the sequence of trials is called "Bernoulli trials," after the Swiss mathematician James Bernoulli (1654–1705).

If we denote a success by the letter S and a failure by the letter F, then a particular outcome for a sequence of $n = 5$ Bernoulli trials might appear: $SSFSF$. If we also let $p = Pr$(success) and $q = 1 - p = Pr$ (failure on any one trial), then we will be able to write $Pr(SSFSF)$ $= p^2qpq = p^3q^2$ for this particular outcome. Note carefully that this result is based on the fact that the trials are independent trials, as defined in the last section.

In order to analyze these trials in a systematic way, let us consider the tree diagram for the cases $n = 2$ and $n = 3$ trials. At the end of each branch will be listed both the probability of this particular outcome and the total number of successes in a particular branch of the tree for n trials, denoted by S_n.

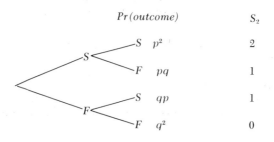

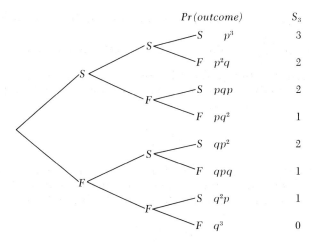

If we organize the results of the two trees in the form of a table, the result would appear as follows. (The student may wish to draw the tree for $n=4$ Bernoulli trials and verify the entries in this table.)

k	$Pr(S_n=k)$		
	$n=2$	$n=3$	$n=4$
0	q^2	q^3	q^4
1	$2qp$	$3q^2p$	$4q^3p$
2	p^2	$3qp^2$	$6q^2p^2$
3		p^3	$4qp^3$
4			p^4

An interesting observation may be made after a careful study of this table. The student will discover that the numerical coefficients in each column, reading from top to bottom, are the rows of Pascal's Triangle, and hence the binomial expansion coefficients from Section 9–2. It is perhaps apparent with a moment's thought that this should be the case for every n in these Bernoulli trials. For, consider the outcome $SFSF$ in $n=4$ trials. The probability of this event is, of course, $pqpq=q^2p^2$. However, the listing of the number of successes in $n=4$ trials does not require that these successes occur in a specified order; but rather that a total of two successes, for example, occurs in the four trials. From Section 9–2, the student will recall that this selection of two S's and two F's can be made in $\binom{4}{2}=6$ different ways. As another example, consider the result $Pr(S_3=2)=3qp^2$ listed in the table. A particular outcome is, for example, SSF, with

$Pr(SSF) = p^2q$; but Pr (exactly two successes in three trials) $= \binom{3}{2} qp^2$,

since there are $\binom{3}{2} = 3$ different ways of listing two successes in three trials. In general, the probability of obtaining exactly r successes in n Bernoulli trials, with $p = Pr$ (success on any one trial) and $q = 1 - p$ $= Pr$ (failure on any one trial) is

$$Pr(S_n = r) = \binom{n}{r} p^r q^{n-r}$$

with n a positive integer, and $r = 0,1,2,3,\ldots,n$. These trials are sometimes called binomial trials, since the various terms of (5.1) for $r = 0,1,2,3,\ldots,n$ are simply the terms in the binomial expansion of

$$1 = (q + p)^n = \sum_{n=0}^{n} \binom{n}{r} p^r q^{n-r}$$

examples

1. The probability of obtaining exactly one tail in six tosses of a fair coin is

$$\binom{6}{1} \left(\frac{1}{2}\right)^1 \left(\frac{1}{2}\right)^5 = 6/64 = .09375.$$

2. If the probability of scoring a hit with a surface-to-air missile is Pr (hit) $= .70$, and the firings form independent trials (an assumption which is probably not realistic!), then in three firings,

$$Pr \text{ (at least one hit)} = 1 - Pr \text{ (no hits)} = 1 - \binom{3}{0} (.70)^0 (.30)^3 = .973.$$

3. A batting average of .333 for a baseball player for a season would be very good, and for some years, a record. Unfortunately, it does not mean that he will get a hit at least once in three times at bat. That probability is only

$$Pr \text{ (at least one hit in three trials)} = 1 - Pr \text{ (no hits)}$$
$$= 1 - \binom{3}{0} (.333)^0 (.667)^3, \text{ or approximately, } 0.704.$$

Finally, we conclude this section with the question: For a given number of Bernoulli trials, n, with fixed Pr (success) $= p$, what is the most probable number of successes that will occur in the n trials? For $r = 0,1,2,3,\ldots,n$, the various terms of $Pr(S_n = r)$ first increase, then decrease, as r increases. We seek the value of r for which the ratio $R = Pr(S_n = r) \div Pr(S_n = r - 1)$ of consecutive terms changes from a number greater than 1 (so terms are increasing) to a number less than 1 (so terms are decreasing). The student may show that

$$R = 1 + \frac{(n+1)p - r}{rq},$$

and since both r and q are both positive ($r=0$ is omitted since there is no previous term, and $q=0$ is omitted, for then every trial is a success), the numerator of the second term changes from positive to negative (hence R changes from a number greater than 1 to a number less than 1), for the following values: If $(n+1)p$ is NOT an integer, then the maximum value of $Pr(S_n=r)$ occurs when $r=[(n+1)p]$, where $[x]=$ greatest integer equal to or less than x. If $(n+1)p$ is an integer, then the two equal maximum values of $Pr(S_n=r)$ occur when $r=(n+1)p$ and when $r=(n+1)p-1$.

examples

1. The most likely number of heads which will occur when 12 fair coins are flipped simultaneously is 6, since $(n+1)p=13/2$. The probability of obtaining exactly 6 heads is only 231/1024, or approximately 1/4, even though it is the maximum value.

2. The probability of obtaining a bridge hand with no ace is

$$\binom{48}{13} \div \binom{52}{13},$$

or approximately .304. If one plays thirteen hands of bridge, the most likely number of hands without aces that he will receive is $(14)(.304)=4$.

exercises

1. The probability of obtaining a bridge hand with no aces is approximately .3, as shown in the above example. What is the probability of having four no-ace bridge hands in four deals?

2. In n Bernoulli trials with $p=1/3$, for what least value of n does the probability of exactly two successes have its only maximum value?

3. What is the probability of obtaining exactly two sevens in five rolls of two fair dice?

4. If a die is loaded in such a way that it is twice as likely to show an even number than to show an odd number, what is the probability of obtaining exactly two fours in four rolls of this die?

5. How many times should a fair coin be flipped in order to have the probability of at least one head appearing be greater than .98?

6. For a baseball player with a .250 batting average, what is the probability he will have at least two hits in four times at bat? Of at least one hit in the four times?

7. If a door-to-door salesman has learned by experience that he will be thrown off the premises at about one house in twenty on the average, what is the probability he will be so ejected at least twice on a day when he plans to make thirty calls?

8. A supposed coffee connoisseur claims he can distinguish between a cup of instant coffee and a cup of percolator coffee 75% of the time. You give

him six cups of coffee and tell him that you will grant his claim if he correctly identifies at least five of the six cups.

  (a) What are his chances of having his claim granted, if he is in fact only guessing?

  (b) What are his chances of having his claim rejected, when in fact he really does have the ability he claims?

9. A fair coin is tossed six times (or six coins are tossed simultaneously).

  (a) What is the probability of obtaining exactly two heads?

  (b) What is the probability of obtaining exactly two heads, if it is known that at least one head appeared?

10. (a) Evaluate the ratio of two consecutive terms, R, given in this section, for the case $n = 10$, $p = 1/2$.

  (b) If ten fair coins are tossed simultaneously, what is the most likely number of heads that will occur?

  (c) Using (a) and (b), what is the probability that the number of heads will be between four and seven, inclusive?

complex numbers

10

Let us turn our attention to an important mathematical problem that required hundreds of years to solve completely. This was the mathematicians' quest to derive formulas that would give the roots of polynomial equations of each degree. For the linear equation $ax+b=0$ where $a \neq 0$, a real (number) solution r_1 always exists and it is given by $r_1 = -b/a$. Hindu and Arabian mathematicians developed the quadratic formula (see Chapter 11) and found that the quadratic equation

$$ax^2 + bx + c = 0 \qquad \text{where } a \neq 0$$

always has real solutions provided $b^2 - 4ac \geq 0$. The solutions are given by

$$x = \frac{-b \pm \sqrt{b^2 - 4ac}}{2a};$$

---

† Portions of this chapter were previously published in Bevan K Youse, *The Number System*, © 1965 by Dickenson Publishing Company, Inc., Belmont, California.

that is, the two solutions are

$$r_1 = \frac{-b + \sqrt{b^2 - 4ac}}{2a} \quad \text{and} \quad r_2 = \frac{-b - \sqrt{b^2 - 4ac}}{2a}.$$

"Solutions" where $b^2 - 4ac < 0$ were not seriously considered until the sixteenth century since no real number exists whose square is negative. There had never been any compelling reasons to consider "numbers" such as x where $x^2 = -4$.

In 1515, Scipio del Ferro discovered that the equation $x^3 + px = q$ had a solution given by

$$x = \sqrt[3]{\sqrt{\frac{p^3}{27} + \frac{q^2}{4}} + \frac{q}{2}} - \sqrt[3]{\sqrt{\frac{p^3}{27} + \frac{q^2}{4}} - \frac{q}{2}}.$$

Since every cubic equation $ay^3 + by^2 + cy + d = 0$ where $a \neq 0$ can be transformed by the linear substitution $y = x - b/3a$ into a cubic equation of the form $x^3 + px = q$, this solution is quite significant. Although the solution is not easy to derive, once obtained it can be shown to be a solution in a straightforward manner using only elementary algebra. Let

$$u = \sqrt{\frac{p^3}{27} + \frac{q^2}{4}} \quad \text{and} \quad v = \frac{q}{2};$$

thus, $(u^2 - v^2)^{1/3} = p/3$. We wish to prove that

$$[(u+v)^{1/3} - (u-v)^{1/3}]^3 + p[(u+v)^{1/3} - (u-v)^{1/3}] = q.$$

The proof follows.

$$(u+v) - 3(u+v)^{2/3}(u-v)^{1/3} + 3(u+v)^{1/3}(u-v)^{2/3} - (u-v)$$
$$+ p(u+v)^{1/3} - p(u-v)^{1/3}$$
$$= 2v - 3(u+v)^{1/3}(u^2 - v^2)^{1/3} + 3(u^2 - v^2)^{1/3}(u-v)^{1/3} + p(u+v)^{1/3}$$
$$- p(u-v)^{1/3}$$
$$= 2v + (u+v)^{1/3}[p - 3(u^2 - v^2)^{1/3}] + (u-v)^{1/3}[3(u^2 - v^2)^{1/3} - p]$$
$$= 2v + (u+v)^{1/3}[p - p] + (u-v)^{1/3}[p - p]$$
$$= 2v$$
$$= q$$

In 1535, the Italian Nicoli Fontana, who received the nickname Tartaglia because of a speech stammer, rediscovered the solution of Ferro. He communicated his solution to Gerolamo Cardano (1501–1576) who published the result in 1545 in his book on algebra. Although Cardano was not primarily responsible for the discovery of the formula for solving the cubic equation, it is generally referred to as Cardano's, or Cardan's, formula.

In 1572, Raffael Bombelli studied the cubic equation $x^3 - 15x = 4$. This equation has three real solutions; they are $r_1 = 4$, $r_2 = -2 + \sqrt{3}$, and $r_3 = -2 - \sqrt{3}$, as the student may verify. Using the cubic formula where $p = -15$ and $q = 4$, we obtain the expression

$$x = \sqrt[3]{\sqrt{-121} + 2} - \sqrt[3]{\sqrt{-121} - 2}.$$

Bombelli's example showed that the cubic equation formula published by Cardan led to the theretofore meaningless expression $\sqrt{-121}$. Prior to this time when such an expression resulted in solving quadratic equations, it was ignored and considered to have no mathematical meaning or practical application. However, Bombelli noticed that treating $\sqrt{-121}$ in a formal algebraic manner led to very desirable results. Formally,

$$\sqrt{-121} = \sqrt{(121)(-1)} = \sqrt{121}\sqrt{-1} = 11\sqrt{-1}.$$

Furthermore,

$$(2 + \sqrt{-1})^3 = 2^3 + 3(2)^2(\sqrt{-1}) + 3(2)(\sqrt{-1})^2 + (\sqrt{-1})^3$$
$$= 8 + 12\sqrt{-1} - 6 - \sqrt{-1}$$
$$= 11\sqrt{-1} + 2.$$

Thus,

$$\sqrt[3]{\sqrt{-121} + 2} = 2 + \sqrt{-1}.$$

Similarly, we can "prove" that

$$\sqrt[3]{\sqrt{-121} - 2} = -2 + \sqrt{-1}.$$

Consequently, substituting in the cubic formula,

$$x = (2 + \sqrt{-1}) - (-2 + \sqrt{-1})$$
$$= 2 + \sqrt{-1} + 2 - \sqrt{-1}$$
$$= 4, \qquad \text{a real root of the given equation!}$$

Having discovered that the "complex numbers" could be put to a practical use—obtaining a real solution to a cubic equation—Bombelli was moved to develop a theory of complex numbers. While this started them along the road to respectability, not until the nineteenth century did they gain full acceptance in the mathematical community.

Before defining the complex numbers, we digress to complete the story of the discovery of formulas to solve polynomial equations. Ferrari, one of Cardan's students, discovered that the problem of solving the biquadratic (or quartic) equation

$$ax^4 + bx^3 + cx^2 + dx + e = 0 \qquad \text{where } a \neq 0$$

could be reduced to that of solving a cubic equation. This result also was published in Cardan's 1545 book, *Ars magna*. Mathematicians searched many years to find a formula to solve not only the general fifth-degree equation but also equations of higher degree. It was proved by the French mathematician Evariste Galois that they were attempting the impossible. The brilliant Galois, who had a profound influence on the development of modern mathematics, proved that *no formula could exist* for solving a general equation of a degree higher than four. Of course, it was necessary for him to give some precise definition of *formula* before such a result could be proved. Essentially, a formula for the solution of an equation means an expression involving only the manipulation of coefficients in the equation through a finite number of algebraic operations. It is difficult to imagine the total influence that Galois might have had on the further development of mathematics had he not been killed in an unfortunate duel in 1832 at the age of 21.

exercise

If $ay^3 + by^2 + cy + d = 0$ and $a \neq 0$, let $y = x - b/3a$ to obtain an equation of the form $x^3 + px = q$. What are p and q in terms of a, b, c, and d?

10–2 complex numbers

It is not necessary to assume that there is a set containing such numbers as $\sqrt{-121}$, having the field properties. We shall define the complex numbers, and prove that this set of numbers has the properties of a field.

A *complex number* is a number that can be denoted by an ordered pair (a,b) of *real numbers*. The ordered pair notation (a,b) is called the *rectangular notation* for complex numbers. Let $z = (a,b)$ and $w = (c,d)$ be two complex numbers; $z = w$ if, and only if, $a = c$ and $b = d$.

As the student already knows, an ordered pair of real numbers represents a unique point in the rectangular coordinate plane. Hence, our definition of equality puts the set of complex numbers in one-to-one correspondence with the points in the coordinate plane. Although this geometric interpretation has nothing to do with the axiomatic development of the complex numbers, it is important in promoting understanding of various properties of the complex numbers.

definition: For any pair of complex numbers $z = (a,b)$ and $w = (c,d)$, the sum and product of z and w, denoted by $z + w$ and zw, respectively, are defined as follows.

1. $z + w = (a + c, b + d)$

2. $zw = (ac - bd, ad + bc)$

Both the sum and product of two complex numbers are complex numbers by definition. Thus, the complex numbers are closed with respect to addition and multiplication. Before proving that the set of complex numbers has the field properties, let us consider the geometric interpretations of addition and multiplication of complex numbers.

10–3   complex plane

The complex number $z = (a,b)$ (where a and b are real numbers) represents a point in the Cartesian coordinate plane. The real number $\sqrt{a^2 + b^2}$ is the distance of this point from the origin of the coordinate system. (See Figure 10–1.)

definition: The real number $\sqrt{a^2 + b^2}$ is called the *absolute value* of the complex number z, or the *modulus* of z. The absolute value of z is denoted by $|z|$.

By definition, $|z|$ is a non-negative real number and $|z| = \sqrt{a^2 + b^2}$.

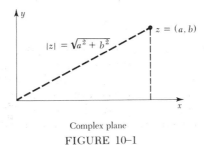

Complex plane
FIGURE 10–1

A directed line segment from the origin to the point (a,b) is called a *vector*. The origin $(0,0)$ is called the *initial point* of the vector and the point associated with the complex number (a,b) is called the *terminal point* of the vector. A vector is often denoted by an arrow, as in Figure 10–2. The length of the vector is the absolute value of the complex number (a,b). The angle that the vector makes with

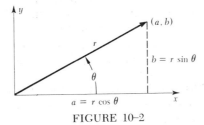

FIGURE 10–2

the positive *x*-axis is called the *amplitude* of *z*, or *argument* of the complex number $z = (a,b)$.

If θ is the amplitude of the complex number $z = (a,b)$ and $r = \sqrt{a^2 + b^2}$ is the absolute value, then $a = r \cos \theta$ and $b = r \sin \theta$.

If $z = (a,b)$ and $w = (c,d)$ are two complex numbers representing points in the complex plane as in Figure 10–3, then $(a+c, b+d)$ is

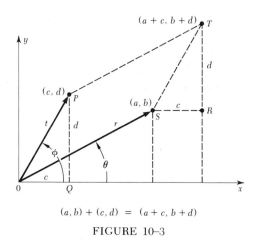

$$(a,b) + (c,d) = (a+c, b+d)$$

FIGURE 10–3

the point diagonally opposite the origin $(0,0)$ in the parallelogram formed by vectors from the origin to *z* and *w*. This should be clear by observing in Figure 10–3 that right triangles *OPQ* and *STR* are congruent. If (a,b) and (c,d) are two complex numbers with moduli *r* and *t* and amplitudes θ and ϕ, respectively, then $(a,b) = (r \cos \theta, r \sin \theta)$ and $(c,d) = (t \cos \phi, t \sin \phi)$. By definition of multiplication,

$$
\begin{aligned}
(a,b)(c,d) &= (r \cos \theta, r \sin \theta)(t \cos \phi, t \sin \phi) \\
&= (rt \cos \theta \cos \phi - rt \sin \theta \sin \phi,\ rt \sin \phi \cos \theta + rt \sin \theta \\
&\qquad\qquad\qquad\qquad\qquad\qquad\qquad\qquad\qquad\qquad \cos \phi) \\
&= (rt \cos(\theta + \phi),\ rt \sin(\theta + \phi)).
\end{aligned}
$$

Thus, the product of (a,b) and (c,d) is that complex number with amplitude $\theta + \phi$ and absolute value *rt*. To multiply *z* and *w* geometrically, one adds the amplitude of one complex number to the amplitude of the other to find the amplitude of the product. The product is represented by the point on the terminal side of the angle with this amplitude and at a distance from the origin equal to the product of the distances from the origin of the two given complex numbers. From this geometric interpretation of multiplication, it should be obvious that $zw = wz$. The complex number $(1,0)$ has $0°$ as amplitude and 1 as modulus. It should also be geometrically clear from the definition of multiplication that the complex number $(1,0)$ is the multiplicative identity for the set of complex numbers.

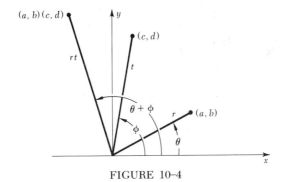

FIGURE 10-4

exercises

1. For the given complex numbers, perform the indicated operation.
   (a) $(2,3) + (-5,8)$ (b) $(\sqrt{3},1) + (-7\sqrt{3},2/3)$
   (c) $(0,1)(2,6)$ (d) $(1,0)(4,7)$
   (e) $(8,11) + (0,0)$ (f) $(\sqrt{3},2)(-\sqrt{3},-2)$

2. Let (a,b) be any complex number. Find the complex number (x,y) such that $(a,b) + (x,y) = (a,b)$.

3. Prove for any complex number (a,b) that $(a,b)(1,0) = (a,b)$.

4. Let (a,b) be any complex number different from $(0,0)$. Find the complex number (x,y) in terms of a and b such that $(a,b)(x,y) = (1,0)$.

5. Give the amplitude and absolute value of each of the following complex numbers.
   (a) $(0,1)$ (b) $(-1,0)$ (c) $(0,-1)$
   (d) $(-1,-1)$ (e) $(1,\sqrt{3})$ (f) $(-\sqrt{3},1)$

6. Give the approximate amplitude (from Table 2) and the absolute value of each of the following complex numbers.
   (a) $(2,3)$ (b) $(3,5)$ (c) $(-8,6)$
   (d) $(-2,-5)$ (e) $(\sqrt{3},\sqrt{2})$ (f) $(17,-3\sqrt{5})$

7. Construct geometrically the sum $(2,5) + (8,2)$ and the product $(2,5)(8,2)$.

10-4   the field properties

We now prove that the set of complex numbers has the field properties. The student should examine the geometric significance of each property in relation to the coordinate system and give a geometric argument to justify the validity of each property.

theorem 10-1 (commutative property of addition):   For complex numbers (a,b) and (c,d)

$$(a,b) + (c,d) = (c,d) + (a,b).$$

proof:

$$(a,b) + (c,d) = (a+c,\ b+d) \qquad \text{definition of addition}$$
$$= (c+a,\ d+b) \qquad \text{commutative property of}$$
$$\qquad \text{addition for real numbers†}$$
$$= (c,d) + (a,b) \qquad \text{definition of addition}$$

theorem 10–2 (commutative property of multiplication): For complex numbers (a,b) and (c,d)

$$(a,b)(c,d) = (c,d)(a,b).$$

proof: Left as an exercise.

theorem 10–3 (associative property of addition): For complex numbers (a,b), (c,d), and (e,f)

$$[(a,b) + (c,d)] + (e,f) = (a,b) + [(c,d) + (e,f)].$$

proof:

$$[(a,b) + (c,d)] + (e,f) = (a+c,b+d) + (e,f) \qquad \text{definition of addition}$$
$$= ((a+c)+e,\ (b+d)+f) \qquad \text{definition of addition}$$
$$= (a+(c+e),\ b+(d+f)) \qquad \text{associative property of}$$
$$\qquad \text{addition}$$
$$= (a,b) + (c+e,\ d+f) \qquad \text{definition of addition}$$
$$= (a,b) + [(c,d) + (e,f)]. \qquad \text{definition of addition}$$

theorem 10–4 (associative property of multiplication): For complex numbers (a,b), (c,d), and (e,f)

$$[(a,b)(c,d)](e,f) = (a,b)[(c,d)(e,f)].$$

proof: Left as an exercise.

theorem 10–5 (existence of additive identity): For any complex number (a,b)

$$(a,b) + (0,0) = (a,b).$$

proof:

$$(a,b) + (0,0) = (a+0,\ b+0) \qquad \text{definition of addition}$$
$$= (a,b). \qquad \text{definition of equality}$$

theorem 10–6 (existence of additive inverses): The complex number (a,b) has an additive inverse, $(-a,-b)$. That is, $(a,b) + (-a,-b) = (0,0)$.

proof: Left as an exercise.

theorem 10–7 (existence of multiplicative identity): For any complex number (a,b)

$$(a,b)(1,0) = (a,b).$$

†Also, equality of ordered pairs.

proof: Left as an exercise.

theorem 10–8 (existence of multiplicative inverses):   Each complex number (a,b) different from the additive identity $(0,0)$ has $(a/(a^2+b^2), -b/(a^2+b^2))$ as its multiplicative inverse.

proof: Left as an exercise for the student.

theorem 10–9 (distributive property):   For the complex numbers, (a,b), (c,d), and (e,f)

$$(a,b)[(c,d)+(e,f)] = (a,b)(c,d)+(a,b)(e,f).$$

proof: Left as an exercise.

exercises

1. Prove Theorem 10–2.
2. Prove Theorem 10–4.
3. Prove Theorem 10–6.
4. Prove Theorem 10–7.
5. Prove Theorem 10–8.
6. Prove Theorem 10–9.

10–5   gaussian notation for complex numbers

We associate the real number a with the complex number $(a,0)$. Geometrically, this is equivalent to associating each real number with a point on the x-axis in the complex plane; for this reason, the x-axis is often called the *real axis*. The set of points on the x-axis is a subset of the coordinate plane, and the set of complex numbers $(a,0)$ is a subset of the set of complex numbers. Since $(a,0)+(b,0)= (a+b,0)$ and $(a,0)(b,0)=(ab,0)$, we can consider $(a,0)$ as another notation for real numbers. From this point of view the set of real numbers is a subset of the set of complex numbers.

The symbol i is used to denote the complex number $(0,1)$. As a consequence of the definition of multiplication for complex numbers, $(b,0)(0,1) = (0,b)$. Hence,

$$(a,b) = (a,0) + (0,b)$$
$$= (a,0) + (b,0)(0,1).$$

Thus, the notation $a+bi$ is used to denote the complex number (a,b); $a+bi$ is called the *Gaussian notation* for the complex number (a,b).

If $z=a+bi$, then a is called the *real part* of the complex number z and we write $a=R(z)$. The real number b is called the *imaginary part* of z and we write $b=I(z)$. The complex number $(0,b)$, or bi, is called a pure imaginary number; since $(0,b)$ is a point on the y-axis, the y-axis is often called the imaginary axis.

The Gaussian notation has a distinct advantage over the rectangular notation. By using the fact that $i^2=-1$, it is possible to add, multiply, subtract, and divide in a formal algebraic manner any pair of complex numbers written in Gaussian notation.

examples

1. $(2+3i)+(6-8i)=(2+6)+(3i-8i)=8-5i$
2. $(8+5i)-(1-2i)=7+7i$
3. $(2+4i)(2-3i)=4+8i-6i-12i^2=16+2i$
4. $\dfrac{3+2i}{2+5i}=\dfrac{3+2i}{2+5i}\dfrac{2-5i}{2-5i}=\dfrac{6-11i-10i^2}{4-25i^2}=\dfrac{16-11i}{29}=\dfrac{16}{29}-\dfrac{11}{29}i$

definition: The complex number $a-bi$ is called the *conjugate* of $a+bi$. If $z=a+bi$, we denote the conjugate of z by $\bar{z}$; thus, $\bar{z}=a-bi$. (Note that the conjugate of $\bar{z}$ is z; symbolically, $\bar{\bar{z}}=z$.)

To find the quotient in Gaussian notation of two complex numbers $(c+di)/a+bi)$, we multiply the numerator and denominator by the conjugate $a-bi$ of the denominator as in Example 4 above.

theorem 10–10:   Let $z=a+bi$ and $w=c+di$ be complex numbers. Then,
(a) $z\cdot\bar{z}=|z|^2=[R(z)]^2+[I(z)]^2$
(b) $|z|\geqslant R(z)$
(c) $\overline{zw}=\bar{z}\cdot\bar{w}$
(d) $|zw|=|z|\,|w|$
(e) $|zw|\geqslant R(z\cdot\bar{w})$
(f) $\overline{z+w}=\bar{z}+\bar{w}$
(g) $z+\bar{z}=2R(z)$

proof:

(a)
$$z\cdot\bar{z}=(a+bi)(a-bi)$$
$$=a^2+b^2$$
$$=|z|^2$$
$$=[R(z)]^2+[I(z)]^2$$

(b) Since $|z|^2=[R(z)]^2+[I(z)]^2$ and since $|z|$, $[R(z)]^2$, and $[I(z)]^2$ are non-negative real numbers,
$$|z|^2\geqslant[R(z)]^2$$

and

$$|z|\geqslant R(z).$$

(c)
$$\overline{zw} = \overline{(a+bi)(c+di)}$$
$$= \overline{(ac-bd)+(ad+bc)i}$$
$$= (ac-bd)-(ad+bc)i$$
$$= (a-bi)(c-di)$$
$$= \bar{z} \cdot \bar{w}$$

(d)
$$|zw|^2 = (zw)(\overline{z \cdot w})$$
$$= (zw)(\bar{z} \cdot \bar{w})$$
$$= (z \cdot \bar{z})(w \cdot \bar{w})$$
$$= |z|^2 |w|^2$$

Since $|zw|$, $|z|$, and $|w|$ are non-negative real numbers, we may take square roots of both sides of the equation

$$|zw|^2 = |z|^2|w|^2$$

and obtain

$$|zw| = |z||w|.$$

In other words, the absolute value of a product of two complex numbers is the product of the absolute values.

(e)
$$|zw| = |z| \, |w| \qquad \text{by part (d)}$$
$$= |z| \, |\bar{w}| \qquad \text{since } |w| = |\bar{w}|$$
$$= |z \cdot \bar{w}| \qquad \text{by part (d)}$$
$$\geq R(z \cdot \bar{w}) \qquad \text{by part (b)}$$

(f)
$$\overline{z+w} = \overline{(a+bi)+(c+di)}$$
$$= \overline{(a+c)+(b+d)i}$$
$$= (a+c)-(b+d)i$$
$$= (a-bi)+(c-di)$$
$$= \bar{z}+\bar{w}$$

In other words, the conjugate of the sum of two complex numbers is the sum of the conjugates of each of the complex numbers.

(g)
$$z+\bar{z} = (a+bi)+(a-bi)$$
$$= 2a$$
$$= 2R(z)$$

We use Theorem 10–10 to prove the important triangular inequality for complex numbers. We wish to prove that $|z+w| \leq |z|+|w|$; that is, the absolute value of the sum of two complex numbers is less than or equal to the sum of the absolute values of the two given numbers.

$$|z+w|^2 = (z+w)(\overline{z+w}) \qquad \text{by part (a)}$$
$$= (z+w)(\bar{z}+\bar{w}) \qquad \text{by part (f)}$$
$$= z \cdot \bar{z}+w \cdot \bar{w}+z \cdot \bar{w}+\bar{z} \cdot w \qquad \text{by the field properties}$$
$$= |z|^2+|w|^2+z \cdot \bar{w}+\bar{z} \cdot w \qquad \text{by part (a)}$$
$$= |z|^2+|w|^2+z \cdot \bar{w}+\overline{z \cdot \bar{w}}) \qquad \text{by part (c)}$$
$$= |z|^2+|w|^2+2R(z \cdot \bar{w}) \qquad \text{by part (g)}$$
$$\leq |z|^2+|w|^2+2 \, |z \cdot w| \qquad \text{by part (e)}$$

$$\le |z|^2 + 2\,|z|\,|w| + |w|^2 \qquad \text{by part (d)}$$
$$\le (|z| + |w|)^2 \qquad \text{by the field properties}$$

Since $|z+w|$ and $|z|+|w|$ are non-negative real numbers, we conclude that

$$|z+w| \le |z| + |w|.$$

Since $|z|$ and $|w|$ are the distances of z and w from the origin and since $|z+w|$ is the distance of $z+w$ from the origin, the theorem is geometrically equivalent to stating that the length of one side of a triangle is less than or equal to the sum of the lengths of the other two sides. This inequality is therefore called the *triangular inequality*.

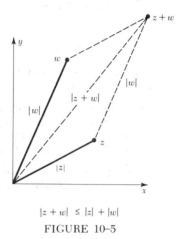

$$|z+w| \le |z| + |w|$$

FIGURE 10-5

It is not difficult to prove that if z_1 is a complex root of the cubic equation $ax^3 + bx^2 + cx + d = 0$ where a, b, c, and d are real numbers then the conjugate $\bar{z}_1$ is also a root of the equation. If z_1 is a root of the equation, then $az_1^3 + bz_1^2 + cz_1 + d$ is zero. Since the conjugate of the real number zero is zero,

$$\overline{az_1^3 + bz_1^2 + cz_1 + d}$$

is also zero. Using the fact that the conjugate of a real number is the number itself, the conjugate of a sum is the sum of the conjugates, and the conjugate of a product is the product of the conjugates, we conclude that $a\bar{z}_1^3 + b\bar{z}_1^2 + c\bar{z}_1 + d$ is zero. Therefore, $\bar{z}_1$ is a root of the equation $ax^3 + bx^2 + cx + d = 0$. In general, it can be proved that if z is a complex root of any polynomial equation with *real* coefficients then the conjugate $\bar{z}$ is also a root of the equation.

Since we proved that the square of any element in an ordered field is non-negative and since there exists a complex number whose square is negative—namely, $i^2 = -1$—the set of complex numbers does not have the ordered field properties; however, the set does have the field properties.

exercises

1. Let z be the complex number $\cos\theta + i\sin\theta$. Prove for every positive integer n that $z^n = \cos n\theta + i\sin n\theta$. *Hint:* Use mathematical induction.

2. Perform each of the indicated operations.
   (a) $(6+7i)(8-11i)$ (b) $(2+17i)/(9-4i)$
   (c) $(3+4i)^3$ (d) $(23+\sqrt{3}\,i)/(1+\sqrt{3}\,i)$
   (e) $(1-i)^{10}$ (f) $(1+\sqrt{3}\,i)^{30}$

3. (a) Prove that $3+i$ is a root of the equation

$$x^4 - 6x^3 + 7x^2 + 18x - 30 = 0.$$

   (b) Prove that the conjugate of $3+i$ is a root of the given equation.

4. Show that $z_1 = 3+4i$ and $z_2 = -3+4i$ are solutions of $x^2 - 8ix - 25 = 0$. Notice that z_1 and z_2 are not conjugate complex numbers. Explain the significance of this fact.

5. For what complex numbers is $|z| = z$?

6. If $2a + 3ai + 6b - 4bi = 5 + 7i$, find what numbers a and b represent.

7. If $7a - 5ai + 3b + 9bi = 6 - 11i$, find what numbers a and b represent.

10–6 powers and roots

Let (a,b) be a complex number. We have already discussed the Gaussian notation $a+bi$ for complex numbers and we now turn our attention to what is called the *polar notation*. If θ is the amplitude of the complex number $a+bi$ and if r is the absolute value, then $a = r\cos\theta$ and $b = r\sin\theta$. Thus,

$$a + bi = r(\cos\theta + i\sin\theta)$$

and $r(\cos\theta + i\sin\theta)$ is called the *polar notation* for the complex number.

In Exercise 1 above, we proved the theorem of DeMoivre. That is, for every positive integer n,

$$(\cos\theta + i\sin\theta)^n = \cos n\theta + i\sin n\theta.$$

This theorem can be proved for both rational numbers n and real numbers n. We shall use the following theorem without proof.

theorem 10–11: If t is any real number, then

$$(\cos\theta + i\sin\theta)^t = \cos t\theta + i\sin t\theta.$$

If $a + bi = r(\cos\theta + i\sin\theta)$, then

$$\begin{aligned}(a+bi)^n &= [r(\cos\theta + i\sin\theta)]^n \\ &= r^n(\cos\theta + i\sin\theta)^n \\ &= r^n(\cos n\theta + i\sin n\theta).\end{aligned}$$

This result is often used with advantage to find powers of complex numbers.

examples

1. To find $(1+i)^8$ using the polar notation for complex numbers, we proceed as follows:

$$1+i = \sqrt{2}(\cos 45° + i \sin 45°).$$

Hence,

$$(1+i)^8 = (\sqrt{2})^8[\cos(8)(45°) + i \sin(8)(45°)]$$
$$= 16(\cos 360° + i \sin 360°)$$
$$= 16.$$

2. To find $(1+i\sqrt{3})^7$, we write $(1+i\sqrt{3})$ in polar notation:

$$(1+i\sqrt{3}) = 2(\cos 60° + i \sin 60°).$$

Thus,

$$(1+i\sqrt{3})^7 = 2^7(\cos 420° + i \sin 420°)$$
$$= 128\left(\frac{1}{2} + i\frac{\sqrt{3}}{2}\right)$$
$$= 64 + 64i\sqrt{3}.$$

Since $(\cos \theta + i \sin \theta)^r = \cos r\theta + i \sin r\theta$ for rational numbers r, we can use DeMoivre's Theorem to find roots of complex numbers. In order to find the two numbers whose squares are $(1+i\sqrt{3})$ we write the complex number in polar notation:

$$(1+i\sqrt{3}) = 2(\cos 60° + i \sin 60°).$$

Thus,

$$(1+i\sqrt{3})^{1/2} = 2^{1/2}(\cos 30° + i \sin 30°)$$
$$= \sqrt{2}\ [\sqrt{3}/2 + i(1/2)]$$
$$= \frac{\sqrt{6}}{2} + \frac{i\sqrt{2}}{2}.$$

Since $(\cos \theta + i \sin \theta) = \cos(\theta + 360°n) + i \sin(\theta + 360°n)$ for every positve integer n, we have for $n=1$ that

$$1 + i\sqrt{3} = 2(\cos 420° + i \sin 420°).$$

Thus,

$$(1+i\sqrt{3})^{1/2} = \sqrt{2}(\cos 210° + i \sin 210°)$$
$$= \sqrt{2}[-\sqrt{3}/2 + i(-1/2)]$$
$$= \frac{-\sqrt{6}}{2} - \frac{i\sqrt{2}}{2}.$$

It can easily be checked that $1+i\sqrt{3}$ is the square of both $\sqrt{6}/2 + i\sqrt{2}/2$ and $-\sqrt{6}/2 - i\sqrt{2}/2$. Furthermore, it can be verified that any even integer n in the equality

$$(1 + i\sqrt{3})^{1/2} = 2^{1/2}[\cos(60° + 360°n) + i\sin(60° + 360°n)]^{1/2}$$

always yields $\sqrt{6}/2 + i\sqrt{2}/2$ and odd integers yield $-\sqrt{6}/2 - i\sqrt{2}/2$.
In general, if $a + bi = r(\cos\theta + i\sin\theta)$ the nth roots of this number can be obtained by the formula

$$(a + bi)^{1/n} = r^{1/n}[\cos(\theta + 360°k) + i\sin(\theta + 360°k)]^{1/n}$$

where $k = 0, 1, 2, 3, 4, 5, \ldots, n-1$.

example

The three cube roots of $(-1 + i)$ are found as follows.

$$-1 + i = \sqrt{2}(\cos 135° + i\sin 135°)$$
$$(-1 + i)^{1/3} = (\sqrt{2})^{1/3}[\cos(135° + 360°k) + i\sin(135° + 360°k)]^{1/3},$$

$k = 0, 1, 2$. For $k = 0$,

$$(-1 + i)^{1/3} = 2^{1/6}(\cos 45° + i\sin 45°)$$
$$= 2^{1/6}\left(\frac{\sqrt{2}}{2} + \frac{i\sqrt{2}}{2}\right)$$
$$= \frac{2^{2/3}}{2} + \frac{i(2^{2/3})}{2}$$
$$= 0.7936 + 0.7936i.$$

For $k = 1$,

$$(-1 + i)^{1/3} = 2^{1/6}(\cos 495° + i\sin 495°)^{1/3}$$
$$= 2^{1/6}(\cos 165° + i\sin 165°)$$
$$= 1.227[-0.9659 + 0.2588i]$$
$$= -1.185 + 0.3175i.$$

For $k = 2$,

$$(-1 + i)^{1/3} = 2^{1/6}(\cos 855° + i\sin 855°)^{1/3}$$
$$= 2^{1/6}(\cos 285° + i\sin 285°)$$
$$= 1.227[0.2588 + i(-0.9659)]$$
$$= 0.3175 - 1.185i.$$

exercises

Find the following powers.

1. $(1 + i)^6$ 2. $(-1 - i)^{15}$ 3. $(\sqrt{2} + i\sqrt{2})^{10}$

4. $[-1/2 + i(\sqrt{3}/2)]^{11}$ 5. $(-\sqrt{3} + i)^6$ 6. $[(\sqrt{3}/2) - i/2]^{20}$

7. $(-\sqrt{2} + i\sqrt{2})^5$ 8. $(1 + 3i)^7$

Find the indicated roots.

9. $(1+i)^{1/2}$ 10. $(-1-i)^{1/2}$ 11. $(\sqrt{2}+i\sqrt{2})^{1/2}$

12. $[-1/2+i(\sqrt{3}/2)]^{1/3}$ 13. $(-\sqrt{3}+i)^{1/3}$ 14. $[(\sqrt{3}/2)-i/2]^{1/5}$

15. $(-i)^{1/4}$ 16. $(-i)^{1/3}$ 17. $27^{1/3}$

18. $(-1)^{1/5}$

19. (a) Prove that

$$(\cos\theta+i\sin\theta)^3 = (\cos^3\theta-3\cos\theta\sin^2\theta) +$$
$$(3\cos^2\theta\sin\theta-\sin^3\theta)i.$$

(b) Use DeMoivre's Theorem, part (a), and the definition of equality of complex numbers to prove that

$$\cos 3\theta = \cos^3\theta - 3\cos\theta\sin^2\theta$$

and

$$\sin 3\theta = 3\cos^2\theta\sin\theta - \sin^3\theta.$$

20. Using the techniques of Exercise 19, derive formulas for $\sin 2\theta$ and $\cos 2\theta$.

21. Using DeMoivre's Theorem, prove that $\cos 4\theta = \cos^4\theta - 6\cos^2\theta\sin^2\theta - \sin^4\theta$. (See Exercise 19.)

22. Using DeMoivre's Theorem, prove that $\sin 4\theta = 4\cos^3\theta\sin\theta - 4\cos\theta\sin^3\theta$. (See Exercises 19 and 21.)

elementary theory of equations

11

11-1 linear and quadratic equations

Let P be a function defined by

$$P(x) = a_0 x^n + a_1 x^{n-1} + a_2 x^{n-2} + \cdots + a_{n-1} x + a_n$$

where n is a positive integer and the coefficients a_i are complex numbers. The function P is a polynomial function of degree n if $a_0 \neq 0$. If r is a number such that $P(r) = 0$, then r is called a *zero of the polynomial* and a *root of the polynomial equation* $P(x) = 0$.

example

Let $P(x) = x^2 - x - 6$. P is a polynomial of degree 2. Since $P(3) = 0$, 3 is a zero of P and 3 is a root of $x^2 - x - 6 = 0$.

If $P(x) = ax + b$ where $a \neq 0$, P is a polynomial of degree 1 and is generally called a *linear function*. The number $r = -b/a$ is the only zero of the function, and $-b/a$ is the root of the linear equation $ax + b = 0$.

Let $P(x) = ax^2 + bx + c$ where $a \neq 0$. This polynomial of degree 2 is generally called a *quadratic function*. If r is a root of the quadratic equation $ax^2 + bx + c = 0$, then

$$ar^2 + br + c = 0.$$

Thus,

$$4a^2r^2 + 4abr = -4ac$$
$$4a^2r^2 + 4abr + b^2 = b^2 - 4ac$$
$$(2ar + b)^2 = b^2 - 4ac$$
$$2ar + b = \pm\sqrt{b^2 - 4ac}$$
$$2ar = -b \pm \sqrt{b^2 - 4ac}$$
$$r = \frac{-b \pm \sqrt{b^2 - 4ac}}{2a}.$$

We have proved that if the equation has a root it is either

$$\frac{-b + \sqrt{b^2 - 4ac}}{2a} \quad \text{or} \quad \frac{-b - \sqrt{b^2 - 4ac}}{2a}.$$

Since the steps in our proof are "reversible," we conclude that both

$$r_1 = \frac{-b + \sqrt{b^2 - 4ac}}{2a} \quad \text{and} \quad r_2 = \frac{-b - \sqrt{b^2 - 4ac}}{2a}$$

are roots; this fact can also be proved by direct substitution. Thus, a quadratic equation has exactly two roots if $b^2 - 4ac \neq 0$; if $b^2 - 4ac = 0$ it has the one root $r = -b/2a$.

If

$$r_1 = \frac{-b + \sqrt{b^2 - 4ac}}{2a} \quad \text{and} \quad r_2 = \frac{-b - \sqrt{b^2 - 4ac}}{2a},$$

then

$$r_1 + r_2 = \frac{-b + \sqrt{b^2 - 4ac} - b - \sqrt{b^2 - 4ac}}{2a} = \frac{-b}{a}$$

and

$$r_1 \times r_2 = \frac{(-b + \sqrt{b^2 - 4ac})(-b - \sqrt{b^2 - 4ac})}{4a^2} = \frac{4ac}{4a^2} = \frac{c}{a}.$$

Furthermore, if a, b, c are *real* numbers and if $b^2 - 4ac < 0$, then the roots are conjugate complex numbers.

Some equations are said to be of quadratic form although they are not quadratic. Essentially, this means that they can be transformed into quadratic equations by algebraic operations or substitutions. For example, $x^4 - 8x^2 - 10 = 0$ is not quadratic but may be treated as quadratic in x^2 as follows.

examples

1. Solve $x^4 - 8x^2 - 10 = 0$.

Solution: Let $y = x^2$. Thus

$$y^2 - 8y - 10 = 0$$

$$y = \frac{8 \pm \sqrt{64 + 40}}{2}$$

$$y_1 = \frac{8 + 2\sqrt{26}}{2} = 4 + \sqrt{26}$$

and

$$y_2 = 4 - \sqrt{26}.$$

Consequently, $x^2 = 4 + \sqrt{26}$ and $x^2 = 4 - \sqrt{26}$, and

$$x_1 = \sqrt{4 + \sqrt{26}}, \quad x_2 = -\sqrt{4 + \sqrt{26}}, \quad x_3 = \sqrt{4 - \sqrt{26}}, \quad \text{and} \quad x_4 = -\sqrt{4 - \sqrt{26}}.$$

2. Solve $\sqrt{x - 9} + \sqrt{2x} = 9$.

Solution: If there is a real number satisfying

$$\sqrt{x - 9} = 9 - \sqrt{2x},$$

then x satisfies

$$x - 9 = 81 - 18\sqrt{2x} + 2x.$$

Thus,

$$18\sqrt{2x} = x + 90.$$

Squaring,

$$324(2x) = x^2 + 180x + 8100$$

$$x^2 - 468x + 8100 = 0$$

$$x = \frac{468 \pm \sqrt{186{,}624}}{2} = \frac{468 \pm 432}{2}$$

$$x_1 = 450$$

and

$$x_2 = 18.$$

We have only proved that if the equation has a solution it must be either x_1 or x_2. If the steps were reversible, we could conclude that both x_1 and x_2 were solutions. However, the steps are not reversible. If $a = b$, then $a^2 = b^2$, but if $a^2 = b^2$ we cannot conclude that $a = b$. [Consider $(-3)^2 = (3)^2$.] We leave as an exercise for the student to check whether or not x_1 and x_2 are solutions.

3. Solve $\sin^2 x - 5\sin x - 7 = 0$.

Solution: Let $y = \sin x$. If there is an x satisfying the equation, then

$$y^2 - 5y - 7 = 0$$

$$y = \frac{5 \pm \sqrt{25 + 28}}{2}$$

$$y_1 = \frac{5 + \sqrt{53}}{2}$$

and

$$y_2 = \frac{5 - \sqrt{53}}{2}.$$

Consequently, $\sin x = (5 + \sqrt{53})/2$ or $\sin x = (5 - \sqrt{53})/2$ for any x satisfying the equation. However, $(5 \pm \sqrt{53})/2$ are not in the closed interval $[-1, 1]$; this is easy to see since $5/2 + \sqrt{53}/2 > 5/2 > 1$ and $5/2 - \sqrt{53}/2 < 5/2 - 7/2 = -1$. Thus, there is no x such that $\sin x = (5 \pm \sqrt{23})/2$. The equation, therefore, has no solutions. (The student might have guessed this result by careful consideration of the original equation.)

exercises

1. Complete the solution of Example 2, page 000.

2. Let $ax^2 + bx + c = 0$ where $a \neq 0$. Prove r_1 and r_2 are roots of this equation if and only if $r_1 + r_2 = -b/a$ and $r_1 \cdot r_2 = c/a$.

3. Give a quadratic equation having 2 and 3 as roots.

4. Give a quadratic polynomial having $7 + 2i$ and $7 - 2i$ as zeros.

5. Solve each of the following equations.
   (a) $3x^2 - 7x + 2 = 0$ (b) $5x^2 - 2x + 1 = 0$

6. Find a real number k such that the roots of $kx^2 + (1 - 3k)x - k = 0$ are negative reciprocal roots.

7. Solve: $x^2 + (1 + 2i)x + (i - 3) = 0$.

8. Solve: $\dfrac{2x + 1}{3x + 5} = \dfrac{x - 6}{5x + 1}$.

9. Solve each of the following equations.
   (a) $\sqrt{2x - 1} + \sqrt{x + 3} = 9$ (b) $\sqrt{x + 8} = \sqrt{3x} - 5$

10. Solve: $2 \cos^2 x + \cos x - 1 = 0$.

11. Solve: $\sin^2 x - 3 \sin x + 2 = 0$.

12. Solve: $x^{2/3} - 3x^{1/3} + 6 = 0$. [Hint: First solve for $x^{1/3}$.]

13. Solve: $2^{2x} - 6(2^x) - 16 = 0$, x a real number.

14. Solve: $x^6 - 2x^3 + 2i + 1 = 0$. [Hint: DeMoivre's Theorem.]

15. Solve: $\sin(x/2) = \cos x - 1/4$.

11–2   remainder and factor theorems

We indicated in Chapter 10 that formulas do not exist to solve general polynomial equations higher than the fourth degree. Formulas giving the solutions to cubic and biquadratic equations can be found in a theory of equations text and are not developed here. However, we discuss methods for finding rational roots of any polynomial equation having rational numbers as *coefficients*.

Let $D(x)$ and $P(x)$ be polynomials of degrees m and n, respectively, and let $n \geqslant m \geqslant 1$. We discuss in elementary algebra how to divide polynomial $P(x)$ by $D(x)$ and obtain polynomials $Q(x)$ called the quotient and $R(x)$ called the remainder such that

$$P(x) = D(x) \cdot Q(x) + R(x)$$

where $R(x) = 0$ or the degree of $R(x)$ is less than the degree of $D(x)$. For example,

$$
\begin{array}{r}
x^2 + x + 4 \\
x^2 + 2x + 1\overline{)\,x^4 + 3x^3 + 7x^2 - 5x - 2} \\
\underline{x^4 + 2x^3 + x^2} \\
x^3 + 6x^2 - 5x \\
\underline{x^3 + 2x^2 + x} \\
4x^2 - 6x - 2 \\
\underline{4x^2 + 8x + 4} \\
-14x - 6
\end{array}
$$

$P(x) = x^4 + 3x^3 + 7x^2 - 5x - 2$, $D(x) = x^2 + 2x + 1$, $Q(x) = x^2 + x + 4$, and $R(x) = -14x - 6$. Thus, $x^4 + 3x^3 + 7x^2 - 5x - 2 = (x^2 + 2x + 1)(x^2 + x + 4) + (-14x - 6)$. This is called the *division algorithm*, and although we do not show it here, it can be proved that the quotient $Q(x)$ and remainder $R(x)$ always exist and are unique. We conclude from the division algorithm that if the divisor $D(x)$ is a linear function, the remainder $R(x)$ is a constant.

Let $P(x)$ be a polynomial with integers as coefficients and let $D(x) = x - r$ where r is a (complex or real) number. Thus, $P(x) = (x - r)Q(x) + R$ where R is a constant. Since $P(x) = (x - r)Q(x) + R$ is an identity for all x, $P(r) = (r - r)Q(r) + R = R$. Thus, we have the following theorem.

theorem 11–1 (remainder theorem): If a polynomial function $P(x)$ is divided by $(x - r)$ such that $P(x) = (x - r)Q(x) + R$, then $R = P(r)$.

example

If we divide $P(x) = x^3 + x^2 - 2x + 1$ by $x - 3$, the remainder R is $P(3) = 27 + 9 - 6 + 1 = 31$.

$$
\begin{array}{r}
x^2 + 4x + 10 \\
x - 3\overline{)\,x^3 + x^2 - 2x + 1} \\
\underline{x^3 - 3x^2} \\
4x^2 - 2x \\
\underline{4x^2 - 12x} \\
10x + 1 \\
\underline{10x - 30} \\
31 = P(3)
\end{array}
$$

An immediate consequence of the division algorithm and the remainder theorem is known as the *factor theorem*.

theorem 11–2 (factor theorem): A polynomial function $P(x)$ has $(x-r)$ as a factor if and only if $P(r)=0$.

proof: If $P(r)=0$, the remainder when dividing $P(x)$ by $(x-r)$ is zero by the remainder theorem. Thus, $(x-r)$ is a factor of $P(x)$. Conversely, if $(x-r)$ is a factor of $P(x)$ the remainder is zero, so $P(r)=0$.

Occasionally, the remainder and factor theorems are used to advantage in solving polynomial equations. For example, consider the equation $x^3-4x^2+2x+1=0$. It is rather obvious that if $P(x)=x^3-4x^2+2x+1$, then $P(1)=0$. Hence, $x-1$ is a factor of x^3-4x^2+2x+1. In fact,

$$x^3-4x^2+2x+1=(x-1)(x^2-3x-1).$$

If $(x-1)(x^2-3x-1)=0$, then either $(x-1)=0$ or $x^2-3x-1=0$. Solving, the solutions to the equation are

$$x_1=1, \quad x_2=\frac{3+\sqrt{13}}{2}, \quad \text{and} \quad x_3=\frac{3-\sqrt{13}}{2}.$$

Consider the equation $3x^3+5x^2-5x+1=0$. An important theorem enabling us to find the rational roots, if any exist, of such a polynomial equation with *integral coefficients* is that if u/v is a rational root of $3x^3+5x^2-5x+1=0$ and is in lowest terms, then u is a factor of 1 and v is a factor of 3. Thus, the only possible rational roots of the given equation are 1, -1, 1/3, and $-1/3$. Before proving the theorem, let us find the roots of the given equation.

Letting $P(x)=3x^3+5x^2-5x+1$. Since $P(1)=4$, $P(-1)=8$, and $P(-1/3)=30/9=10/3$, it follows that 1, -1, and $-1/3$ are not rational roots of the equation $3x^3+5x^2-5x+1=0$. However, $P(1/3)=0$; consequently, 1/3 is the only rational root of $P(x)=0$ and $x-(1/3)$ is a factor of $P(x)$. In fact,

$$3x^3+5x^2-5x+1=(x-1/3)(3x^2+6x-3).$$

Solving,

$$3x^3+5x^2-5x+1=0,$$

we have

$$x-1/3=0 \quad \text{or} \quad 3x^2+6x-3=0.$$

Dividing $3x^2+6x-3=0$ by 3 and using the quadratic formula, $x=(-2\pm\sqrt{8})/2$. Consequently, $x_1=1/3$, $x_2=-1+\sqrt{2}$, $x_3=-1-\sqrt{2}$.

theorem 11–3: Let $a_0x^n+a_1x^{n-1}+\cdots+a_{n-1}x+a_n=0$ be an nth degree polynomial equation where $n>1$ and the coefficients a_i are integers. If the rational number u/v is a non-zero rational root of $P(x) = 0$ where u and v are integers with no common factors, except 1 and -1, then u is a factor of a_n and v is a factor of a_0.

proof: The rational number u/v is a root of the equation if and only if

(A) $$a_0 \left(\frac{u}{v}\right)^n + a_1 \left(\frac{u}{v}\right)^{n-1} + \cdots + a_{n-1}\frac{u}{v} + a_n = 0.$$

Equality (A) is true if and only if

$$a_n = \frac{-a_0 u^n}{v^n} - \frac{a_1 u^{n-1}}{v^{n-1}} - \cdots - \frac{a_{n-1}u}{v}.$$

(B) $$a_n v^n = u(-a_0 u^{n-1} - a_1 u^{n-2}v - \cdots - a_{n-1}v^{n-1})$$

Since a_i are integers for $i = 1, 2, 3, \ldots, n-1$, and since u and v are integers, $-a_0 u^{n-1} - a_1 u^{n-2}v - \cdots - a_{n-1}v^{n-1}$ is an integer. Thus, if (B) is true, then u is a factor of $a_n v^n$. Since u and v have no common factor except 1 and -1, if u is a factor of $a_n v^n$ then u is a factor of a_n.

From (A), we obtain

$$a_0 u^n + a_1 u^{n-1}v + \cdots + a_{n-1}uv^{n-1} + a_n v^n = 0$$

and

$$a_0 u^n = v(-a_1 u^{n-1} - \cdots - a_{n-1}uv^{n-2} - a_n v^{n-1}).$$

By an argument similar to that in the first part of the proof, v is a factor of a_0. Thus, u is a factor of a_n and v is a factor of a_0 if u/v is a root of the equation.

11-3   fundamental theorem of algebra

We have already proved for a polynomial function

$$P(x) = a_0 x^n = a_1 x^{n-1} + a_2 x^{n-2} + \cdots + a_{n-1}x + a_n$$

that if a number r exists such that $P(r) = 0$, then $(x-r)$ is a factor of $P(x)$ and r is a root of the polynomial equation $P(x) = 0$. However, it is not obvious that for any polynomial function $P(x)$ a number r always exists such that $P(r) = 0$. The great German mathematician Karl Frederick Gauss proved in his doctoral thesis (1799) that for a polynomial equation $P(x) = 0$ of any degree at least one number r exists such that $P(r) = 0$. This important theorem is called the fundamental theorem of algebra.

theorem 11–4 (fundamental theorem of algebra):   Let $P(x)$ be a polynomial function of degree n where $n \geq 1$. Then, there exists at least one (complex) number r such that $P(r) = 0$.

Although we do not prove the fundamental theorem of algebra here, we do state and prove some of its immediate consequences. Let

$P(x)$ be a polynomial function of degree $n \geqslant 1$. The fundamental theorem of algebra implies that there exists a number r_1 such that

$$P(r_1) = 0;$$

thus, it follows from the factor theorem that

$$P(x) = (x - r_1) Q_1(x).$$

Now, $Q_1(x)$ is a polynomial of degree $n-1$ and if $n-1 \geqslant 1$ there exists an r_2 such that $Q_1(r_2) = 0$. Hence, $Q_1(x) = (x - r_2) Q_2(x)$. Consequently,

$$P(x) = (x - r_1)(x - r_2) Q_2(x).$$

Continuing, we conclude that

$$P(x) = a_0(x - r_1)(x - r_2)(x - r_3) \ldots (x - r_n).$$

Although the numbers r_i where $1 \leqslant i \leqslant n$ need not be different from each other, we have the following theorem.

theorem 11–5:   Let $P(x) = 0$ be a polynomial equation of degree n. The equation has at most n roots.

A polynomial equation of degree three has at most three roots. If the coefficients are real numbers, the complex roots appear in conjugate pairs; thus, a cubic equation with real coefficients has at least one real root. In fact, any polynomial equation with real coefficients of an odd degree must have at least one real root. Geometrically, the graph of a polynomial function with real coefficients of an odd degree must cross the x-axis at least once.

exercises

Express each polynomial as the product of linear factors.

1. $P(x) = 2x^3 - x^2 - 5x - 2$
2. $P(x) = 2x^3 - 5x^2 - 39x - 18$
3. $P(x) = 30x^3 + 13x^2 - 13x - 6$
4. $P(x) = 6x^4 - 7x^3 - 60x^2 + 63x + 45$

Solve each of the following equations.

5. $x^3 + 3x^2 + 3x + 2 = 0$
6. $x^3 - 14x - 15 = 0$
7. $12x^3 + 113x^2 + 86x - 15 = 0$
8. $x^4 - 9x^3 + 21x^2 - 9x + 20 = 0$
9. $4 \sin^3 x - 2 \sin^2 x - 6 \sin x + 3 = 0$
10. $x^3 - \dfrac{5}{6} x^2 - \dfrac{17}{3} x - \dfrac{5}{2} = 0$

11. $\dfrac{3}{2} x^3 - x^2 - x - \dfrac{5}{2} = 0$

12. $x^4 + \dfrac{1}{6} x^3 + \dfrac{11}{3} x^2 + \dfrac{2}{3} x - \dfrac{4}{3} = 0$

13. $10^{3x+1} - 31(10^{2x}) + 17(10^x) - 2 = 0$.   [Hint: $10^{3x+1} = 10(10^{3x})$.]

14. For what values of k does $P(x) = x^3 + k^2x^2 - 2kx - 4$ have $(x-1)$ as a linear factor?

15. For what values of k does $P(x) = k^2x^3 - k^2x^2 + 3kx + 11$ have $(x+3)$ as a linear factor? Why can you conclude that k is not a rational number before finding the solution?

16. If $-2 + i$ is a root of $x^5 + 4x^4 + 5x^3 + 8x^2 + 32x + 40 = 0$, find the other roots.

17. If $4 + i \sqrt{2}$ is a root of $x^4 - 11x^3 + 43x^2 - 62x + 18 = 0$, find the other roots.

18. If $3 + i$ is a root of $x^4 - 6x^3 + 7x^2 + 18x - 30 = 0$, find the other roots.

19. Solve: $4 \sin^3 x - 2 \sin^2 x - 2 \sin x + 1 = 0$.

20. Solve: $\sin 3 x + \sin x = 1/2$. Approximate roots. [Hint: Use $\sin A + \sin B = 2 \sin (A+B/2) \cos (A-B/2)$.]

21. Solve: $1 + \tan x + \tan^2 x + \tan^3 x = 0$.

analytic geometry

12

The student might wish to review briefly the discussion of the rectangular coordinate system in Chapter 4. We recall the following facts.

Let P_1 and P_2 be two points in the rectangular coordinate plane with coordinates (x_1,y_1) and (x_2,y_2), respectively.

1. The distance d between the two points P_1 and P_2 is given by

$$d = \sqrt{(x_2 - x_1)^2 + (y_2 - y_1)^2}.$$

2. If P_1 and P_2 are distinct points,

$$\left(\frac{x_1 + x_2}{2}, \frac{y_1 + y_2}{2}\right)$$

are the coordinates of the midpoint of the line segment connecting the two points.

3. If P_1 and P_2 are distinct points and if the segment joining the two points is divided into n equal segments,

$$\left(\frac{(n-k)x_1+kx_2}{n}, \frac{(n-k)y_1+ky_2}{n}\right)$$

are the coordinates of the endpoint of the kth segment from P_1 to P_2.

4. If $x_1 \neq x_2$, then $m = (y_2-y_1)/(x_2-x_1)$ is the slope of the line containing the two points.

12–2   slope

Let (x_1,y_1) and (x_2,y_2) be the coordinates of two distinct points P_1 and P_2. Consider the line containing the two points. (See Figure 12–1.) If $y_1 \neq y_2$, the line containing P_1 and P_2 intersects the x-axis.

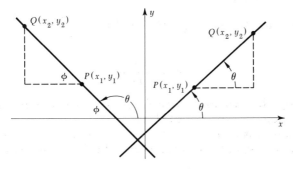

FIGURE 12–1

The angle with positive measure θ where $0° < \theta < 180°$ having the x-axis as initial side and the line as terminal side is called the *angle of inclination* of the line. A line parallel to the x-axis is defined to have an angle of inclination with $0°$ as measure. Thus, if θ is the measure of the angle of inclination of a given line, $0° \le \theta < 180°$.

Let L be a line not perpendicular to the x-axis; that is, the measure θ of the angle of inclination of L is not $90°$. Let P_1 and P_2 be two points on L with coordinates (x_1,y_1) and (x_2,y_2), respectively. Then, $\tan \theta = (y_2-y_1)/(x_2-x_1)$ is the slope of the line. If θ is acute this follows immediately from the definition of slope and Figure 12–1. If θ is obtuse,

$$\tan \theta = -\tan \phi = -\frac{y_2-y_1}{x_1-x_2} = \frac{y_2-y_1}{x_2-x_1}.$$

Let L_1 and L_2 be nonvertical lines with slopes m_1, m_2 and θ_1, θ_2 as measures of the angles of inclination. Lines L_1 and L_2 are parallel if and only if $\theta_1 = \theta_2$. Since $0° \le \theta_1 < 180°$, $0° \le \theta_2 < 180°$, $\theta_1 \neq 90°$, and $\theta_2 \neq 90°$, $\tan \theta_1 = \tan \theta_2$ if and only if $\theta_1 = \theta_2$, Consequently, L_1 and L_2 are parallel if and only if $m_1 = m_2$.

Let L_1 and L_2 be two nonvertical lines with slopes $m_1 = \tan \theta_1$ and $m_2 = \tan \theta_2$. If lines L_1 and L_2 are perpendicular to each other, then either $\theta_1 > 90°$ or $\theta_2 > 90°$. We assume $\theta_2 > 90°$. (See Figure 12–2.)

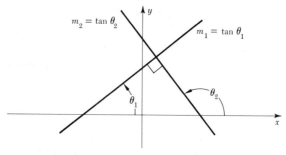

FIGURE 12-2

Thus, $\theta_2 = \theta_1 + 90°$ and

$$m_2 = \tan \theta_2 = \tan (\theta_1 + 90°) = -\cot \theta_1 = \frac{-1}{\tan \theta_1} = \frac{-1}{m_1},$$

or

$$m_2 = -\frac{1}{m_1}.$$

Consequently, the two nonvertical lines are perpendicular if and only if they have negative reciprocal slopes.

Let $m_1 = \tan \theta_1$ and $m_2 = \tan \theta_2$ be the slopes of two nonvertical lines L_1 and L_2, respectively. (See Figure 12-3.) Let θ be the measure

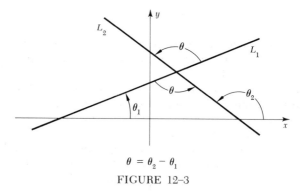

$$\theta = \theta_2 - \theta_1$$

FIGURE 12-3

of the angle generated counterclockwise with L_1 as initial side and L_2 as terminal side. Then,

$$\theta = \theta_2 - \theta_1$$

and

$$\tan \theta = \tan (\theta_2 - \theta_1)$$
$$= \frac{\tan \theta_2 - \tan \theta_1}{1 + \tan \theta_1 \tan \theta_2}$$
$$= \frac{m_2 - m_1}{1 + m_1 m_2}.$$

If L_1 and L_2 are not perpendicular, $m_1 \neq -1/m_2$ and $1 + m_1 m_2 \neq 0$.

examples

1. Let $(3,-7)$ and $(8,5)$ be the coordinates of two points in the plane.
   (a) $d = \sqrt{(8-3)^2 + [5-(-7)]^2} = \sqrt{5^2+12^2} = \sqrt{169} = 13$ is the distance of the line segment joining the two points.
   (b) The slope of the line containing the two points is
   $$m = \frac{-7-5}{3-8} = \frac{12}{5}.$$
   (c) The coordinates of the midpoint of the line segment joining the two are $[(8+3)/2, (-7+5)/2]$, or $(11/2, -1)$.

2. Let A, B, C be points in the plane with coordinates $(-4,1)$, $(-2,-4)$, $(3,-2)$, respectively.
   (a) Find the length of each side of the triangle formed.
   $$|AB| = \sqrt{(-4+2)^2+(1+4)^2} = \sqrt{2^2+5^2} = \sqrt{29}$$
   $$|BC| = \sqrt{(-2-3)^2+(-4+2)^2} = \sqrt{5^2+2^2} = \sqrt{29}$$
   $$|AC| = \sqrt{(-4-3)^2+(1+2)^2} = \sqrt{7^2+5^2} = \sqrt{58}$$

   (b) Find the slopes of each side of the triangle. (A line segment joining two points is said to have the same slope as the line containing the two points.) Let m_{AB}, m_{AC}, m_{BC} be the slopes of the sides AB, AC, BC, respectively.
   $$m_{AB} = \frac{-4-1}{-2+4} = \frac{-5}{2},$$
   $$m_{AC} = \frac{-2-1}{3+4} = \frac{-3}{7},$$
   $$m_{BC} = \frac{-2+4}{3+2} = \frac{2}{5}$$

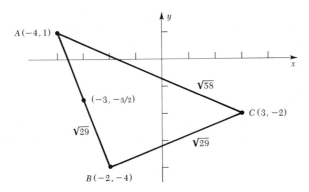

$$m_{AC} = -3/7, \quad m_{AB} = -5/2, \quad m_{BC} = 2/5$$

FIGURE 12-4

   (c) Prove that the triangle is a right triangle. Since $m_{AB} = -1/m_{BC}$, side AB is perpendicular to side BC. (Also, since $|AB|^2 + |BC|^2 = |AC|^2$, we conclude from the Pythagorean Theorem that the triangle is a right triangle with B as right angle and hypotenuse AC.)

(d) Find the coordinates of the midpoint of each side. Midpoint of AB has coordinates

$$\left(\frac{-4+(-2)}{2}, \frac{1+(-4)}{2}\right),$$

or $(-3, -3/2)$. Midpoint of AC has coordinates $(-1/2, -1/2)$ and midpoint of BC has coordinates $(1/2, -3)$.

(e) Prove that the medians are concurrent in a point which is 2/3 of the distance from a vertex to midpoint of the opposite side. The point 2/3 of the distance from A to the midpoint of BC has coordinates

$$\left(\frac{(-4)+2(1/2)}{3}, \frac{1+2(-3)}{3}\right),$$

or $(-1, -5/3)$. The point 2/3 of the distance from B to the midpoint of AC has coordinates $(-1, -5/3)$. Similarly, the point 2/3 of the distance from C to the midpoint of AB has coordinates $(-1, -5/3)$.

(f) Find the tangent of the measure of each of the acute angles in the triangle.

$$\tan A = \frac{m_{AC} - m_{AB}}{1 + m_{AC} m_{AB}} = \frac{-3/7 - (-5/2)}{1 + \left(\frac{-3}{7}\right)\left(\frac{-5}{2}\right)} = 1$$

If we notice that the right triangle is isosceles, it is obvious that $\tan A = \tan B = 1$ since $A = B = 45°$.

exercises

1. Find the distance between each pair of points and the coordinates of the midpoint of the segment joining the two points.
   (a) $(2,3)$ and $(-7,5)$ (b) $(6,3)$ and $(9,7)$
   (c) $(-2/3, 7/9)$ and $(5/9, 1/3)$ (d) $(2\sqrt{3}, -3)$ and $(\sqrt{3}, 5)$

2. Find the distance between each pair of points and the coordinates of the midpoint of the segment joining the two points.
   (a) $(3,5)$ and $(-2,-5)$ (b) $(-3,2)$ and $(3,10)$
   (c) $(-2/3, 2/5)$ and $(5/3, -7/5)$ (d) $(3\sqrt{5}, 6)$ and $(\sqrt{5}, 10)$

3. Find the slopes of the lines containing the pairs of points given in Exercise 1.

4. Find the slopes of the lines containing the pairs of points in Exercise 2.

5. Prove by two different methods that the points $(-3,4)$, $(6,-2)$, and $(-6,6)$ are collinear.

6. Prove by two different methods that the points $(-2,-3)$, $(18,5)$, and $(8,1)$ are collinear.

7. Find the coordinates of the point on the x-axis equidistant from $(1,3)$ and $(3,5)$.

8. Find the coordinates of the point on the y-axis equidistant from $(1,2)$ and $(-5,-2)$.

9. Find the coordinates of the point which divides the segment from $(-1,3)$ to $(5,7)$ into the ratio of 3 to 4.

10. Find the coordinates of the point which divides the segment from $(-3,-2)$ to $(5,4)$ into the ratio of 3 to 5.

11. Find the point on the y-axis such that the line containing it and the point with coordinates $(3,4)$ is parallel to the line containing $(-3,7)$ and $(2,-5)$.

12. Find the point on the x-axis such that the line containing it and the point with coordinates $(-5,7)$ is parallel to the line containing the points $(-7,-6)$ and $(-4,2)$.

13. Let $(-2,5)$, $(6,3)$, $(5,0)$, $(-3,2)$ be the coordinates of four points in the plane. Prove that the quadrilateral having these four points as vertices is a parallelogram.

14. Let (a,b), (c,d), (e,f), (g,h) be the coordinates of any four points in the plane which form a quadrilateral. Prove by analytic methods that the line segments joining the midpoints of the sides (in the order given) form a parallelogram.

15. Find the measure of the interior angles in each of the triangles with the given points as vertices.
    (a) $(22/3,6)$, $(4,-4)$, $(10,4)$
    (b) $(1,1)$, $(2,0)$, $(3,1)$

16. Find the measure of the interior angles in each of the triangles with the given points as vertices.
    (a) $(3,-4)$, $(6,7)$, $(1,0)$
    (b) $(-1,7)$, $(3,4)$, $(0,4)$

17. Find the coordinates (a,b) of the point equidistant from the three points in the plane with coordinates $(1,2)$, $(5,7)$, and $(3,-3)$.

18. Find the coordinates (a,b) of the point equidistant from the three points in the plane with coordinates $(3,5)$, $(-8,11)$, and $(-2,-5)$.

19. Let T be any triangle in the plane. Show that a coordinate system may be introduced so that the vertices of T are given by $(0,0)$, $(u,0)$, and (v,w). Then prove that four times the sum of the squares of the lengths of the medians of any triangle is equal to three times the sum of the squares of the lengths of the sides.

20. Prove by analytic methods that the segments which join the midpoints of opposite sides of any quadrilateral bisect each other. [Hint: Show that a coordinate system can be introduced so that $(0,0)$, $(a,0)$, (b,c), (d,e) are coordinates of the vertices of the quadrilateral.]

12–3   the line

Two important problems in analytic geometry are the following. (1) Given an equation $P(x,y)=0$ in two variables, how do we find the collection of points in the plane which make up the graph of the equation? (2) Given a collection of points in the coordinate plane, how do we find an equation $P(x,y)=0$ which has the set of points as its graph? In Chapter 4, we found that the line with slope m and y-intercept $(0,b)$ has equation $y=mx+b$.

Since a line can also be determined by two points, let us consider the method for finding the equation of the line containing two given points with coordinates (x_1,y_1) and (x_2,y_2). If $x_1=x_2$, then every point on the line through the two points has coordinates (x_1,y) where y is any real number. Thus, $x=x_1$ is the equation of the line; that is, the equation is the linear equation $Ax+By=C$ where $A=1$, $B=0$, and $C=x_1$. Notice that the collection of all points where $x=6$ on the real coordinate line is a point while the collection of all points where $x=6$ in the plane is a line parallel to the y-axis containing $(6,0)$.

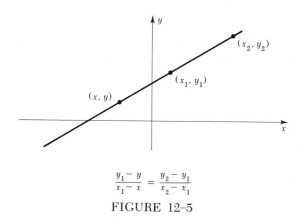

$$\frac{y_1-y}{x_1-x}=\frac{y_2-y_1}{x_2-x_1}$$

FIGURE 12-5

If (x_1,y_1) and (x_2,y_2) are the coordinates of two points and if $x_1 \neq x_2$, then $m=(y_2-y_1)/(x_2-x_1)$ is the slope of the line containing the two points. If, and only if, (x,y) is any point on the line distinct from (x_1,y_1),

$$\frac{y-y_1}{x-x_1}=\frac{y_2-y_1}{x_2-x_1}.$$

Thus,

$$y-y_1=\frac{y_2-y_1}{x_2-x_1}(x-x_1)$$

is the equation of the line containing (x_1,y_1) and (x_2,y_2). If $(2,3)$ and $(7,-5)$ are two points, then

$$y-3=\frac{-5-3}{7-2}(x-2),$$

or

$$8x+5y=31$$

is the equation of the straight line containing the two points.
We should note three things:

1. It is easy to check the preceding solution by noticing that (2,3) and (7,–5) satisfy the equation $8x + 5y = 31$.
2. We cease distinguishing between a point in the plane and its coordinates so we may use such phrases as "consider the point (2,3)" instead of "consider the point with coordinates (2,3)."
3. We do not distinguish between equations such as $8x + 5y = 31$ and $16x + 10y = 62$, since any ordered pair of real numbers satisfies one equation if, and only if, it satisfies the other. Thus, we talk about $8x + 5y = 31$ as *the* equation of the line containing (2,3) and (7,–5) instead of *an* equation of the line. In other words, although the equations are not identical in form, the sets $S = \{(x,y) | 8x + 5y = 31\}$ and $T = \{(x,y) | 16x + 10y = 62\}$ are equal. We call such equations *equivalent equations*.

Consider the linear equation $Ax + By = C$ where A and B are not both zero. If $B = 0$, then $A \neq 0$ and $x = C/A$ is the equation of the line parallel to the y-axis and containing the point $(C/A, 0)$. If $B \neq 0$, then $y = (-A/B) x + C/B$; this is the equation of the line with slope $-A/B$ and y-intercept $(0, C/B)$. We conclude that every linear equation of the form $Ax + By = C$ represents a straight line. Also, every line can be represented by a linear equation of the form $Ax + By = C$.

example

Find the equation of the line through (2,5) with slope $-3/2$.

Solution: Since $3x + 2y = k$ is the equation of a straight line with slope $-3/2$, we need only to determine k. If the line is to contain the point (2,5), then $3(2) + 2(5) = k$ since (2,5) must satisfy the equation. Thus, $k = 16$ and $3x + 2y = 16$ is the equation of the line.

Consider any line in the plane not containing the origin. This line could be determined by the perpendicular distance from the origin (0,0) to the line and the positive generated angle this line from the origin makes with the positive x-axis. (See Figure 12–6.) Notice if ω

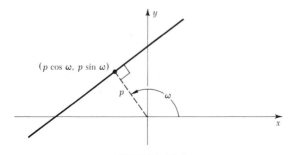

FIGURE 12–6

is the measure of the angle and p is the distance of the line from the origin, $0° \le \omega < 360°$ and $p > 0$. The coordinates of the point of intersection of the given line and the normal (perpendicular) line are $(p \cos \omega, p \sin \omega)$; furthermore, the slope of the normal line is $\tan \omega$ (if $\omega \ne 90°$ or $270°$) so the slope of the given line is

$$\frac{-1}{\tan \omega} = \frac{-\cos \omega}{\sin \omega}.$$

Hence, the equation of the line is

$$y - p \sin \omega = \frac{-\cos \omega}{\sin \omega}(x - p \cos \omega).$$
$$(\sin \omega)y - p \sin^2 \omega = -(\cos \omega)x + p \cos^2 \omega$$
$$(\cos \omega)x + (\sin \omega)y = p(\sin^2 \omega + \cos^2 \omega) = p$$

The equation $(\cos \omega)x + (\sin \omega)y = p$ is called the *normal equation* of the given line. Since the normal equation determines the lines $x = p$ and $x = -p$ when $\omega = 90°$ and $270°$, respectively, we need make no restriction on ω for the normal equation except $0° \le \omega < 360°$.

If $Ax + By = C$ and $(\cos \omega)x + (\sin \omega)y = p$ are both equations of the same line, then there exists a real number k such that

$$kA = \cos \omega, \quad kB = \sin \omega, \quad kC = p.$$

Thus,

$$k^2A^2 = \cos^2 \omega, \quad k^2B^2 = \sin^2 \omega, \text{ and } k^2(A^2 + B^2) = \cos^2 \omega + \sin^2 \omega.$$
$$k^2 = \frac{1}{A^2 + B^2}$$
$$k = \pm \frac{1}{\sqrt{A^2 + B^2}}$$

Consequently,

$$p = \pm \frac{C}{\sqrt{A^2 + B^2}}.$$

Therefore,

$$p = \frac{|C|}{\sqrt{A^2 + B^2}}$$

is the distance of the line $Ax + By = C$ from the origin. Note that if the line contains the origin $C = 0$ and $p = 0$, thus,

$$p = \frac{|C|}{\sqrt{A^2 + B^2}}$$

is the distance of any line from the origin.

example

1. For the line $3x + 4y = 13$, we have that $13/\sqrt{9+16} = 13/5$ is the perpendicular distance of the line from the origin.

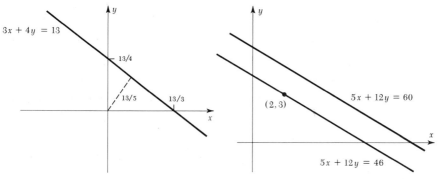

FIGURE 12–7

2. Find the distance of the point $(2,3)$ from the line $5x + 12y = 60$.

Solution: Since a line parallel to $5x + 12y = 60$ has equation $5x + 12y = C$, and since $5(2) + 12(3) = C$ if $(2,3)$ is on the line, $5x + 12y = 46$ is the equation of the line containing $(2,3)$ and parallel to $5x + 12y = 60$. The distance of $5x + 12y = 60$ from the origin is $60/13$ and the distance of $5x + 12y = 46$ from the origin is $46/13$. Since both lines are on the same side of the origin, $60/13 - 46/13 = 14/13$ is the distance between the parallel lines, the perpendicular distance from $(2,3)$ to $5x + 12y = 60$.

exercises

1. Graph each of the following lines, give the coordinates of the x- and y-intercepts, and find the area of the triangle formed by the line and the coordinate axes.
   (a) $3x + 5y = 15$ (b) $5x - 4y = 11$
   (c) $3x - 7y = 14$ (d) $11x + 13y = 15$

2. Graph each of the following lines, give the coordinates of the x- and y-intercepts, and find the area of the triangle formed by the line and the coordinate axes.
   (a) $11x - 3y = 6$ (b) $4x + 3y = 12$
   (c) $6x - 17y = 39$ (d) $4x - 13y = 2$

3. Find the equation of the line containing the given point and which has the given slope.
   (a) $(3,-5)$; $m = 1/2$ (b) $(7,-15)$; $m = -2/3$
   (c) $(2/5,-9/4)$; $m = -6/5$ (d) $(3,8)$; $m = \sqrt{3}$

4. Find the equation of the line containing the given point and which has the given slope.
   (a) $(3/2,7/3)$; $m = -7/13$ (b) $(6,4)$; $m = 3/5$
   (c) $(1,0)$; $m = 0$ (d) $(1,1)$; $m = -1$

5. Find the equation of the line containing the two given points.
    (a) $(2,7)$ and $(-5,-11)$ (b) $(7,-3)$ and $(-5,13)$
    (c) $(2/3,-7/5)$ and $(3,11/6)$ (d) $(5/6,7/3)$ and $(2,2)$

6. Find the equation of the line containing the two given points.
    (a) $(6,0)$ and $(-9,0)$ (b) $(6,3)$ and $(-7,3)$
    (c) $(0,3)$ and $(0,-5)$ (d) $(1+\sqrt{3}, 1-\sqrt{3})$ and $(7,2)$

7. Find the equation of the line parallel to the given line and containing the given point.
    (a) $3x-7y=11$; $(-7,5)$ (b) $2x+3y=8$; $(0,2)$
    (c) $5x-9y=13$; $(2/3,-5/7)$

8. Find the equation of the line parallel to the given line and containing the given point.
    (a) $12x-4y=1$; $(2,5)$ (b) $2x-3y=11$; $(-8,5)$
    (c) $6x+7y=15$; $(2/3,-7/5)$

9. Find the equation of the line perpendicular to the given line and containing the given point.
    (a) $3x-7y=11$; $(-7,5)$ (b) $2x+3y=8$; $(0,2)$
    (c) $5x-9y=13$; $(2/3,-5/7)$

10. Find the equation of the line perpendicular to the given line and containing the given point.
    (a) $12x-4y$; $(2,5)$ (b) $2x-3y=11$; $(-8,5)$
    (c) $6x+7y=15$; $(2/3,-7/5)$

11. Find the equation of the perpendicular bisector of the line segment joining the given points.
    (a) $(5,11)$ and $(3,4)$ (b) $(2,6)$ and $(-11,-4)$
    (c) $(6,9)$ and $(6,15)$

12. Find the equation of the perpendicular bisector of the line segment joining the given points.
    (a) $(7/5,11)$ and $(2/3-5/8)$ (b) $(3,7)$ and $(-19,14)$
    (c) $(8,-5)$ and $(8,3)$

13. Prove that the perpendicular distance from the point (x_1,y_1) to the line $Ax+By=C$ is

$$\frac{|Ax_1+By_1-C|}{\sqrt{A^2+B^2}}.$$

14. (a) Find the coordinates of the foot of the perpendicular drawn through the point $(3,5)$ to the line $5x+12y=30$.
    (b) Find the distance from $(3,5)$ to the line by using the distance formula for the distance between two points.
    (c) Check your answer in (b) by using the formula for the distance from a point to a line. [See Exercise 13.]

15. (a) Find the coordinate of the foot of the perpendicular drawn through the point $(-7,4)$ to the line $7x+24y=13$.
    (b) Find the distance from $(-7,4)$ to the line by using the distance formula for the distance between two points.
    (c) Check your answer in (b) by using the formula for the distance from a point to a line. [See Exercise 13.]

16. Find the equations of the bisectors of the angles of intersection of the lines $3x + 4y = 15$ and $8x + 15y = 11$.

17. (a) Graph $(3x + 2y + 6) + k(3x - 4y - 12) = 0$ for $k = 0$, $k = 1$, $k = 2$, $k = -1$, $k = -2$, $k = -5$.

(b) Prove that $(3x + 2y - 6) + k(3x - 4y - 12) = 0$ is the equation of a line containing the intersection (a,b) of the two lines given by $3x + 2y = 6$ and $3x - 4y = 12$.

(c) Find the equation of the line containing the intersection of $3x + 2y = 6$ and $3x - 4y = 12$ and the point $(4,2)$.

18. Without finding the point of intersection, find the equation of the line containing the intersection of the lines $2x + 5y = 11$ and $7x - 8y = 14$ and the point $(-3,5)$.

12-4 graphing algebraic equations

In the last section, we completely solved the problems of graphing a given linear equation in two variables and of finding the equation when given the graph of a straight line. In general, it is not a simple task to graph an arbitrary equation in x and y; however, some of the properties of the graph of algebraic equation can be found by studying the equation. A knowledge of some of the curve properties makes it possible to sketch the graph of the equation without the necessity of plotting so many different points. Although a complete analysis of the properties of a curve usually requires calculus, we discuss in this section some of the methods for finding the elementary properties of a curve that do not require techniques of calculus.

The x- and y-intercepts of a curve are the points where the curve crosses the x- and y-axis, respectively. Since a point on the x-axis has y-coordinate 0, the x-intercepts of a curve represented by an equation in x and y can be found by letting $y = 0$ and solving the resulting equation for x. Similarly, to find the y-intercepts, we let $x = 0$ and solve the resulting equation for y.

example

For the curve represented by

$$y = \frac{(x-3)(x+2)}{(x+5)(x-6)},$$

we find, by letting $y = 0$ and solving for x, that the x-intercepts are 3 and -2. The coordinates $(3,0)$ and $(-2,0)$ satisfy the equation. By letting $x = 0$, we find there is only one y-intercept; it is 1/5. The coordinates $(0,1/5)$ satisfy the equation. The curve contains the intercept-points $(3,0)$, $(0,1/5)$, and $(-2,0)$.

definition: Two points P_1 and P_2 are said to be *symmetric with respect to a point* P if P is the midpoint of the line segment joining P_1 and P_2. A curve is said to be *symmetric with respect to a point P* if, for every point P_1 on the curve, there is a corresponding point P_2 on the curve such that P_1 and P_2 are symmetric with respect to P.

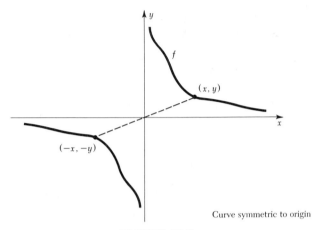

Curve symmetric to origin

FIGURE 12–8

Since $(0,0)$ is the midpoint of the line segment joining (x,y) and $(-x,-y)$, the points (x,y) and $(-x,-y)$ are symmetric with respect to the origin. It follows that a curve represented by an equation in x and y is *symmetric with respect to the origin* if and only if the substitution of $-x$ for x and $-y$ for y in the given equation results in an equation equivalent to the given equation.

example

The curve $x^2 + xy = y^3(x+y)$ is symmetric with respect to the origin since substituting $-x$ for x and $-y$ for y results in the equation

$$(-x)^2 + (-x)(-y) = (-y)^3[(-x) + (-y)],$$

which is equivalent to the original equation.

We have already said that two points P_1 and P_2 are symmetric with respect to a line if the line is the perpendicular bisector of the segment joining P_1 and P_2. Furthermore, a curve is said to be symmetric with respect to a line if for every point P_1 on the curve there is a corresponding point P_2 on the curve such that P_1 and P_2 are symmetric to the line.

Since (x,y) and $(-x,y)$ are symmetric with respect to the y-axis, a curve represented by an equation in x and y is symmetric with respect to the y-axis if and only if the substition of $-x$ for x results in an equivalent equation. Similarly, since (x,y) and $(x,-y)$ are symmetric with respect to the x-axis, a curve represented by an equation in x

and y is symmetric with respect to the x-axis if and only if the substitution of $-y$ for y results in an equivalent equation.

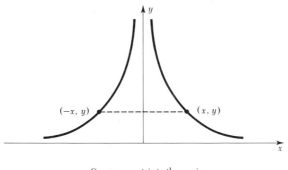

Curve symmetric to the y-axis

FIGURE 12–9

example

The curve represented by $x^2 + x^4 y = 3y^2$ is symmetric with respect to the y-axis; however, it is not symmetric with respect to the x-axis.

It should be noted that if a curve is symmetric with respect to both the x-axis and the y-axis it is symmetric with respect to the origin. This follows from the fact that if the curve is symmetric to the y-axis then $P(x,y) = P(-x,y)$, and if the curve is symmetric to the x-axis then $P(-x,y) = P(-x,-y)$. Consequently, $P(x,y) = P(-x,-y)$ and the curve is symmetric to the origin. Finally, it should be noted that a curve, such as that represented by $y = x^3$, can be symmetric with respect to the origin but not symmetric with respect to either axis.

If the perpendicular distances from a point (x,y) on a curve to a fixed vertical straight line tend to zero as y becomes infinitely large, the line is said to be a *vertical asymptote* to the curve. For example, if

$$y = \frac{1}{(x-2)^4}$$

the line $x = 2$ is a vertical asymptote for the graph of the equation. If the perpendicular distances from a point (x,y) on a curve to a fixed vertical straight line tend to zero as x becomes infinitely large, the line is said to be a *horizontal asymptote* to the curve. In other words, an asymptote is a line which approximates the curve for large values of x or y.

Consider the equation $y^2 = x^2 + 2$. The graph of this equation is symmetric to the x-axis, y-axis, and the origin. Furthermore, for large values of x, y^2 is approximately equal to x^2; thus, $y = x$ or $y = -x$ are asymptotes for the curve.

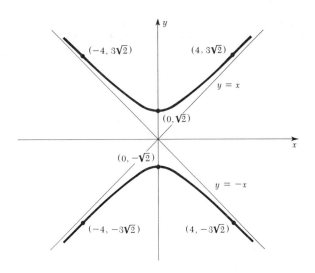

Graph of $y^2 = x^2 + z$: symmetric to x-axis, y-axis, and origin

FIGURE 12–10

Assume we have an equation of the form $y^n = f(x)/g(x)$ where $f(x)$ and $g(x)$ are polynomial functions and n is a positive integer. If $(x-a)$ is a factor of the denominator and not the numerator, then the line $x=a$ is a vertical asymptote for the curve. This is obvious if we notice that if x is a number "close" to a, then y is large. Similarly, if $(y-b)$ is a factor of the denominator and not the numerator of an equation in x and y written as $x^n = f(y)/g(y)$ where n is a positive integer and $f(y)$ and $g(y)$ are polynomial functions, then the line $y=b$ is a horizontal asymptote for the curve.

example

(1) To find the vertical asymptotes for the curve given by $xy + 4x - 6y = 11$, we solve the equation for y in terms of x. Thus,

$$(x-6)y = 11 - 4x$$

and

$$y = \frac{11 - 4x}{x - 6}.$$

Hence, $x=6$ is a vertical asymptote.

(2) To find the horizontal asymptote, we solve the equation for x in terms of y.

$$(y+4)x = 6y + 11$$
$$x = \frac{6y + 11}{y - (-4)}$$

Hence, $y=-4$ is a horizontal asymptote.

A final technique that is often useful in graphing algebraic equations is finding the excluded regions for the curve. *Excluded regions* for the curve are parts of the coordinate plane not containing any points of the curve. For example, if some real values of x in an equation in x and y result in imaginary values for y, then the graph of the equation has no points in the region of the plane with these x-coordinates. If $y = \sqrt{x+4}$, it is obvious that there can be no points on the graph of this equation in the coordinate plane if x is less than -4. Excluded regions are also often found by solving for x in terms of y and finding those real values of y which give imaginary values of x.

Excluded regions can often be found without explicitly solving the equation for one variable in terms of the other or even without finding what real values for one variable make the other variable have imaginary values to satisfy the equation. For example, if $y = x^6 + 3x^4 + 2x^2$, it is obvious since x^2, x^4, and x^6 are non-negative real numbers. For any real number x, y is always non-negative; hence, the region below the x-axis is an excluded region for the graph of this equation.

examples

1. Find excluded regions for $x^2 + 16 = y^4$.

   Solution:

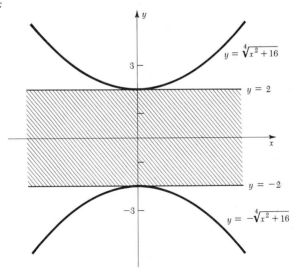

FIGURE 12–11

(1) Solving for x,

$$x = \pm\sqrt{y^4 - 16}.$$

Since $y^4 - 16 < 0$ when $-2 < y < 2$, an excluded region is the part of the plane between $y = 2$ and $y = -2$.

(2) Solving for y,

$$y = \pm \sqrt[4]{x^2 + 16}.$$

Since $x^2 + 16 > 0$ for all x, we find no excluded regions. Note: There are no x-intercepts; the y-intercepts are 2 and -2; the curve is symmetric with respect to the x-axis, y-axis, and the origin; there are no horizontal or vertical asymptotes. Furthermore, excluded regions could have been found by observing that $y^4 \geq 16$ for all real x.

2. Discuss and sketch the graph of $xy^2 + 2y^2 - x = 8$.

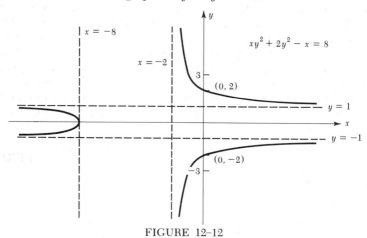

FIGURE 12-12

Solution:
(1) Let $x = 0$, and we get $y = \pm 2$. Thus, the y-intercepts are 2 and -2. Let $y = 0$ and we get $x = -8$. Thus, the x-intercept is -8.
(2) Since substituting $-y$ for y results in an equivalent equation, the curve is symmetric with respect to the x-axis. The curve is not symmetric with respect to the origin or the y-axis.
(3) Solving for y^2,

$$(x+2)y^2 = x + 8$$
$$y^2 = \frac{x+8}{x+2}.$$

Since $x - (-2)$ is a factor of the denominator, $x = -2$ is a vertical asymptote. Solving for y,

$$y = \pm \sqrt{\frac{x+8}{x+2}}.$$

Since $(x+8)/(x+2) < 0$ when $-8 < x < -2$, the plane region between $x = -8$ and $x = -2$ is an excluded region for the curve.
(4) Solving for x,

$$xy^2 - x = 8 - 2y^2$$
$$(y^2 - 1)x = 8 - 2y^2$$
$$x = \frac{8 - 2y^2}{y^2 - 1}.$$

Since $(y-1)$ and $(y+1)$ are factors of the denominator and not the numerator, $y=1$ and $y=-1$ are horizontal asymptotes.

3. Discuss and sketch the graph of $xy^2 - 6x + 2y = 0$.

Solution:
(1) Let $x=0$, and we get $y=0$. When $y=0$, $x=0$; thus, the origin is the only point at which the curve crosses the axes.
(2) Since substituting $-x$ for x and $-y$ for y results in an equivalent equation, the curve is symmetric with respect to the origin. It is not symmetric with respect to the x- or y-axes.
(3) Solving for y,

$$xy^2 + 2y - 6x = 0$$
$$y = \frac{-2 \pm \sqrt{24 + 24x^2}}{2x}$$
$$= \frac{-1 \pm \sqrt{1 + 6x^2}}{x}.$$

The line $x=0$, the y-axis, is an asymptote for the curve. Since $1 + 6x^2 > 0$ for all real x, there is no excluded region indicated.
(4) Solving for x,

$$xy^2 - 6x = -2y$$
$$x = \frac{-2y}{y^2 - 6}.$$

Since $(y - \sqrt{6})$ and $(y + \sqrt{6})$ are factors of the denominator, $y = \sqrt{6}$ and $y = -\sqrt{6}$ are horizontal asymptotes for the curve.

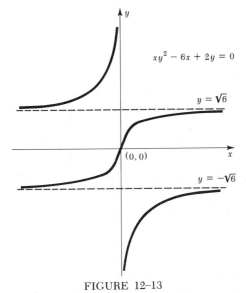

$$xy^2 - 6x + 2y = 0$$

$y = \sqrt{6}$

$(0, 0)$

$y = -\sqrt{6}$

FIGURE 12–13

4. Discuss and sketch the graph of

$$y = \frac{x(x-3)}{(x-1)(x+3)}.$$

Solution:

(1) Let $x=0$, and we get $y=0$. Thus, the origin is one intercept of the curve. Let $y=0$ and we get $x=0$ or $x=3$. Thus, the only other intercept is the point $(3,0)$.

(2) By the symmetry tests, we find the curve is not symmetric with respect to the x-axis, y-axis, or the origin.

(3) Since $(x-1)$ and $(x+3)$ are factors of the denominator when y is given explicitly in terms of x, the lines $x=1$ and $x=-3$ are vertical asymptotes for the curve.

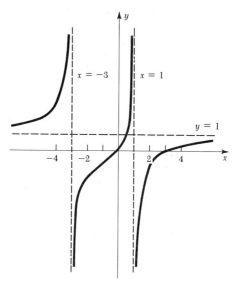

$$y = \frac{x(x-3)}{(x-1)(x+3)}$$

FIGURE 12–14

(4) Since

$$\frac{x(x-3)}{(x-1)(x+3)} = \frac{1(1-3/x)}{(1-1/x)(1+3/x)},$$

y approaches 1 as x becomes positively (or negatively) infinite; thus, the line $y=1$ is a horizontal asymptote.

5. Discuss and sketch the graph

$$y = \frac{x+2}{x^2-3x}.$$

Solution:

(1) For $x=0$, y is undefined. Hence, there are no y-intercepts and the curve does not cross the y-axis. Let $y=0$, and we get $x=-2$. Thus, the x-intercept is -2.

(2) By the symmetry tests we find the curve is not symmetric with respect to the x-axis, y-axis, or origin.

(3) Since x and $(x-3)$ are factors of the denominator, the lines $x=0$ and $x=3$ are the vertical asymptotes for the curve.

(4) Solving for x,

$$yx^2 - 3xy = x + 2$$
$$yx^2 + (-3y-1)x - 2 = 0$$
$$x = \frac{3y+1 \pm \sqrt{9y^2+6y+1+8y}}{2y}$$
$$x = \frac{3y+1 \pm \sqrt{9y^2+14y+1}}{2y}.$$

We see that $y=0$ is an asymptote for the curve.
Solving $9y^2 + 14y + 1 = 0$, we get

$$y = \frac{-14 \pm \sqrt{196-36}}{18}$$
$$y = \frac{-14 \pm 4\sqrt{10}}{18}$$
$$= \frac{-7 \pm 2\sqrt{10}}{9}.$$

By the graphic method for solving inequalities, we find that $9y^2 + 14y + 1 < 0$ when

$$\frac{-7-2\sqrt{10}}{9} < y < \frac{-7+2\sqrt{10}}{9}.$$

Hence, the part of the plane between the lines

$$y = (-7-2\sqrt{10})/9 \quad \text{and} \quad y = (-7+2\sqrt{10})/9$$

is an excluded region.

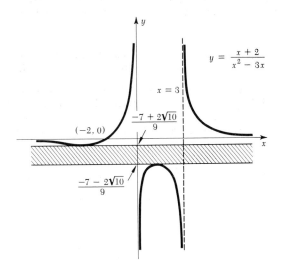

FIGURE 12–15

12–5 locus problems

In the last section, we discussed how to sketch the graph of a given equation. In this section, we shall discuss the problem of finding the equation of a given locus of points. A set of points, usually a curve, is given as the set of all points satisfying some geometric condition. This set of points is called the *locus* determined by the given condition. We set up a coordinate system (if one is not already given in the description of the locus) and find an equation in x and y which is satisfied by the coordinates of each point on the locus and only by such points. We call this the equation of the locus relative to the chosen axes. When we set up a coordinate system, we usually try to choose the axes so that the final equation will be in a convenient and simple form.

examples

1. Find the collection of all points at distance r from the point (h,k) in the coordinate plane.

   Solution: Let (x,y) be any point in the coordinate plane at distance r from the point (h,k). Then,

   $$\sqrt{(x-h)^2+(y-k)^2}=r.$$

   Since $(x-h)^2$, $(y-k)^2$, and r are non-negative, the coordinates (x,y) satisfy the preceding equation if and only if they satisfy

   $$(x-h)^2+(y-k)^2=r^2.$$

   Since the collection of all points equidistant from a fixed point is a circle, $(x-h)^2+(y-k)^2=r^2$ is the equation of a circle with center (h,k) and radius r.

2. A and B are points on the x- and y-axis, respectively, such that AB subtends a right angle at $C(1,2)$. Find the locus of the midpoint of AB.

   Solution: Let P, with coordinates (x,y), be a typical position of the midpoint of AB. Since the x-coordinate of B is 0, the x-coordinate of A, say a, is such that $(a+0)/2=x$. Hence A is $(2x,0)$. Similarly, B is $(0,2y)$. Now ABC is a right-angle triangle with $C=90°$ if and only if

   $$|AC|^2+|BC|^2=|AB|^2.$$

   Hence, AB subtends a right angle at C if and only if x and y satisfy

   $$[(1-2x)^2+(2-0)^2]+[(1-0)^2+(2-2y)^2]=[(0-2x)^2+(2y-0)^2].$$

   That is,

   $$1-4x+4x^2+4+1+4-8y+4y^2=4x^2+4y^2$$
   $$2x+4y-5=0.$$

   Thus, the locus is the straight line $2x+4y-5=0$.

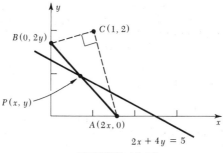

FIGURE 12–16

3. B is any point on the line $x=2$. The point P is on the line segment OB and $|OB| \cdot |OP| = 1$. Find the locus of P as B takes all positions on the line $x=2$.

Solution: Let $P(x,y)$ be a typical point on the required locus. If B is $(2,t)$, by similar triangles, $t/y = 2/x$—that is, $t = 2y/x$, and so B is $(2,2y/x)$. Since $|OB| \cdot |OP| = 1$, the coordinates of P satisfy

$$\sqrt{4 + \frac{4y^2}{x^2}} \cdot \sqrt{x^2+y^2} = 1 \qquad (x \neq 0).$$

$$2\,\frac{x^2+y^2}{x} = 1 \qquad (x \neq 0).$$

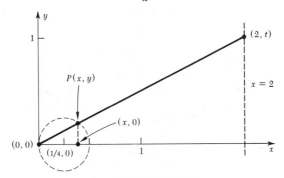

FIGURE 12–17

Hence, the locus is $x^2 + y^2 - (1/2)x = 0$ [except for the point $(0,0)$]. Since $[x - (1/4)]^2 + y^2 = 1/16$ is equivalent to $x^2 + y^2 - (1/2)x = 0$, this is a circle with center $(1/4,0)$ and radius $1/4$.

4. Find the locus of all points P such that the product of the slopes of the lines through P and $A(1,0)$, $B(-1,0)$, respectively, is 1.

Solution: Let (x,y) be the coordinates of a point on the locus. The slope of PA is $y/(x-1)$, where $x \neq 1$. The slope of PB is $y/[x-(-1)]$, where $x \neq -1$. Hence, the coordinates of P satisfy

$$\left(\frac{y}{x-1}\right) \cdot \left(\frac{y}{x+1}\right) = 1.$$

That is, $y^2 = x^2 - 1$ or $x^2 - y^2 = 1$, where $x \neq \pm 1$. Conversely, any point [except for $(1,0)$ and $(-1,0)$] whose coordinates satisfy this equation will satisfy the condition of the locus. Hence, the locus is given by $x^2 - y^2 = 1$ with the points $(1,0)$, $(-1,0)$ omitted.

5. Find the locus of all points which satisfy the condition that the sum of the squares of the distances of each point from two fixed intersecting lines is a positive constant.

Solution: Take the perpendicular bisectors of the angles between the lines as coordinate axes. Then the two lines will have equations $y = mx$, $y = -mx$, respectively, where $m \neq 0$. Let P with coordinates (x,y) be a typical point on the locus. The perpendicular distance of P from the line $y = mx$ is $|mx - y|/\sqrt{m^2 + 1}$ and from the line $y = -mx$ is $|mx + y|\sqrt{m^2 + 1}$. Hence, the coordinates of P satisfy

$$\frac{(mx - y)^2}{m^2 + 1} + \frac{(mx + y)^2}{m^2 + 1} = K,$$

where K is a positive constant. Conversely, if x, y satisfy this equation, then P satisfies the given condition. Simplifying this equation we get

$$\frac{2m^2}{m^2 + 1} x^2 + \frac{2}{m^2 + 1} y^2 = K$$

$$m^2 x^2 + y^2 = \frac{K(m^2 + 1)}{2}.$$

For $m = 1$, this is a circle with center at the origin and radius $\sqrt{K}$.

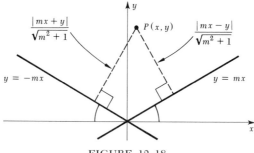

FIGURE 12-18

exercises

Discuss and sketch the graph of each of the equations in Exercises 1 through 12.

1. $xy = 4$

2. $x(y - 2) = 9$

3. $(x - 2)(y + 4) = 8$

4. $x^2 y - x^2 = 4$

5. $x^2 y = 16$

6. $y = x^3$

7. $y(x - 9) = x^2 - 9$

8. $x^3 y - 4x^2 y = x - 1$

9. $xy - 2y - 4x = 8$

10. $x^3 + xy = 0$

11. $(x^2 - 9)y = 3x$

12. $y^2 x = 16x$

13. Find the equation of the locus of points at distance 5 from the point $(2,-1)$. Sketch the graph.

14. Let A, B, and C have coordinates $(-1,0)$, $(0,0)$, and $(1,0)$, respectively. Find the equation of the locus of points P with coordinates (x,y) if the product of the slopes of AP and CP equals the slope of BP. Sketch the graph.

15. Find the equation of the locus of points P such that the sum of the distance from P to $(3,0)$ and $(-3,0)$ is always 10. Sketch the graph.

16. Find the equation of the locus of points that are equal distance from the line $x=2$ and the point $(-2,0)$. Sketch the graph.

17. Find the equation of the locus of points that are equal distance from the line $x=6$ and the point $(2,4)$. Sketch the graph.

18. Find the equation of the locus of points that are equal distance from the line $3x+4y=12$ and the point $(6,8)$. Sketch the graph and prove that it is symmetric to the line $4x-3y=0$.

12–6 ellipse

We turn our attention now to the study of three important plane curves: the *ellipse, hyperbola,* and *parabola.* We shall define each of these curves in terms of plane properties; however, as we shall see, each can also be defined as a section of a cone — thus, the name *conic sections.*

Let F and F' be two fixed points in the plane. These points determine a line segment with a given length; for convenience, we let $2c$ be the length $|FF'|$. See Figure 12–19. Let $a > c$ and consider the locus of

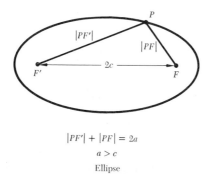

$$|PF'| + |PF| = 2a$$
$$a > c$$
Ellipse

FIGURE 12–19

points P in the plane such that the sum of the distances between any point P and the two fixed points F and F' is $2a$; that is,

$$|PF| + |PF'| = 2a .$$

This set of points is called an *ellipse.*

If we introduce a coordinate system in the plane as in Figure 12–20

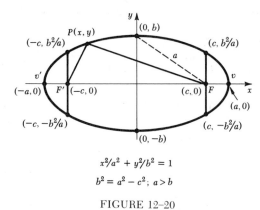

$$x^2\!/a^2 + y^2\!/b^2 = 1$$

$$b^2 = a^2 - c^2;\ a > b$$

FIGURE 12-20

so that the x-axis coincides with the segment FF' and the origin is the midpoint of the segment, then

(1) $\sqrt{(x - c)^2 + (y - 0)^2} + \sqrt{(x + c)^2 + (y - 0)^2} = 2a$.

We leave as an exercise for the reader to prove that the coordinates $(x,\ y)$ satisfy this equation if and only if they satisfy the following equation:

(2) $(a^2 - c^2)x^2 + a^2y^2 = a^2(a^2 - c^2)$.

Thus, equation (2) is that of an ellipse. Since $a > c$, $a^2 > c^2$ and $a^2 - c^2$ is positive. Hence, we can *let* $b^2 = a^2 - c^2$; this substitution is done for notational convenience. Consequently, equation (2) may be written as follows:

$$b^2x^2 + a^2y^2 = a^2b^2 ,$$

or

(3) $\dfrac{x^2}{a^2} + \dfrac{y^2}{b^2} = 1$.

From equation (3), we can conclude the following about the graph of the ellipse. First, the curve is symmetric to the x-axis, the y-axis, and the origin. Second, the x-intercepts are a and $-a$ and the y-intercepts are b and $-b$. Notice since $a^2 = b^2 + c^2$ that the distance from $(0,\ b)$ to $(c,\ 0)$ is a.

We call the fixed points F and F' the *foci* of the ellipse; the midpoint of the line segment FF' is the *center* of the ellipse; the points $(a,\ 0)$ and $(-a,\ 0)$ are *vertices*; the line segment joining $(a,\ 0)$ and $(-a,\ 0)$ is the *major axis*; and the line segment joining $(0,\ b)$ and $(0,\ -b)$ is the *minor axis*. The line segment that is perpendicular to the major axis at the focus with endpoints on the ellipse is called the *latus rectum*; the two such segments are called *latera recta*. Substituting c for x in equation (3) and solving for y, we find the y-coordinates of the endpoints of the latera recta:

$$\frac{c^2}{a^2} + \frac{y^2}{b^2} = 1 \ ,$$

$$\frac{y^2}{b^2} = \frac{a^2 - c^2}{a^2} = \frac{b^2}{a^2} \ ,$$

$$y^2 = \frac{b^4}{a^2} \ ,$$

$$y = \pm \frac{b^2}{a} \ .$$

For, the equation $x^2/169 + y^2/25 = 1$, $a = 13$, $b = 5$, and $c = 12$. Since $b^2/a = 25/13$, the endpoints of the latera recta are $(12, 25/13)$, $(12, -25/13)$, $(-12, 25/13)$, and $(-12, -25/13)$. See Figure 12–21.

We always let $2c$ be the distance between the fixed points, let $2a$ be the fixed distance, and let $b^2 = a^2 - c^2$. Thus, $b^2 < a^2$, and in the equation

$$\frac{x^2}{36} + \frac{y^2}{100} = 1 \ ,$$

$b^2 = 36$ and $a^2 = 100$. In other words, the major axis is always longer than the minor axis. Furthermore, since $c^2 = 100 - 36 = 64$, the foci are at $(0, 8)$ and $(0, -8)$ on the y-axis. See Figure 12–21.

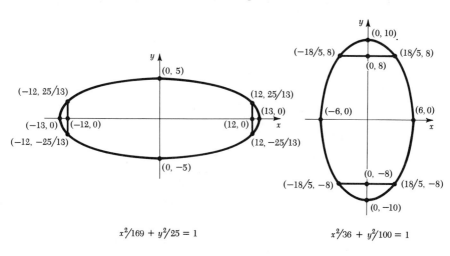

FIGURE 12–21

Consider a right circular cone as in Figure 12–22. The intersection of plane I and the cone is an ellipse, the intersection of plane II and the

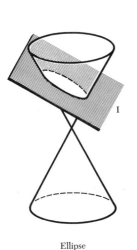
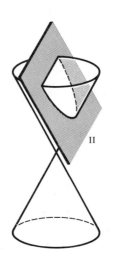
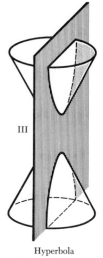

Ellipse	Parabola	Hyperbola
(Plane I intersects only one nappe)	(Plane II is parallel to line of cone through vertex)	(Plane III intersects upper and lower nappes)

FIGURE 12–22

cone is a parabola; and the intersection of plane III and the cone is a hyperbola. Let us *prove* that curve C – the intersection of plane I and the cone – has the properties of an ellipse.

Let S_1 be a sphere inscribed in the cone with plane of intersection as tangent plane. See Figure 12–23. Let F be the point of tangency

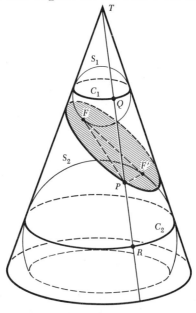

FIGURE 12–23

of the plane and the sphere. Similarly, let S_2 be the other sphere in-scribed in the cone with the given plane as tangent plane; let F' be the point of tangency of this sphere and the plane. Consider *any* point P on curve C and draw a generator (line) from T through P intersecting curves C_1 and C_2 at Q and R, respectively. Now, PF' and PR are tangent lines to sphere S_2 from the exterior point P; from solid geometry, we know that $|PF'| = |PR|$. Similarly, $|PF| = |PQ|$. Furthermore, $|PR| + |PQ| = |RQ|$. Since the length $|RQ|$ is independent of the point P chosen on C,

$$|PF'| + |PF| = |RQ| ,$$

a constant. Consequently, the curve C is an ellipse with F and F' as foci and $|RQ| = 2a$.

exercises

1. Let $a > 0$. Prove that the coordinates (x, y) satisfy the equation

$$\sqrt{(x + c)^2 + y^2} + \sqrt{(x - c)^2 + y^2} = 2a$$

if and only if they satisfy

$$(a^2 - c^2)x^2 + a^2y^2 = a^2(a^2 - c^2) .$$

In Exercises 2 through 10, graph the equation and label coordinates of the foci, vertices, endpoints of minor axis, and endpoints of latera recta.

2. $\dfrac{x^2}{25} + \dfrac{y^2}{9} = 1$

3. $\dfrac{x^2}{25} + \dfrac{y^2}{144} = 1$

4. $\dfrac{x^2}{16} + \dfrac{y^2}{9} = 1$

5. $25x^2 + 36y^2 = 100$

6. $2x^2 + y^2 = 1$

7. $4x^2 + 9y^2 = 36$

8. $x^2 + 4y^2 = 4$

9. $16x^2 + y^2 = 16$

10. $9x^2 + y^2 = 1$

11. (a) Prove that if an ellipse has center at the origin of the coordinate system and foci on the x-axis, then the ratio of the perpendicular distance of each point P on the ellipse from the line $x = a^2/c$ to the distance of P from the focus $(c, 0)$ is a constant.

(b) What is the constant ratio? Is it less than 1 or greater than 1? (The line $x = a^2/c$ is called the *directrix* of the ellipse and the constant ratio is called the *eccentricity*.)

In Exercises 12 through 19, find the equation of the ellipse determined by the given information.

12. Center at $(0, 0)$, focus at $(0, 6)$, and vertex at $(0, 8)$.

13. Center at $(0, 0)$, focus at $(4, 0)$, and vertex at $(5, 0)$.

14. Center at $(0, 0)$, endpoint of major axis at $(12, 0)$, and endpoint of minor axis at $(0, -5)$.

15. Center at $(0,0)$, focus at $(4,0)$, and directrix the line $x = 9$. (See Exercise 11.)

16. Center at $(0, 0)$, vertex at $(8, 0)$, and directrix the line $x = 12$. (See Exercise 11.)

17. Center at $(-5, 1)$, focus at $(-5 + \sqrt{5}, 1)$, and vertex at $(-2, 1)$.

    where $(h + a, k)$ and $(h - a, k)$ are the vertices.

18. Show that an ellipse with center at (h, k) has equation

$$\frac{(x - h)^2}{a^2} + \frac{(y - k)^2}{b^2} = 1 \, ,$$

    where $(h + a, k)$ and $(h - a, k)$ are the vertices.

19. Let $y = x$ be the major axis of an ellipse. Let $(3, 3)$ and $(11, 11)$ be the foci and $(2, 2)$ and $(12, 12)$ be the vertices. Find the equation of the ellipse.

12–7   hyperbola

We also define the hyperbola in terms of two fixed points in the plane and a given distance. The student should be careful to note the difference from the definition of the ellipse.

Let F and F' be two fixed points in the plane and let $2c$ be the length $|FF'|$. Assume a is a *positive* number *less than* c; that is, $0 < a < c$. The locus of points P in the plane such that the *difference* of the distances from P to the two fixed points F and F' is $2a$ is called a *hyperbola*. Algebraically, if $|PF| \geqslant |PF'|$, then $|PF| - |PF'| = 2a$; if $|PF| < |PF'|$, then $|PF'| - |PF| = 2a$, or $|PF| - |PF'| = -2a$. Thus, P is on the hyperbola if and only if

$$|PF| - |PF'| = \pm 2a \, .$$

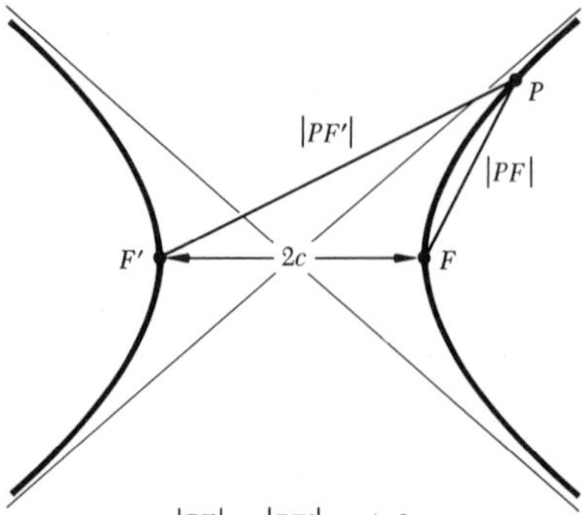

$$|PF| - |PF'| = \pm 2a$$

$$0 < a < c$$

FIGURE 12–24

If we introduce a coordinate system in the plane, as in Figure 12–24, where the x-axis coincides with the segment FF' and the origin is the midpoint of the segment, then

(1) $\sqrt{(x - c)^2 + (y - 0)^2} - \sqrt{(x + c)^2 + (y - 0)^2} = \pm 2a$.

We leave as an exercise for the reader to prove that the coordinates (x, y) satisfy this equation if and only if they satisfy the following equation:

(2) $(c^2 - a^2)x^2 - a^2y^2 = a^2(c^2 - a^2)$.

Thus, equation (2) is that of a hyperbola. Since $a < c$, $a^2 < c^2$, and $c^2 - a^2$ is positive. Hence, we can let $b^2 = c^2 - a^2$. As for the ellipse, this is done for notational convenience. The student should note that here $b^2 = c^2 - a^2$ instead of $b^2 = a^2 - c^2$ as for the ellipse; furthermore, no conclusion can be reached as to whether $a < b$, $a = b$, or $a > b$, since $b^2 = c^2 - a^2$. With the substitution $b^2 - a^2$, equation (2) can be written as follows:

$$b^2x^2 - a^2y^2 = a^2b^2 \ ,$$

or

(3) $\dfrac{x^2}{a^2} - \dfrac{y^2}{b^2} = 1$.

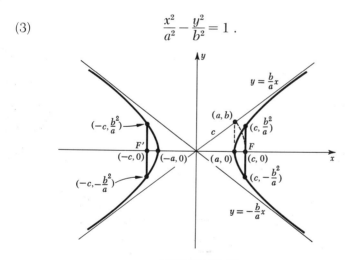

FIGURE 12–25

From equation (3), we can conclude the following about the graph of the ellipse. First, the curve is symmetric to the x-axis, the y-axis, and the origin. Second, the x-intercepts are a and $-a$ and there are no y-intercepts.

We call the fixed points F and F' the *foci* of the hyperbola; the midpoint of the line segment FF' is the *center* of the hyperbola; the points $(a, 0)$ and $(-a, 0)$ are *vertices*; the line segment joining $(a, 0)$ and $(-a, 0)$ is the *transverse axis*; and the line segment joining $(0, b)$ and $(0, -b)$ is called the *conjugate axis*. The line segment with endpoints on the hyperbola that is perpendicular to the transverse axis at a focus is called the *latus rectum*; the two such segments are called *latera recta*. Substituting c for x in equation (3) and solving for y, we find the y-coordinates of the endpoints of the latera recta are $\pm b^2/a$.

Since

$$\frac{y^2}{b^2} = \frac{x^2}{a^2} - 1 \ ,$$

then, for "large" values of x,

$$\frac{y^2}{b^2} \approx \frac{x^2}{a^2} \ .$$

Thus, $y \approx \pm(b/a)x$ and $y = (b/a)x$ and $y = -(b/a)x$ are asymptotes for hyperbola.

For the equation $x^2/169 - y^2/25 = 1$, $a = 13$, $b = 5$, and $c = \sqrt{169 + 25} = \sqrt{194}$. See Figure 12–26. Since a is the distance from the center to a vertex (the point where the curve intersects the transverse axis), in the equation $y^2/36 - x^2/64 = 1$ we have $a = 6$, $b = 8$, and $c = \sqrt{36 + 64} = 10$.

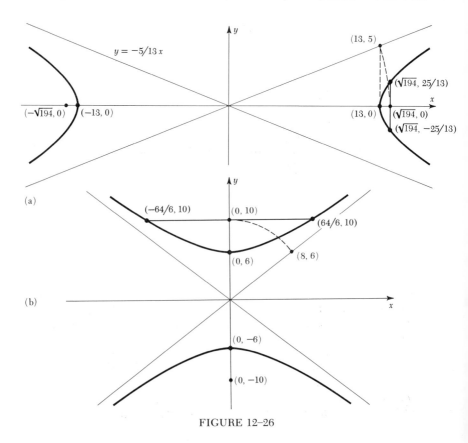

FIGURE 12–26

exercises

1. Let $a > 0$. Prove that the coordinates (x, y) satisfy the equation

$$\sqrt{(x + c)^2 + y^2} - \sqrt{(x - c)^2 + y^2} = \pm 2a$$

if and only if they satisfy

$$(c^2 - a^2)x^2 - a^2 y^2 = a^2(c^2 - a^2) .$$

*2. Prove that the definition of the hyperbola using two fixed points in the plane and a fixed distance is equivalent to the definition of the hyperbola as a section of a cone. *Hint*: See proof on page 206.

In Exercises 3 through 11, graph the equation and label coordinates of the foci, vertices, and endpoints of latera recta. Graph asymptotes and give their equations.

3. $\dfrac{x^2}{9} - \dfrac{y^2}{16} = 1$

4. $\dfrac{x^2}{144} - \dfrac{y^2}{25} = 1$

5. $\dfrac{y^2}{64} - \dfrac{x^2}{225} = 1$

6. $25x^2 - 36y^2 = 100$

7. $2x^2 - y^2 = 1$

8. $9y^2 - 4x^2 = 36$

9. $x^2 - 4y^2 = 4$

10. $16x^2 - y^2 = -16$

11. $x^2 - 9y^2 = -1$

12. (a) Prove that if a hyperbola has center at the origin of the coordinate system and foci on the x-axis, then the ratio of the distance of each point P on the hyperbola from the line $x = a^2/c$ to the distance of P from the focus $(c, 0)$ is a constant.
    (b) What is the constant ratio? Is it less than 1 or greater than 1? (The line $x = a^2/c$ is called the *directrix* of the hyperbola, and the constant ratio is called the eccentricity.)

In Exercises 13 through 18, find the equation of the hyperbola determined by the given information.

13. Center at $(0, 0)$, focus at $(8, 0)$, and vertex at $(6, 0)$.

14. Center at $(0, 0)$, focus at $(0, -10)$, and vertex at $(0, -6)$.

15. Center at $(0, 0)$, endpoint of transverse axis at $(2, 0)$, endpoint of conjugate axis at $(0, 2)$.

16. Center at $(0, 0)$, foci on x-axis, and endpoint of one latus rectum at $(\sqrt{17}, 1/4)$.

12–8   parabola

We define the parabola in terms of fixed point F and a fixed line d not containing the point. The collection of points P in the plane such that the distance from point P to point F is equal to the perpendicular distance from P to line d is called a *parabola*. The point F is called the *focus*, the line d is called the *directrix*, and the line containing F perpendicular to the directrix is called the *axis* of the parabola. The midpoint between F and the point where the axis and directrix intersect is on the parabola; it is called the *vertex*. The line segment perpendicular to the axis through the focus with its intersection points with the curve as endpoints is called the *latus rectum*.

We let $2p$ be the perpendicular distance from the focus to the directrix. If we introduce a coordinate system in the plane, as in Figure 12–28, where the x-axis coincides with the axis of the parabola and the origin coincides with the vertex, then

(1)
$$x + p = \sqrt{(x - p)^2 + (y - 0)^2} \qquad (x \geq 0, \, p > 0).$$

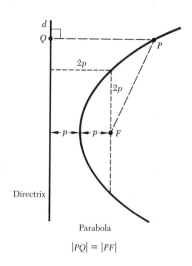

FIGURE 12–27

We leave as an exercise for the reader the proof that the coordinates (x, y) satisfy this equation if and only if they satisfy

(2) $y^2 = 4px$.

From equation (2), we can conclude the following about the graph of the parabola. First, the curve is symmetric to the x-axis. Second, the curve contains the origin, and since $x \geq 0$, the rest of the graph is in the first and fourth quadrants. Since $y = \pm 2p$ when $x = p$, $(p, 2p)$ and $(p, -2p)$ are the endpoints of the latus rectum. In Figure 12–28, we indicate the equations of parabolas with different orientations in the coordinate system. We leave as an exercise for the reader the verification of the equations given there.

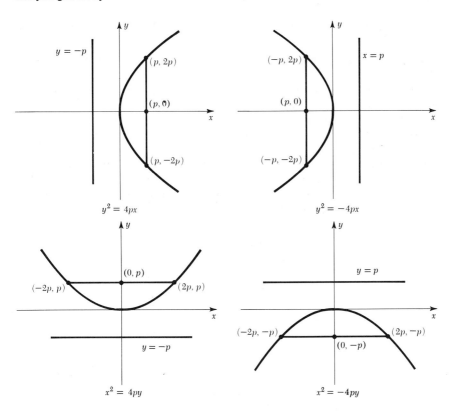

FIGURE 12–28

exercises

1. Prove that equations (1) and (2) for the parabola are equivalent equations.

*2. Prove that the definition of the parabola using a fixed point and a fixed line is equivalent to the definition of the parabola as a section of a cone. *Hint:* The directrix is the line of intersection of the plane of the parabola and the plane of the circle where the tangent sphere intersects the cone.

In Exercises 3 through 11, graph the equation and label the coordinates of the focus and endpoints of latus rectum.

3. $y^2 = 8x$ 4. $y^2 = -16x$ 5. $y^2 = -32x$

6. $y^2 = 4x$ 7. $y^2 = x$ 8. $x^2 = -8y$

9. $x^2 = 20y$ 10. $x^2 = 25y$ 11. $x^2 = -36y$

12. Find the equation of the parabola with $(2, 3)$ as focus and $x = 12$ as directrix.

13. Find the equation of the parabola with $(-3, 4)$ as focus and $x = -7$ as directrix.

14. Find the equation of the parabola with $(2, 4)$ as focus and $y = 8$ as directrix.

15. Find the equation of the parabola with $(5, 8)$ as focus and $y = 2$ as directrix.

*16. Find the equation of the parabola with $(4, 4)$ as focus and the line $y = -x$ as directrix.

12–9   three-dimensional cartesian coordinate system

A variety of different coordinate systems can be introduced for three-dimensional space. The one we shall discuss is called the Cartesian coordinate system for three-space. Essentially, we consider any plane in three dimensions and construct the familiar *xy* rectangular coordinate system in this plane. A number line is then constructed perpendicular to this plane through the origin of the *xy* coordinate system; this line is called the *z-axis*. One of the rays from the origin is the positive *z*-axis and the other is the negative *z*-axis. Points in three-space are assigned coordinates relative to these three coordinate axes in much the same way as coordinates were assigned to points in two dimensions.

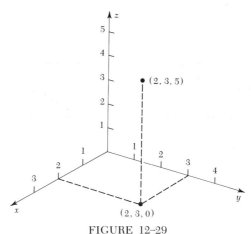

FIGURE 12–29

If (2,3) is a point in the *xy*-plane, then the ordered triple of numbers (2,3,0) is assigned to the point and is called the three-dimensional coordinates of the point. If the positive *z*-axis is up, (2,3,5) represents a point five units above the point (2,3,0). The point (2,3,−7) is the point seven units below the point (2,3,0). An ordered triple (x,y,z) of real numbers is the coordinates of a point in three-space; conversely, any point in three-space has an ordered triple (x,y,z) as its coordinates. The first number in the ordered triple is called the *x*-coordinate; the second number is called the *y*-coordinate; and the third number is called the *z*-coordinate.

If when we look "down" from the side of the *xy*-plane with the positive *z*-axis we see the positive *y*-axis is 90° counterclockwise from the positive *x*-axis, the system is called a *right-hand* coordinate system. If when we look "down" from the side of the *xy*-plane with positive *z*-axis we see the positive *x*-axis is 90° counterclockwise from the positive *y*-axis, then this is called a *left-hand* coordinate system. We shall restrict our study to the right-hand rectangular coordinate system.

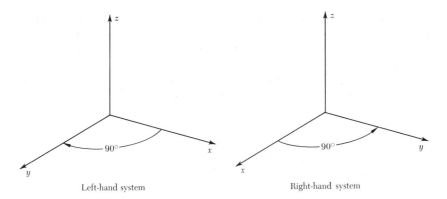

Left-hand system   Right-hand system

FIGURE 12-30

The three-dimensional rectangular coordinate system divides space into eight equal parts called *octants*. The collection of points where x, y, and z are all positive is often referred to as the first octant. The other octants are usually not named.

If $P(x_1,y_1,z_1)$ and $Q(x_2,y_2,z_2)$ are two points in three-space, the orthogonal projections of the two points on the xy-plane are $R(x_1,y_1,0)$ and $S(x_2,y_2,0)$, respectively. (See Figure 12-31.) We have

$$|RS| = \sqrt{(x_2-x_1)^2+(y_2-y_1)^2}$$

from the formula for the distance between two points in two dimensions. In the rectangle $RPTS$, $|PT|=|RS|$ and T has coordinates

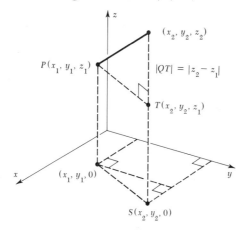

FIGURE 12-31

(x_2,y_2,z_1). Furthermore, $|TQ|=|z_2-z_1|$ and by the Pythagorean Theorem,

$$|PQ| = \sqrt{|PT|^2+|QT|^2}$$
$$= \sqrt{(x_2-x_1)^2+(y_2-y_1)^2+(z_2-z_1)^2}.$$

We recognize the similarity between the formulas for finding the distance between two points in two dimensions and three dimensions. If $P(x_1,y_1,z_1)$ and $Q(x_2,y_2,z_2)$ are two points in three dimensions, then the coordinates of the midpoint of the line segment joining P and Q are found in a fashion similar to that for two dimensions. We leave as an exercise for the student to prove that the midpoint is

$$\left(\frac{x_1+x_2}{2}, \frac{y_1+y_2}{2}, \frac{z_1+z_2}{2}\right).$$

It can be proved that every linear equation $ax+by+cz=d$ represents a plane in three dimensions. We shall not give a proof of this fact; instead, we focus our attention on techniques of graphing planes given by linear equations. The student will find that an ability to construct three-dimensional graphs is quite valuable in the study of several topics in calculus.

If $2x+3y+6z=18$ is the equation of a plane, then $(9,0,0)$ is a point in the plane since the coordinates of the point satisfy the equation. Since $(9,0,0)$ is on the x-axis, it is the point of intersection of the plane and the x-axis; it is called the x-intercept of the plane. Similarly, $(0,6,0)$ is the y-intercept and $(0,0,3)$ is the z-intercept. (See Figure 12–32.)

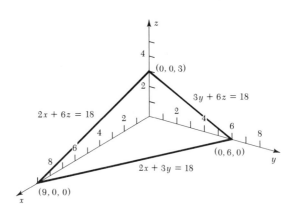

FIGURE 12–32

Since $z=0$ for every point in the xy-plane, $2x+3y=18$ is the equation of the line of intersection of the plane $2x+3y+6z=18$ and the xy-plane. This line of intersection is called the *trace* of $2x+3y+6z=18$ in the xy-plane. Similarly, the line $2x+6z=18$ is the trace of $2x+3y+6z=18$ in the xz-plane and $3y+6z=18$ is the trace of the given plane in the yz-plane.

Consider the plane whose equation is $x-2y-z=0$. This plane contains the origin $(0,0,0)$ of the coordinate system. The trace in the xy-plane of $x-2y-z=0$ is $x=2y$ and the trace in the xz-plane is $x=z$. (See Figure 12–33.) To find the intersection point of the

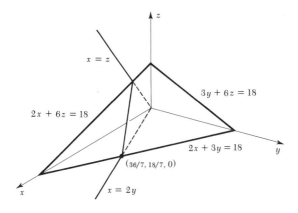

Intersection of $x - 2y - z = 0$ and $2x + 3y + 6z = 18$

FIGURE 12-33

traces of $x-2y-z=0$ and $2x+3y+6z=18$ in the xy-plane, we solve the following system of equations.

$$\begin{cases} 2x+3y=18 & (1) \\ x=2y & (2) \end{cases}$$

Substituting (2) in (1), $4y+3y=18$. Thus, $y=18/7$ and $x=36/7$.

Since two points determine a line, we can determine the line of intersection of the two given planes by finding the intersection of the traces of the planes in the xz-plane and then joining this point and the point $(36/7,18/7,0)$. (See Figure 12-33.)

In two dimensions, two distinct points determine a line. In three dimensions, three distinct non-collinear points determine a plane. Let us consider one method for finding the equation of the plane containing the three non-collinear points $(2,1,1)$, $(3,5,6)$, and $(1,-5,-4)$. Since $ax+by+cz=d$ is the equation of a plane, each point must satisfy the equation. Thus, we need to determine a, b, c, and d such that

$$\begin{cases} 2a+b+c=d & (1) \\ 3a+5b+6c=d & (2) \\ a-5b-4c=d & (3) \end{cases}$$

By subtracting five times equation (1) from equation (2) and by adding equation (2) to equation (3), we get

$$\begin{cases} -7a+c=-4d & (4) \\ 4a+2c=2d. & (5) \end{cases}$$

Dividing equation (5) by two, we have

$$\begin{cases} -7a+c=-4d & (6) \\ 2a+c=d. & (7) \end{cases}$$

Subtracting (6) from (7), we obtain

$$9a = 5d$$

or

$$a = \frac{5}{9} d. \qquad (8)$$

Substituting (8) in (7), we get

$$\frac{10}{9} d + c = d,$$

or

$$c = -\frac{d}{9}. \qquad (9)$$

Finally, substituting (8) and (9) in (1), we get

$$\frac{10}{9} d + b - \frac{d}{9} = d$$

or

$$b = 0.$$

Consequently, $a = 5d/9$, $b = 0$, and $c = -d/9$. Since the three points are non-collinear, a fact that can be proved by the distance formula, not all a, b, and c are zero; thus $d \neq 0$. If $d \neq 0$, we can let d be any real number other than zero. For convenience, let $d = 9$. Consequently,

$$a = 5, \quad b = 0, \quad \text{and} \quad c = -1.$$

Therefore, $5x - z = 9$ is the equation of the plane containing $(2,1,1)$, $(3,5,6)$, and $(1,-5,-4)$. Notice that this plane does not intersect the y-axis.

exercises

In Exercises 1 through 4, find the distance between the given points.

1. $(2,3,4)$ and $(-5,-3,2)$

2. $(1,1,1)$ and $(2,3,3)$

3. $(-3,-2,5)$ and $(1/2,2/3,7)$

4. $(0,0,3)$ and $(3,5,-11)$

5. Let $P(x_1,y_1,z_1)$ and $Q(x_2,y_2,z_2)$ be two points in three-space. Give a geometric proof that the coordinates of the midpoint of the line segment joining the two points are

$$\left(\frac{x_1 + x_2}{2}, \; \frac{y_1 + y_2}{2}, \; \frac{z_1 + z_2}{2} \right).$$

6. Find the coordinates of the midpoints of the line segments obtained by joining the points given in Exercises 1 through 4.

7. Show that $(5,7,13)$, $(-1,6,8)$, and $(3,8,7)$ are vertices of a right triangle.

8. Show that $(-1,0,-2)$, $(2,5,6)$, and $(7,-3,3)$ are the vertices of a right triangle.

9. Let $P(2,3,6)$ and $Q(6,8,4)$ be two points and let $S = \{(x,y,z)$ is equidistant from P and $Q\}$.
   (a) Give a geometric description of S and find its equation.
   (b) Find the coordinates of the midpoint of the segment joining P and Q.
   (c) Should the coordinates of the midpoint satisfy the equation found in (a)?

10. Let $2x + 6y - 3z = 12$ be the equation of a plane.
   (a) What are the x-intercept, y-intercept, and z-intercept?
   (b) What is an equation of the trace of the plane in the xz-plane?

11. Find an equation of the plane containing the points $(3,-1,2)$, $(7,-2,5)$, and $(8,-9,2)$. First prove they are not collinear points.

12. Find an equation of the plane containing the points $(1/2, 2/3, 5)$, $(0,0,2)$, and $(1,-2,5)$. First prove they are not collinear points.

13. Let $(2,3,5)$ and $(-1,2,4)$ be two points in three-space. Find the coordinates of any points on the line containing the two points that is not between the given points.

linear equations and determinants

13

13-1   determinants of order two

In this chapter we will develop some of the theory and techniques needed to solve systems of linear equations. In doing this we shall meet the useful notion of a *determinant* and study some of the elementary properties of determinants. We begin by recalling the familiar problem of solving two linear equations in two unknowns. We wish to find numbers x, y such that

(1)
$$ax + by = h$$
$$cx + dy = k$$

given the coefficients a, b, c, and d and the numbers h, k. For the moment we will assume that there are numbers x, y which satisfy both equations; we will solve the equations in the usual way. Multiply both sides of the first equation by d, both sides of the second equation by $-b$, and add corresponding sides. We get

(2)
$$(ad - bc)x = hd - bk.$$

In the same way, if we multiply both sides of the first equation by $-c$, both sides of the second equation by a, and add, we get

(3) $(ad-bc)y = ak-hc.$

Hence, if the coefficients a, b, c, and d are such that $ad-bc$ is not zero, then

(4) $x = \dfrac{hd-bk}{ad-bc}, \qquad y = \dfrac{ak-hc}{ad-bc}$

is the solution of the two equations (1). Of course, we began by assuming that the equations had a solution, but it is a matter of elementary algebra to verify that the values of x and y given by (4) satisfy the original equations.

If $ad-bc = 0$, we cannot solve for x and y as in (4). We see from equations (2) and (3) that, in this case, if the equations (1) have a solution, then necessarily $hd-bk$ and $ak-hc$ are both zero.

Since the number $ad-bc$ plays an important part in the problem of solving the linear equations (1), let us denote it by

$$\begin{vmatrix} a & b \\ c & d \end{vmatrix}$$

to indicate that it is associated with the coefficients in the two linear equations. In fact, it will be convenient at this point to give a name to arrays of numbers such as the square array of coefficients in the equations. We will call a 2×2 square array of numbers a *square matrix of order two*, or a 2×2 *matrix*, and enclose the array in square brackets

$$\begin{bmatrix} a & b \\ c & d \end{bmatrix}$$

to show that we are considering it as a single entity. This particular matrix is called the *matrix of coefficients* in the system of linear equations (1), and the number $ad-bc$ will be called the *determinant* of the matrix. Note that the determinant of a 2×2 matrix is computed as the product of the numbers in the main diagonal (that is, from upper-left to lower-right) minus the product of the numbers in the cross-diagonal. The numbers occurring in a matrix are called its *entries* and we refer to them by the horizontal row and vertical column positions they occupy. For example, in the matrix above, we say that b is the entry in the first row, second column.

Since $hd-bk$ is the determinant of the matrix

$$\begin{bmatrix} h & b \\ k & d \end{bmatrix}$$

and $ak-hc$ is the determinant of the matrix

$$\begin{bmatrix} a & h \\ c & k \end{bmatrix},$$

the solution we described earlier for the equations $ax + by = h$ and $cx + dy = k$ in the case where

$$\begin{vmatrix} a & b \\ c & d \end{vmatrix} \neq 0,$$

may be written as

$$x = \frac{\begin{vmatrix} h & b \\ k & d \end{vmatrix}}{\begin{vmatrix} a & b \\ c & d \end{vmatrix}}, \qquad y = \frac{\begin{vmatrix} a & h \\ c & k \end{vmatrix}}{\begin{vmatrix} a & b \\ c & d \end{vmatrix}}.$$

This is known as *Cramer's Rule* for the solution of the equations. Note that the numerators are determinants obtained from the determinant of coefficients by replacing the entries in the first and second columns respectively, by h and k, the right-hand members of the equations. As an example of these ideas consider the system of linear equations

$$3x - 2y = 1$$
$$2x + 7y = 4.$$

The matrix of coefficients is

$$\begin{bmatrix} 3 & -2 \\ 2 & 7 \end{bmatrix}.$$

The determinant of this matrix is

$$\begin{vmatrix} 3 & -2 \\ 2 & 7 \end{vmatrix} = 3 \cdot 7 - (-2) \cdot 2 = 25.$$

Since the determinant of the matrix of coefficients is not zero, we may apply Cramer's Rule to obtain the solution. We get

$$x = \frac{\begin{vmatrix} 1 & -2 \\ 4 & 7 \end{vmatrix}}{\begin{vmatrix} 3 & -2 \\ 2 & 7 \end{vmatrix}}, \qquad y = \frac{\begin{vmatrix} 3 & 1 \\ 2 & 4 \end{vmatrix}}{\begin{vmatrix} 3 & -2 \\ 2 & 7 \end{vmatrix}};$$

or

$$x = \frac{15}{25} = \frac{3}{5}, \qquad y = \frac{10}{25} = \frac{2}{5}.$$

We will often denote a matrix by a single capital letter. For example, we may let **A** denote the matrix

$$\begin{bmatrix} a & b \\ c & d \end{bmatrix}.$$

If we do this, then we denote the determinant of $\mathbf{A}$ by $|\mathbf{A}|$. That is, if

$$\mathbf{A} = \begin{bmatrix} a & b \\ c & d \end{bmatrix},$$

then

$$|\mathbf{A}| = \begin{vmatrix} a & b \\ c & d \end{vmatrix} = ad - bc.$$

The main properties of 2×2 determinants may all be verified by straightforward calculation, and we leave most of the proofs of the following properties to the student as exercises. In all that follows, $\mathbf{A}$ is a 2×2 matrix

$$\begin{bmatrix} a & b \\ c & d \end{bmatrix}$$

and $|\mathbf{A}|$ is its determinant.

(i)   If $\mathbf{A}$ has a row or column of zeros, then $|\mathbf{A}| = 0$. For example,

$$\begin{vmatrix} a & b \\ 0 & 0 \end{vmatrix} = a(0) - b(0) = 0.$$

(ii)   If two rows of $\mathbf{A}$ are identical (or two columns are identical), then $|\mathbf{A}| = 0$. For example,

$$\begin{vmatrix} a & a \\ c & c \end{vmatrix} = ac - ac = 0.$$

(iii)   If one row of $\mathbf{A}$ is a multiple of the other row (or one column a multiple of the other column), then $|\mathbf{A}| = 0$. For example,

$$\begin{vmatrix} a & b \\ ka & kb \end{vmatrix} = a(kb) - b(ka) = 0.$$

(iv)   If a matrix $\mathbf{B}$ is obtained from $\mathbf{A}$ by multiplying the entries in one row (or one column) of $\mathbf{A}$ by a real number k, then $|\mathbf{B}| = k|\mathbf{A}|$. For example,

$$\begin{vmatrix} ka & b \\ kc & d \end{vmatrix} = kad - bkc = k(ad - bc) = k \begin{vmatrix} a & b \\ c & d \end{vmatrix}.$$

(v)   If a matrix $\mathbf{B}$ is obtained from $\mathbf{A}$ by interchanging the two rows (or interchanging the columns), then $|\mathbf{B}| = -|\mathbf{A}|$. For example, if we interchange the rows,

$$\mathbf{B} = \begin{bmatrix} c & d \\ a & b \end{bmatrix}$$

and

$$|\mathbf{B}| = cb - da = -|\mathbf{A}|.$$

(vi)   If a matrix $\mathbf{B}$ is obtained from $\mathbf{A}$ by adding a multiple of one row to the other row (or adding a multiple of one column to the other column), then $|\mathbf{B}| = |\mathbf{A}|$. For example, if we obtain $\mathbf{B}$ by adding k

times the entries in the first column of $\mathbf{A}$ to the corresponding entries in the second column, then

$$\mathbf{B} = \begin{bmatrix} a & b+ka \\ c & d+kc \end{bmatrix}$$

and

$$|\mathbf{B}| = a(d+kc) - (b+ka)c = ad - bc = |\mathbf{A}|.$$

(vii)

$$\begin{vmatrix} a_1+a_2 & b \\ c_1+c_2 & d \end{vmatrix} = \begin{vmatrix} a_1 & b \\ c_1 & d \end{vmatrix} + \begin{vmatrix} a_2 & b \\ c_2 & d \end{vmatrix}$$

Similar results hold if the entries in the second column or in either row are written as sums.

By the *transpose* of a 2×2 matrix

$$\mathbf{A} = \begin{bmatrix} a & b \\ c & d \end{bmatrix},$$

we mean the matrix

$$\begin{bmatrix} a & c \\ b & d \end{bmatrix}$$

obtained by interchanging rows and columns of $\mathbf{A}$ so that the rows of $\mathbf{A}$ are the columns of its transpose. The following property is easily verified.

(viii) The determinant of the transpose of a matrix is equal to the determinant of the original matrix.

These properties may be used to simplify the computation of a determinant. For example,

$$\begin{vmatrix} 36 & 48 \\ 46 & 61 \end{vmatrix} = 12 \begin{vmatrix} 3 & 4 \\ 46 & 61 \end{vmatrix} \qquad \text{[property (iv)]}$$

$$= 12 \begin{vmatrix} 3 & 4 \\ 1 & 1 \end{vmatrix} \qquad \text{[by property (vi); subtracting 15 times row 1 from row 2]}$$

$$= 12(3-4) = -12.$$

Also,

$$\begin{vmatrix} a+b+d & b+d \\ a+c+d & c+d \end{vmatrix} = \begin{vmatrix} a & b+d \\ a & c+d \end{vmatrix} \qquad \text{[by property (vi); subtracting col. 2 from col. 1]}$$

$$= a \begin{vmatrix} 1 & b+d \\ 1 & c+d \end{vmatrix} \qquad \text{[by property (iv)]}$$

$$= a\{(c+d) - (b+d)\} = a(c-b).$$

exercises

1. Compute the following determinants.

$$\begin{vmatrix} 1 & 0 \\ 0 & 1 \end{vmatrix}, \quad \begin{vmatrix} 0 & -1 \\ 1 & 0 \end{vmatrix}, \quad \begin{vmatrix} a & -b \\ b & a \end{vmatrix}, \quad \begin{vmatrix} 3-x & -1 \\ 5 & 2-x \end{vmatrix}$$

2. Compute the determinants of the following matrices.

$$\begin{bmatrix} x+y & -x+y \\ x-y & -x-y \end{bmatrix}, \quad \begin{bmatrix} a+bi & -c+di \\ c+di & a-bi \end{bmatrix} \quad \text{(where } i^2 = -1)$$

3. Use Cramer's Rule, if applicable, to solve the following pairs of linear equations.
   (a) $2x - 11y = 5$
   $\quad 4x + 7y = 2$
   (b) $3x + 9y = 2$
   $\quad x + 3y = 0$
   (c) $4x + 3y = 0$
   $\quad 3x - 2y = 0$
   (d) $\quad 97x + 37y = 18$
   $\quad -46x + 21y = 31$

4. Prove the basic properties of determinants listed at the end of this section.

5. Use the given properties of determinants to simplify the computation of

$$\begin{vmatrix} 1001 & 99 \\ 999 & 101 \end{vmatrix}, \quad \begin{vmatrix} a+b+c & b+c+d \\ a+c+d & c+2d \end{vmatrix}.$$

6. Prove that two distinct points (x_1, y_1), (x_2, y_2) are collinear with the origin if and only if

$$\begin{vmatrix} x_1 & y_1 \\ x_2 & y_2 \end{vmatrix} = 0.$$

7. Find an expression in determinant form for the area of the parallelogram having $(0,0)$, (x_1, y_1), (x_2, y_2), and $(x_1 + x_2, y_1 + y_2)$ as vertices.

8. Prove that

$$\begin{vmatrix} a_1 + a_2 & b_1 + b_2 \\ c_1 + c_2 & d_1 + d_2 \end{vmatrix}$$

is equal to the sum of four determinants, each of the form

$$\begin{vmatrix} a_i & b_j \\ c_i & d_j \end{vmatrix}$$

where $i, j = 1, 2$.

9. Prove that the linear equations

$$ax + by = 0$$
$$cx + dy = 0$$

have a nonzero solution—that is, one other than $x = 0$, $y = 0$—if and only if

$$\begin{vmatrix} a & b \\ c & d \end{vmatrix} = 0.$$

Give a nonzero solution in this case.

10. Prove that if

$$\begin{vmatrix} a & b \\ c & d \end{vmatrix} = 0,$$

then the equations

$$ax + by = h$$
$$cx + dy = k$$

have a solution if and only if

$$\begin{vmatrix} h & b \\ k & d \end{vmatrix} = \begin{vmatrix} a & h \\ c & k \end{vmatrix} = 0.$$

Give a solution in this case.

11. Verify that the linear equations in p, q, and r

$$b_1 p + b_2 q + b_3 r = 0$$
$$c_1 p + c_2 q + c_3 r = 0$$

have

$$p = \begin{vmatrix} b_2 & c_2 \\ b_3 & c_3 \end{vmatrix}, \qquad q = -\begin{vmatrix} b_1 & c_1 \\ b_3 & c_3 \end{vmatrix}, \qquad r = \begin{vmatrix} b_1 & c_1 \\ b_2 & c_2 \end{vmatrix}$$

as a solution.

13–2   determinants of order three

We have defined determinants of order two and described their connection with systems of two linear equations in two unknowns. Now we extend these ideas to third-order determinants. First, we define the determinant of a 3×3 matrix and then show how the idea arises in solving a system of three linear equations in three unknowns.

By a 3×3 *matrix* (or a *square matrix of order three*), we mean an array of nine numbers, arranged in three rows and three columns

$$M = \begin{bmatrix} a_1 & b_1 & c_1 \\ a_2 & b_2 & c_2 \\ a_3 & b_3 & c_3 \end{bmatrix}.$$

As usual, we enclose the array in square brackets and we use capitals to denote matrices. We define the determinant of $\mathbf{M}$, denoted by $|\mathbf{M}|$, to be the number

$$(1) \qquad \begin{vmatrix} a_1 & b_1 & c_1 \\ a_2 & b_2 & c_2 \\ a_3 & b_3 & c_3 \end{vmatrix} = a_1 \begin{vmatrix} b_2 & c_2 \\ b_3 & c_3 \end{vmatrix} - a_2 \begin{vmatrix} b_1 & c_1 \\ b_3 & c_3 \end{vmatrix} + a_3 \begin{vmatrix} b_1 & c_1 \\ b_2 & c_2 \end{vmatrix}$$

Written out in full, the right-hand side is

$$a_1(b_2c_3 - c_2b_3) - a_2(b_1c_3 - c_1b_3) + a_3(b_1c_2 - c_1b_2),$$

and hence,

(2) $|\mathbf{M}| = a_1b_2c_3 + a_2b_3c_1 + a_3b_1c_2 - a_1b_3c_2 - a_2b_1c_3 - a_3b_2c_1$

This explicit expression (2) for the determinant of $\mathbf{M}$ may also be taken as the definition of $|\mathbf{M}|$ rather than the form we have given in (1).

We will call the 2×2 matrix obtained from $\mathbf{M}$ by omitting the row and column containing a particular entry the *minor* of that entry and denote it by the corresponding capital. Thus, in $\mathbf{M}$ above,

$$\mathbf{A}_1 = \begin{bmatrix} b_2 & c_2 \\ b_3 & c_3 \end{bmatrix}, \qquad \mathbf{A}_2 = \begin{bmatrix} b_1 & c_1 \\ b_3 & c_3 \end{bmatrix}, \qquad \cdots, \qquad \mathbf{C}_3 = \begin{bmatrix} a_1 & b_1 \\ a_2 & b_2 \end{bmatrix}.$$

One definition (1) may now be written in the compact form

$$|\mathbf{M}| = a_1|\mathbf{A}_1| - a_2|\mathbf{A}_2| + a_3|\mathbf{A}_3|.$$

As an example of these ideas, let $\mathbf{M}$ be given by

$$\mathbf{M} = \begin{bmatrix} 3 & 1 & -1 \\ 2 & 0 & 4 \\ -1 & 1 & 2 \end{bmatrix}.$$

The minor of the entry in the second row, first column is

$$\mathbf{A}_{21} = \begin{bmatrix} 1 & -1 \\ 1 & 2 \end{bmatrix}$$

and the minor of the entry in the third row, third column is

$$\mathbf{A}_{33} = \begin{bmatrix} 3 & 1 \\ 2 & 0 \end{bmatrix}.$$

Our definition for $|\mathbf{M}|$ gives

$$\begin{vmatrix} 3 & 1 & -1 \\ 2 & 0 & 4 \\ -1 & 1 & 2 \end{vmatrix} = 3 \begin{vmatrix} 0 & 4 \\ 1 & 2 \end{vmatrix} - 2 \begin{vmatrix} 1 & -1 \\ 1 & 2 \end{vmatrix} + (-1) \begin{vmatrix} 1 & -1 \\ 0 & 4 \end{vmatrix}$$

$$= 3(-4) - 2(3) + (-1)(4) = -22.$$

The notion of a determinant arises naturally in the study of the following system of linear equations having $\mathbf{M}$ as *matrix of coefficients*.

(3)
$$\begin{aligned} a_1x + b_1y + c_1z &= d_1 \\ a_2x + b_2y + c_2z &= d_2 \\ a_3x + b_3y + c_3z &= d_3 \end{aligned}$$

To solve for x, we wish to find numbers p, q, and r, say, such that if we multiply both sides of the first equation by p, both sides of the second by q, both sides of the third by r, and add, then the resulting sums on the left contain no y or z terms. To find such numbers p, q, and r we may use the result given in Exercise 11 at the end of the preceding section. The numbers

$$(4) \quad p=\begin{vmatrix} b_2 & c_2 \\ b_3 & c_3 \end{vmatrix}, \quad q=-\begin{vmatrix} b_1 & c_1 \\ b_3 & c_3 \end{vmatrix}, \quad \text{and} \quad r=\begin{vmatrix} b_1 & c_1 \\ b_2 & c_2 \end{vmatrix}$$

satisfy the equations

$$b_1p+b_2q+b_3r=0$$
$$c_1p+c_2q+c_3r=0.$$

Using these values given in (4) for p, q, and r, we now solve the system of linear equations (3) by multiplying the first by p, the second by q, the third by r, and adding. We get

$$\left\{ a_1\begin{vmatrix} b_2 & c_2 \\ b_3 & c_3 \end{vmatrix} - a_2\begin{vmatrix} b_1 & c_1 \\ b_3 & c_3 \end{vmatrix} + a_3\begin{vmatrix} b_1 & c_1 \\ b_2 & c_2 \end{vmatrix} \right\} \cdot x$$

$$= d_1\begin{vmatrix} b_2 & c_2 \\ b_3 & c_3 \end{vmatrix} - d_2\begin{vmatrix} b_1 & c_1 \\ b_3 & c_3 \end{vmatrix} + d_3\begin{vmatrix} b_1 & c_1 \\ b_2 & c_2 \end{vmatrix}.$$

In terms of our *minor* notation, this may be written as

$$(5) \quad (a_1|\mathbf{A}| - a_2|\mathbf{A}_2| + a_3|\mathbf{A}_3|)x = d_1|\mathbf{A}_1| - d_2|\mathbf{A}_2| + d_3|\mathbf{A}_3|$$

The coefficient of x in (5) is the number we have called the determinant of the matrix of coefficients, M, in the original system of linear equations. Similarly, the right-hand side of (5) is the determinant of the matrix we obtained from $\mathbf{M}$ by replacing the entries in the first column by d_1, d_2, and d_3 respectively.

Although we wish merely to illustrate here that determinants arise naturally in the study of linear equations, it is appropriate to include at this point *Cramer's Rule* for the solution of a system of three linear equations in three unknowns.

$$a_1x+b_1y+c_1z=d_1$$
$$a_2x+b_2y+c_2z=d_2$$
$$a_3x+b_3y+c_3z=d_3$$

If the determinant of the matrix of coefficients is not zero, then these equations have a unique solution given by

$$x=\frac{\begin{vmatrix} d_1 & b_1 & c_1 \\ d_2 & b_2 & c_2 \\ d_3 & b_3 & c_3 \end{vmatrix}}{\begin{vmatrix} a_1 & b_1 & c_1 \\ a_2 & b_2 & c_2 \\ a_3 & b_3 & c_3 \end{vmatrix}}, \quad y=\frac{\begin{vmatrix} a_1 & d_1 & c_1 \\ a_2 & d_2 & c_2 \\ a_3 & d_3 & c_3 \end{vmatrix}}{\begin{vmatrix} a_1 & b_1 & c_1 \\ a_2 & b_2 & c_2 \\ a_3 & b_3 & c_3 \end{vmatrix}}, \quad z=\frac{\begin{vmatrix} a_1 & b_1 & d_1 \\ a_2 & b_2 & d_2 \\ a_3 & b_3 & d_3 \end{vmatrix}}{\begin{vmatrix} a_1 & b_1 & c_1 \\ a_2 & b_2 & c_2 \\ a_3 & b_3 & c_3 \end{vmatrix}}.$$

Note that the numerators are obtained from the determinant of coefficients by replacing the first, second, and third columns respectively by d_1, d_2, d_3, the column of numbers on the right-hand sides of the equations. We will return to the proof of this result after we have discussed some properties of 3×3 determinants.

As an example of the use of Cramer's Rule, consider the equations

$$\begin{aligned} 2x - y + z &= 4 \\ x + 2y - 3z &= 1 \\ 2x + 3y - 5z &= -2. \end{aligned}$$

The determinant of the matrix of coefficients is:

$$\begin{vmatrix} 2 & -1 & 1 \\ 1 & 2 & -3 \\ 2 & 3 & -5 \end{vmatrix} = 2 \begin{vmatrix} 2 & -3 \\ 3 & -5 \end{vmatrix} - 1 \begin{vmatrix} -1 & 1 \\ 3 & -5 \end{vmatrix} + 2 \begin{vmatrix} -1 & 1 \\ 2 & -3 \end{vmatrix}$$

$$= -2 - 2 + 2 = -2.$$

Since this is not zero, we may apply Cramer's Rule to obtain the solution. We get

$$x = \frac{\begin{vmatrix} 4 & -1 & 1 \\ 1 & 2 & -3 \\ -2 & 3 & -5 \end{vmatrix}}{\begin{vmatrix} 2 & -1 & 1 \\ 1 & 2 & -3 \\ 2 & 3 & -5 \end{vmatrix}}, \quad y = \frac{\begin{vmatrix} 2 & 4 & 1 \\ 1 & 1 & -3 \\ 2 & -2 & -5 \end{vmatrix}}{\begin{vmatrix} 2 & -1 & 1 \\ 1 & 2 & -3 \\ 2 & 3 & -5 \end{vmatrix}}, \quad z = \frac{\begin{vmatrix} 2 & -1 & 4 \\ 1 & 2 & 1 \\ 2 & 3 & -2 \end{vmatrix}}{\begin{vmatrix} 2 & -1 & 1 \\ 1 & 2 & -3 \\ 2 & 3 & -5 \end{vmatrix}}$$

or

$$x = -8/2 = 4, \quad y = -30/-2 = 15, \quad z = -22/-2 = 11.$$

It is perhaps worth remarking that although Cramer's Rule gives an explicit solution of the system of equations, it is usually not the most efficient computational method for solving systems of linear equations with numerical coefficients.

We noted earlier that

$$\begin{vmatrix} a_1 & b_1 & c_1 \\ a_2 & b_2 & c_2 \\ a_3 & b_3 & c_3 \end{vmatrix} = a_1 b_2 c_3 + a_2 b_3 c_1 + a_3 b_1 c_2 - a_1 b_3 c_2 - a_2 b_1 c_3 - a_3 b_2 c_1.$$

This expression contains six terms and each term is the product of three entries—one from each of columns 1, 2, 3, with no two from the same row. That is, each term is of the form $\pm a_i b_j c_k$ where i, j, and k are 1, 2, and 3 in some order. The simplest way to remember and compute this expression for a 3×3 determinant is to write down the determinant and then repeat the first two columns

The triple products going down from left to right are the positive terms. The triple products going down from right to left are the negative terms. For example, to compute

$$\begin{vmatrix} 1 & 2 & 3 \\ -4 & 1 & 5 \\ 2 & 1 & 4 \end{vmatrix}, \quad \text{we write} \quad -4 \overset{1}{\underset{2}{\diagdown}} \overset{2}{\underset{1}{\diagdown}} \overset{3}{\underset{4}{\diagdown}} \overset{1}{\underset{2}{\diagdown}} \overset{2}{\underset{1}{\diagdown}} \cdot$$

Hence, the determinant is

$$1 \cdot 1 \cdot 4 + 2 \cdot 5 \cdot 2 + 3(-4) \cdot 1 - 3 \cdot 1 \cdot 2 - 1 \cdot 5 \cdot 1 - 2(-4) \cdot 4$$
$$= 4 + 20 - 12 - 6 - 5 + 32$$
$$= 33.$$

exercises

1. Use the definition of a 3×3 determinant in terms of 2×2 determinants to compute the following.

$$\begin{vmatrix} 1 & 0 & 0 \\ 0 & 1 & 0 \\ 0 & 0 & 1 \end{vmatrix}, \quad \begin{vmatrix} 3 & 5 & -9 \\ 1 & 1 & 0 \\ 8 & 0 & 1 \end{vmatrix}, \quad \begin{vmatrix} 1 & -1 & 2 \\ 0 & 4 & 3 \\ 0 & -2 & 1 \end{vmatrix}, \quad \begin{vmatrix} 0 & 0 & a \\ a & b & 0 \\ c & 0 & d \end{vmatrix}, \quad \begin{vmatrix} a & b & c \\ c & a & b \\ b & c & a \end{vmatrix}$$

2. Use the computational technique described at the end of this section to compute the determinants in Exercise 1. Write out in full the six-term expression for each determinant.

3. Use Cramer's Rule to solve the following systems of linear equations.
   (a) $3x - y + z = 1$
       $2x - 9y + z = -5$
       $x + 2y - 5z = 0$
   (b) $x \quad - z = 1$
       $2x + y \quad = -1$
       $4y + 3z = 0$
   (c) $4x + 4y - z = 1$
       $3x - y + 2z = 4$
       $x + 5y - 3z = 2$
   (d) $x + y + z = 0$
       $3x - y + 2z = 0$
       $2x + 5y - 7z = 1$

4. Compute all the determinants $|A_1|$, etc., of the minors $A_1, A_2, \ldots, C_3$ of

$$M = \begin{bmatrix} a_1 & b_1 & c_1 \\ a_2 & b_2 & c_2 \\ a_3 & b_3 & c_3 \end{bmatrix}.$$

Compute the following and show that they are all equal to $|M|$.
   (a) $-b_1|B_1| + b_2|B_2| - b_3|B_3|$
   (b) $c_1|C_1| - c_2|C_2| + c_3|C_3|$
   (c) $a_1|A_1| - b_1|B_1| + c_1|C_1|$
   (d) $-a_2|A_2| + b_2|B_2| - c_2|C_2|$
   (e) $a_3|A_3| - b_3|B_3| + c_3|C_3|$

5. Prove that the equation in x and y

$$\begin{vmatrix} x & x_1 & x_2 \\ y & y_1 & y_2 \\ 1 & 1 & 1 \end{vmatrix} = 0$$

represents the line through the points (x_1, y_1) and (x_2, y_2) in a coordinate plane.

13–3   properties of 3 × 3 determinants

It will be helpful in studying properties of determinants of 3×3 matrices if we change our notation for the entries in a matrix. We will denote the entry in the ith row and jth column of a 3×3 matrix $\mathbf{A}$ by a_{ij}. That is,

$$\mathbf{A} = \begin{bmatrix} a_{11} & a_{12} & a_{13} \\ a_{21} & a_{22} & a_{23} \\ a_{31} & a_{32} & a_{33} \end{bmatrix}.$$

Note that the first subscript, i, gives the row and the second, j, gives the column in which the entry a_{ij} occurs. The minor of the entry a_{ij} in A will be denoted by $\mathbf{A}_{ij}$. That is, $\mathbf{A}_{ij}$ is the 2×2 matrix obtained by omitting row i and column j from $\mathbf{A}$. For example, in $\mathbf{A}$ above,

$$\mathbf{A}_{11} = \begin{bmatrix} a_{22} & a_{23} \\ a_{32} & a_{33} \end{bmatrix} \quad \text{and} \quad \mathbf{A}_{32} = \begin{bmatrix} a_{11} & a_{13} \\ a_{21} & a_{23} \end{bmatrix}.$$

Using this new notation, we obtain the following version of our original definition of $|\mathbf{A}|$:

(1) $$|\mathbf{A}| = a_{11}|\mathbf{A}_{11}| - a_{21}|\mathbf{A}_{21}| + a_{31}|\mathbf{A}_{31}|.$$

The six-term expansion of $\mathbf{A}$ becomes:

(2) $|\mathbf{A}| = a_{11}a_{22}a_{33} + a_{12}a_{23}a_{31} + a_{13}a_{21}a_{32}$
$$-a_{11}a_{23}a_{32} - a_{12}a_{21}a_{33} - a_{13}a_{22}a_{31}.$$

We note again that each term on the right-hand side of (2) contains exactly one entry from each row and exactly one entry from each column.

We now show that 3×3 determinants have similar properties to those described in the 2×2 case in Section 13–1. These properties may all be verified by direct computation, although much of the computation may be avoided by a little ingenuity. In the following list of properties, $\mathbf{A}$ is a 3×3 matrix.

1. If $\mathbf{A}$ has a row or column of zeros—that is, if every entry in some row or in some column is zero—then $|\mathbf{A}| = 0$.

proof: This follows from the description of $|\mathbf{A}|$ given by (2) above.

2. If the 3×3 matrix **B** is obtained from **A** by multiplying each entry in one row (or in one column) by a number k, then $|\mathbf{B}| = k|\mathbf{A}|$.

proof: This also follows from the expression for $|\mathbf{A}|$ given in (2).

As an example of this property

$$\begin{vmatrix} a & a^2 & a^3 \\ b & b^2 & b^3 \\ c & c^2 & c^3 \end{vmatrix} = a \begin{vmatrix} 1 & a & a^2 \\ b & b^2 & b^3 \\ c & c^2 & c^3 \end{vmatrix} = ab \begin{vmatrix} 1 & a & a^2 \\ 1 & b & b^2 \\ c & c^2 & c^3 \end{vmatrix} = abc \begin{vmatrix} 1 & a & a^2 \\ 1 & b & b^2 \\ 1 & c & c^2 \end{vmatrix}.$$

3. If the 3×3 matrix **B** is obtained from **A** by interchanging two rows (or interchanging two columns), then $|\mathbf{B}| = -|\mathbf{A}|$.

proof: If **B** is obtained from **A** by interchanging two rows, say the first and second, then

$$|\mathbf{B}| = \begin{vmatrix} a_{21} & a_{22} & a_{13} \\ a_{11} & a_{12} & a_{13} \\ a_{31} & a_{32} & a_{23} \end{vmatrix}$$

$$= a_{21} \begin{vmatrix} a_{12} & a_{13} \\ a_{32} & a_{33} \end{vmatrix} - a_{11} \begin{vmatrix} a_{22} & a_{23} \\ a_{32} & a_{33} \end{vmatrix} + a_{31} \begin{vmatrix} a_{22} & a_{23} \\ a_{12} & a_{13} \end{vmatrix}$$

$$= -\{a_{11}|\mathbf{A}_{11}| - a_{21}|\mathbf{A}_{21}| + a_{31}|\mathbf{A}_{31}|\}$$

$$\text{(note that } \begin{vmatrix} a_{22} & a_{23} \\ a_{12} & a_{13} \end{vmatrix} = -\begin{vmatrix} a_{12} & a_{13} \\ a_{22} & a_{23} \end{vmatrix} = -|\mathbf{A}_{31}|$$

by properties of 2×2 determinants)

$$= -|\mathbf{A}|.$$

Similar proofs may be given for the interchange of any other pair of rows. If **B** is obtained from **A** by the interchange of column 1 with column 2 or column 1 with column 3, the simplest proof consists of computing $|\mathbf{B}|$ using the expression (2) and verifying that one gets $-|\mathbf{A}|$. If **B** is obtained from **A** by interchanging columns 2 and 3, we have

$$|\mathbf{B}| = a_{11} \begin{vmatrix} a_{23} & a_{22} \\ a_{33} & a_{32} \end{vmatrix} - a_{21} \begin{vmatrix} a_{13} & a_{12} \\ a_{33} & a_{32} \end{vmatrix} + a_{31} \begin{vmatrix} a_{13} & a_{12} \\ a_{23} & a_{22} \end{vmatrix}$$

$$= a_{11}(-|\mathbf{A}_{11}|) - a_{21}(-|\mathbf{A}_{21}|) + a_{31}(-|\mathbf{A}_{31}|)$$

(by properties of 2×2 determinants — interchanging columns!)

$$= -\{a_{11}|\mathbf{A}_{11}| - a_{21}|\mathbf{A}_{21}| + a_{31}|\mathbf{A}_{31}|\} = -|\mathbf{A}|.$$

4. If **A** has two rows identical (or two columns identical), then $|\mathbf{A}| = 0$.

proof: We apply property 3 above and find that $|A| = -|A|$. Hence, $|A| = 0$.

As an example of property 4, let (x_1, y_1), (x_2, y_2) be two points in a plane. Consider the determinant

$$\begin{vmatrix} x & x_1 & x_2 \\ y & y_1 & y_2 \\ 1 & 1 & 1 \end{vmatrix}.$$

Using the definition of a determinant, we see that this is a linear expression in x and y. Furthermore, if we replace x and y by x_1 and y_1 respectively, we obtain a determinant with two identical columns. Hence, the equation

$$(3) \qquad \begin{vmatrix} x & x_1 & x_2 \\ y & y_1 & y_2 \\ 1 & 1 & 1 \end{vmatrix} = 0$$

represents a line through the point (x_1, y_1) since it is satisfied by the coordinates of the point. Similarly, the line represented by the equation (3) passes through the point (x_2, y_2). Hence, the equation (3) is simply an equation in determinant form of the line through (x_1, y_1) and (x_2, y_2).

5. Let **A**, **M**, and **N** be 3×3 matrices identical except for one row (or one column) and let each entry in that row (or column) of **A** be the sum of the corresponding entries in **M** and **N**. Then

$$|A| = |M| + |N|.$$

proof: We will look at one case only as an example. Let **A**, **M**, and **N** be given by

$$\mathbf{M} = \begin{bmatrix} a_{11} & a_{12} & a_{13} \\ a'_{21} & a'_{22} & a'_{23} \\ a_{31} & a_{32} & a_{33} \end{bmatrix}, \ \mathbf{N} = \begin{bmatrix} a_{11} & a_{12} & a_{13} \\ a''_{21} & a''_{22} & a''_{23} \\ a_{31} & a_{32} & a_{33} \end{bmatrix},$$

$$\mathbf{A} = \begin{bmatrix} a_{11} & a_{12} & a_{13} \\ a'_{21} + a''_{21} & a'_{22} + a''_{22} & a'_{23} + a''_{23} \\ a_{31} & a_{32} & a_{33} \end{bmatrix}.$$

Thus, **A**, **M**, and **N** differ only in their second rows and each entry in the second row of **A** is the sum of the corresponding entries of **M** and **N**.

$$|A| = a_{11}(a'_{22} + a''_{22})a_{33} + a_{12}(a'_{23} + a''_{23})a_{31} + a_{13}(a'_{21} + a''_{21})a_{32}$$
$$- a_{11}(a'_{23} + a''_{23})a_{32} - a_{12}(a'_{21} + a''_{21})a_{33} - a_{13}(a'_{22} + a''_{22})a_{31}$$
$$= \{a_{11}a'_{22}a_{33} + \cdots + \cdots - a_{11}a'_{23}a_{32} \cdots\}$$
$$+ \{a_{11}a''_{22}a_{33} + \cdots + \cdots - a_{11}a''_{23}a_{32} - \cdots - \cdots\}$$
$$= |M| + |N|$$

A similar proof may be used to prove the theorem for the other cases. This theorem is useful in proving the following very important property of determinants.

6. Let the matrix **B** be obtained from **A** by adding k times each entry in one row (or column) to the corresponding entry in another row (or column). Then $|\mathbf{B}| = |\mathbf{A}|$.

proof: We will prove one case as an example. Let **B** be obtained from **A** by adding k times the first column to the third column. That is,

$$\mathbf{B} = \begin{bmatrix} a_{11} & a_{12} & a_{13} + ka_{11} \\ a_{21} & a_{22} & a_{23} + ka_{21} \\ a_{31} & a_{32} & a_{33} + ka_{31} \end{bmatrix}.$$

Then, by property 5,

$$|\mathbf{B}| = |\mathbf{A}| + \begin{vmatrix} a_{11} & a_{12} & ka_{11} \\ a_{21} & a_{22} & ka_{21} \\ a_{31} & a_{32} & ka_{31} \end{vmatrix}$$

$$= |\mathbf{A}| + k \begin{vmatrix} a_{11} & a_{12} & a_{11} \\ a_{21} & a_{22} & a_{21} \\ a_{31} & a_{32} & a_{31} \end{vmatrix} \qquad \text{(by property 2)}$$

$$= |\mathbf{A}| + k \cdot 0 \qquad\qquad\qquad\quad \text{(by property 4)}$$

$$= |\mathbf{A}|.$$

This property is extremely useful in simplifying the computation of determinants. We give two examples.

(i) $\begin{vmatrix} 2 & 4 & 1 \\ 8 & 17 & -3 \\ -5 & 2 & 0 \end{vmatrix} = \begin{vmatrix} 2 & 4 & 1 \\ 0 & 1 & -7 \\ -5 & 2 & 0 \end{vmatrix}$ (subtracting 4 times row 1 from row 2)

$$= \begin{vmatrix} 2 & 4 & 1 \\ 0 & 1 & -7 \\ 0 & 12 & 5/2 \end{vmatrix} \qquad \text{(adding 5/2 times row 1 to row 3)}$$

$$= 2 \begin{vmatrix} 1 & -7 \\ 12 & 5/2 \end{vmatrix} \qquad \text{(by our original definition of a determinant)}$$

$$= 2(5/2 + 84) = 173$$

(ii) $\begin{vmatrix} 1 & a & a^2 \\ 1 & b & b^2 \\ 1 & c & c^2 \end{vmatrix} = \begin{vmatrix} 1 & a & a^2 \\ 0 & b-a & b^2-a^2 \\ 1 & c & c^2 \end{vmatrix}$ (subtracting row 1 from row 2)

$$= (b-a) \begin{vmatrix} 1 & a & a^2 \\ 0 & 1 & b+a \\ 1 & c & c^2 \end{vmatrix} \quad \text{(by property 2)}$$

$$= (b-a) \begin{vmatrix} 1 & a & a^2 \\ 0 & 1 & b+a \\ 0 & c-a & c^2-a^2 \end{vmatrix} \quad \begin{array}{l} \text{(subtracting} \\ \text{row 1 from} \\ \text{row 3)} \end{array}$$

$$= (b-a)(c-a) \begin{vmatrix} 1 & a & a^2 \\ 0 & 1 & b+a \\ 0 & 1 & c+a \end{vmatrix} \quad \begin{array}{l} \text{(by property} \\ \text{2)} \end{array}$$

$$= (b-a)(c-a) \begin{vmatrix} 1 & b+a \\ 1 & c+a \end{vmatrix}$$

$$= (b-a)(c-a)\{(c+a)-(b+a)\}$$
$$= (b-a)(c-a)(c-b)$$

7. By the *transpose* **B** of **A** we mean the 3×3 matrix having the rows of **A** as its columns. More precisely, the entry in the ith row, jth column of **B** is a_{ji}, so that

$$\mathbf{B} = \begin{bmatrix} a_{11} & a_{21} & a_{31} \\ a_{12} & a_{22} & a_{32} \\ a_{13} & a_{23} & a_{33} \end{bmatrix}.$$

The determinant of the transpose of **A** is equal to the determinant of **A**—that is, $|\mathbf{B}| = |\mathbf{A}|$.

proof: The simplest way to prove this is by direct computation. We leave this to the student.

As an example of the use of this property we will prove that if **A** is a *skew-symmetric* matrix—that is, a matrix with $a_{ji} = -a_{ij}$,—so that **A** is of the form

$$\mathbf{A} = \begin{bmatrix} 0 & a & b \\ -a & 0 & c \\ -b & -c & 0 \end{bmatrix},$$

then $|\mathbf{A}| = 0$. For

$$|\mathbf{A}| = \begin{vmatrix} (-1)\cdot 0 & (-1)\cdot(-a) & (-1)\cdot(-b) \\ (-1)\cdot a & (-1)\cdot 0 & (-1)\cdot(-c) \\ (-1)\cdot b & (-1)\cdot c & (-1)\cdot 0 \end{vmatrix}$$

$$= (-1)^3 \begin{vmatrix} 0 & -a & -b \\ a & 0 & -c \\ b & c & 0 \end{vmatrix} \quad \text{(by property 2)}$$

$$= (-1)\cdot |\mathbf{A}|. \quad\quad\quad \text{(by property 7)}$$

Hence,

$$|\mathbf{A}| = 0.$$

Before proceeding with further properties we sum up those we have examined so far. Briefly, we may state these as:

(i)   A determinant with a row or column of zeros has value zero.

(ii)   If a row or column is multiplied by a number k, then the value of the determinant is multiplied by k.

(iii)   Interchanging two rows (or two columns) changes the sign of the determinant.

(iv)   A determinant with two rows the same (or two columns the same) has value zero.

(v)   Adding a multiple of one row to another row (or adding a multiple of one column to another column) does not change the value of the determinant.

(vi)   If we interchange the rows and columns, the value of the determinant is unchanged.

In order to describe the remaining properties, we need some new terminology. We define the *cofactor* of the entry a_{ij} in $\mathbf{A}$ to be $(-1)^{i+j}|A_{ij}|$ and will denote it by C_{ij}. Thus,

$$C_{ij} = (-1)^{i+j}|A_{ij}|.$$

The cofactor of an entry is either plus or minus the determinant of the minor of the entry. The following table shows for which entries the cofactor is *plus* and for which it is *minus* the determinant of the minor.

$$\begin{vmatrix} + & - & + \\ - & + & - \\ + & - & + \end{vmatrix}$$

For example,

$$C_{13} = (-1)^{1+3}|A_{13}| = \begin{vmatrix} a_{21} & a_{22} \\ a_{31} & a_{32} \end{vmatrix},$$

$$C_{32} = (-1)^{3+2}|A_{32}| = -\begin{vmatrix} a_{11} & a_{13} \\ a_{21} & a_{23} \end{vmatrix}.$$

In terms of cofactors our original definition of $|\mathbf{A}|$,

$$|\mathbf{A}| = a_{11}|\mathbf{A}_{11}| - a_{21}|\mathbf{A}_{21}| + a_{31}|\mathbf{A}_{31}|$$

may be written as

$$|\mathbf{A}| = a_{11}\,\mathbf{C}_{11} + a_{21}\,\mathbf{C}_{21} + a_{31}\,\mathbf{C}_{31}.$$

We will call both the original definition and this expression in terms of cofactors, the *expansion of* $|\mathbf{A}|$ *by its first column*.

It is easily verified by direct computation that

$$|\mathbf{A}| = -a_{12}|\mathbf{A}_{12}| + a_{22}|\mathbf{A}_{22}| - a_{32}|\mathbf{A}_{32}|$$
$$= a_{12}\ \mathbf{C}_{12} + a_{22}\ \mathbf{C}_{22} + a_{32}\ \mathbf{C}_{32}.$$

We call this the *expansion of* $|\mathbf{A}|$ *by its second column*. Similarly, we get

$$|\mathbf{A}| = a_{13}|\mathbf{A}_{13}| - a_{23}|\mathbf{A}_{23}| + a_{33}|\mathbf{A}_{33}|$$
$$= a_{13}\ \mathbf{C}_{13} + a_{23}\ \mathbf{C}_{23} + a_{33}\ \mathbf{C}_{33}.$$

We call this the *expansion of* $|\mathbf{A}|$ *by its third column*.

Note that in each expression for $|\mathbf{A}|$, we multiply each entry in a fixed column by its cofactor and add the resulting three products. The expressions for $|\mathbf{A}|$ as expansions by its second and third columns occur naturally if we attempt to solve the three linear equations (1) in Section 13–2 for y and z respectively in the same way in which we solved for x in obtaining our original description of the determinant. As an example of these ideas, consider the matrix

$$\mathbf{A} = \begin{bmatrix} 2 & 5 & -1 \\ 0 & 3 & 7 \\ 1 & -4 & 2 \end{bmatrix}.$$

The expansion of $|\mathbf{A}|$ by its third column is

$$|\mathbf{A}| = (-1) \cdot \begin{vmatrix} 0 & 3 \\ 1 & -4 \end{vmatrix} - 7 \cdot \begin{vmatrix} 2 & 5 \\ 1 & -4 \end{vmatrix} + 2 \cdot \begin{vmatrix} 2 & 5 \\ 0 & 3 \end{vmatrix}$$
$$= 3 + 91 + 12 = 106.$$

If we consider the expression for $|\mathbf{A}|$ in terms of products of the entries of $\mathbf{A}$,

$$|\mathbf{A}| = a_{11}\ a_{22}\ a_{33} + a_{12}\ a_{23}\ a_{31} + a_{13}\ a_{21}\ a_{32} - a_{11}\ a_{23}\ a_{32}$$
$$- a_{12}\ a_{21}\ a_{33} - a_{13}\ a_{22}\ a_{31},$$

we see that the expansion of $|\mathbf{A}|$ by its second column, for example, may be obtained by collecting together the terms in each second column entry.

$$|\mathbf{A}| = a_{12}(a_{23}a_{31} - a_{21}a_{33}) + a_{22}(a_{11}a_{33} - a_{13}a_{31}) + a_{32}(a_{13}a_{21} - a_{11}a_{23})$$
$$= a_{12}\ \mathbf{C}_{12} + a_{22}\ \mathbf{C}_{22} + a_{32}\ \mathbf{C}_{32}$$

This suggests we try the same procedure with the entries in each row. We get,

$$|\mathbf{A}| = a_{11}(a_{22}a_{33} - a_{23}a_{32}) + a_{12}(a_{23}a_{31} - a_{21}a_{33}) + a_{13}(a_{21}a_{32} - a_{22}a_{31})$$
$$= a_{11}\ \mathbf{C}_{11} + a_{12}\ \mathbf{C}_{12} + a_{13}\ \mathbf{C}_{13}.$$

This is called the *expansion of* $\mathbf{A}$ *by its first row*. In terms of minors, this expression may be written as

$$|A| = a_{11}|A_{11}| - a_{12}|A_{12}| + a_{13}|A_{13}|.$$

In the same way, we get the *expansion of* A *by its second row*,

$$|A| = a_{21}\,C_{21} + a_{22}\,C_{22} + a_{23}\,C_{23}$$
$$= -a_{21}|A_{21}| + a_{22}|A_{22}| - a_{23}|A_{23}|,$$

and the *expansion of* A *by its third row*,

$$|A| = a_{31}\,C_{31} + a_{32}\,C_{32} + a_{33}\,C_{33}$$
$$= a_{31}|A_{31}| - a_{32}|A_{32}| + a_{33}|A_{33}|.$$

As an example, the expansion of

$$|A| = \begin{vmatrix} 2 & 5 & -1 \\ 0 & 3 & 7 \\ 1 & -4 & 2 \end{vmatrix}$$

by its second row is:

$$A = -a_{21}|A_{21}| + a_{22}|A_{22}| - a_{23}|A_{23}|$$
$$= 0 \cdot \begin{vmatrix} 5 & -1 \\ -4 & 2 \end{vmatrix} + 3 \cdot \begin{vmatrix} 2 & -1 \\ 1 & 2 \end{vmatrix} - 7 \cdot \begin{vmatrix} 2 & 5 \\ 1 & -4 \end{vmatrix}$$
$$= 0 + 15 + 91$$
$$= 106.$$

To sum up, we have shown that if we take the entries in any row (or in any column), multiply each by its cofactor, and add the resulting three products, we obtain the determinant.

An important application of the row and column expansions of a determinant is obtained if we expand a determinant which has two identical rows (or two identical columns). We know from property 4 that such a determinant is zero. As an example, let B be the matrix obtained from A by replacing row 2 of A by row 1.

$$B = \begin{bmatrix} a_{11} & a_{12} & a_{13} \\ a_{11} & a_{12} & a_{13} \\ a_{31} & a_{32} & a_{33} \end{bmatrix}$$

Now we expand $|B|$ by its second row. We get

$$0 = a_{11}\,C_{21} + a_{12}\,C_{22} + a_{13}\,C_{23}.$$

That is, if we multiply each entry a_{1j} in the first row of A by the cofactor C_{2j} of the corresponding entry in the second row of A, then the sum of these products is zero.

The general result for rows is obtained similarly. Let row m in $\mathbf{A}$ be replaced by row i of $\mathbf{A}$ and expand the resulting determinant by its mth row. We get

$$0 = a_{i1}\,\mathbf{C}_{m1} + a_{i2}\,\mathbf{C}_{m2} + a_{i3}\,\mathbf{C}_{m3}, \qquad i \neq m.$$

Similarly, if we expand by its nth column a determinant obtained from $|\mathbf{A}|$ by replacing the nth column of $|\mathbf{A}|$ by its jth column, we get

$$0 = a_{1j}\,\mathbf{C}_{1n} + a_{2j}\,\mathbf{C}_{2n} + a_{3j}\,\mathbf{C}_{3n}.$$

We collect the above properties and our earlier results on expansions of a determinant in the following comprehensive statements.

8. (i) If each entry in one row (or column) is multiplied by its cofactor, then the sum of these products is the determinant.
   (ii) If each entry in one row (column) is multiplied by the cofactor of the corresponding entry in another row (column), then the sum of these products is zero.

exercises

Exercises 1–8 refer to the eight properties of determinants listed in this section.

1. Give the details in the proof of property 1.

2. Give the details in the proof of property 2.

3. Give the proof of property 3 in the cases
   (i) where rows 2 and 3 are interchanged.
   (ii) where columns 1 and 3 are interchanged.

4. Give the details in the proof of property 4.

5. Prove property 5 for the case where column 1 of $\mathbf{A}$ is the sum of columns 1 in $\mathbf{M}$ and $\mathbf{N}$.

6. Prove property 6 for one case other than that given.

7. Prove property 7.

8. Prove property 8
   (i) for all expansions by rows, and
   (ii) for the expansion using the entries from row 3 and the cofactors from row 1.

Use the properties of determinants to prove the following.

9.
$$\begin{vmatrix} a & b & c \\ b & c & a \\ c & a & b \end{vmatrix} = (a+b+c)(bc+ca+ab-a^2-b^2-c^2)$$

10.
$$\begin{vmatrix} 1 & 1 & 1 \\ a & b & c \\ b+c & c+a & a+b \end{vmatrix} = 0$$

11.
$$\begin{vmatrix} x-y & y-z & z-x \\ y-z & z-x & x-y \\ z-x & x-y & y-z \end{vmatrix} = 0$$

12.
$$\begin{vmatrix} 1 & 1 & 1 \\ a^2 & b^2 & c^2 \\ a^4 & b^4 & c^4 \end{vmatrix} = (a+b)(b+c)(c+a)(a-b)(b-c)(c-a)$$

13.
$$\begin{vmatrix} 1 & 1 & 1 \\ a & b & c \\ a^3 & b^3 & c^3 \end{vmatrix} = (a-b)(b-c)(c-a)(a+b+c)$$

14. Use the properties of determinants to compute the following.

(a) $\begin{vmatrix} 99 & 103 & -4 \\ 73 & 74 & 1 \\ 82 & 91 & -5 \end{vmatrix}$
(b) $\begin{vmatrix} 1 & 5 & 9 \\ 13 & 17 & 21 \\ 25 & 29 & 31 \end{vmatrix}$

15. Let $\mathbf{A}$ be a 3×3 matrix with entries a_{ij} such that the determinant $|\mathbf{A}|$ is zero. Verify that $x = \mathbf{C}_{11}$, $y = \mathbf{C}_{12}$, $z = \mathbf{C}_{13}$ is a solution of the equations

$$a_{11}x + a_{12}y + a_{13}z = 0$$
$$a_{21}x + a_{22}y + a_{23}z = 0$$
$$a_{31}x + a_{32}y + a_{33}z = 0.$$

(Hint: Use property 8.)

13-4 linear equations in three unknowns

We will describe in this section the general solution of the system of linear equations in three unknowns x, y, and z,

(1)
$$a_{11}x + a_{12}y + a_{13}z = b_1$$
$$a_{21}x + a_{22}y + a_{23}z = b_2$$
$$a_{31}x + a_{32}y + a_{33}z = b_3.$$

We begin by using the information obtained in Section 13-3 (property 8) to prove Cramer's Rule. Let $\mathbf{A}$ denote the matrix of coefficients in the equations (1) and let $\mathbf{A}_1$, $\mathbf{A}_2$, and $\mathbf{A}_3$ denote the matrices obtained from $\mathbf{A}$ by replacing columns 1, 2, and 3 respectively by b_1, b_2, and b_3, the column of numbers on the right-hand sides of the equations. As usual, $\mathbf{C}_{11}$, $\mathbf{C}_{12}$, ... will denote cofactors of entries in $|\mathbf{A}|$. Note that

$$|\mathbf{A}_j| = b_{i1}\,\mathbf{C}_{ij} + b_{2j}\,\mathbf{C}_{2j} + b_{3j}\,\mathbf{C}_{3j}, \qquad j = 1, 2, 3.$$

cramer's rule: If $|\mathbf{A}| \neq 0$, then the equations (1) have the unique solution

$$x = \frac{|\mathbf{A}_1|}{|\mathbf{A}|}, \qquad y = \frac{|\mathbf{A}_2|}{|\mathbf{A}|}, \qquad z = \frac{|\mathbf{A}_3|}{|\mathbf{A}|}.$$

proof: First we show that these values for x, y, and z, are in fact a solution. We do this for the first equation only, leaving the other verifications to the student. Consider

$$a_{11}\frac{|\mathbf{A_1}|}{|\mathbf{A}|}+a_{12}\frac{|\mathbf{A_2}|}{|\mathbf{A}|}+a_{13}\frac{|\mathbf{A_3}|}{|\mathbf{A}|}$$

$$=\frac{1}{|\mathbf{A}|}\{a_{11}(b_1\,\mathbf{C_{11}}+b_2\,\mathbf{C_{21}}+b_3\,\mathbf{C_{31}})$$
$$+a_{12}(b_1\,\mathbf{C_{12}}+b_2\,\mathbf{C_{22}}+b_3\,\mathbf{C_{32}})$$
$$+a_{13}(b_1\,\mathbf{C_{13}}+b_2\,\mathbf{C_{23}}+b_3\,\mathbf{C_{33}})\}$$

$$=\frac{1}{|\mathbf{A}|}\{b_1(a_{11}\,\mathbf{C_{11}}+a_{12}\,\mathbf{C_{12}}+a_{13}\,\mathbf{C_{13}})$$
$$+b_2(a_{11}\,\mathbf{C_{21}}+a_{12}\,\mathbf{C_{22}}+a_{13}\,\mathbf{C_{23}})$$
$$+b_3(a_{11}\,\mathbf{C_{31}}+a_{12}\,\mathbf{C_{32}}+a_{13}\,\mathbf{C_{33}})\}$$

$$=\frac{1}{|\mathbf{A}|}\{b_1|\mathbf{A}|+b_2\cdot 0+b_3\cdot 0\}\quad\text{(by property 8 of Section 13–3)}$$
$$=b_1.$$

Similarly, we show that

$$x=\frac{|\mathbf{A_1}|}{|\mathbf{A}|},\qquad y=\frac{|\mathbf{A_2}|}{|\mathbf{A}|},\qquad z=\frac{|\mathbf{A_3}|}{|\mathbf{A}|}$$

is a solution of the other two equations.

It remains to show that this is the only solution. Let x_1, y_1, z_1 be a solution. That is, x_1, y_1, and z_1 satisfy

$$a_{11}x_1+a_{12}y_1+a_{13}z_1=b_1$$
$$a_{21}x_1+a_{22}y_1+a_{23}z_1=b_2$$
$$a_{31}x_1+a_{32}y_1+a_{33}z_1=b_3.$$

Multiply both sides of the first equation by $\mathbf{C_{11}}$, both sides of the second by $\mathbf{C_{21}}$, and both sides of the third by $\mathbf{C_{31}}$. Add corresponding sides of the three equations. Using the properties of cofactors given in 8, Section 13–3, we obtain

$$|\mathbf{A}|\cdot x_1=|\mathbf{A_1}|.$$

That is,

$$x_1=|\mathbf{A_1}|/|\mathbf{A}|.$$

Similarly, we show that the assumption that there is a solution x_1, y_1, z_1 leads to the conclusion $y_1=|\mathbf{A_2}|/|\mathbf{A}|$, and $z_1=|\mathbf{A_3}|/|\mathbf{A}|$.

Hence, if the linear equations (1) have a solution, it must be the solution stated in Cramer's Rule. Since we have shown that this is a solution, it is the only solution. This concludes the proof.

The information we have obtained about cofactors in Section 13–3 (property 8) also enables us to describe nonzero solutions for the case of three linear equations in three unknowns with constant terms zero:

$$\begin{aligned}a_{11}x+a_{12}y+a_{13}z=0\\a_{21}x+a_{22}y+a_{23}z=0\\a_{31}x+a_{32}y+a_{33}z=0.\end{aligned}$$

(2)

We call such a system of equations *homogeneous*. Clearly, $x=0$, $y=0$, and $z=0$ is one solution. We call this the *zero solution*. Now if

$|\mathbf{A}| \neq 0$, by Cramer's Rule, this is the only solution. Hence, in order that the equations (2) have a nonzero solution it is certainly necessary that $|\mathbf{A}| = 0$. We now show that this condition is sufficient also.

(i) If not all the cofactors $\mathbf{C}_{ij}$ of $|\mathbf{A}|$ are zero, then one of the following solutions of (2) is a nonzero solution:

$x = \mathbf{C}_{11}, \; y = \mathbf{C}_{12}, \; z = \mathbf{C}_{13};$
$x = \mathbf{C}_{21}, \; y = \mathbf{C}_{22}, \; z = \mathbf{C}_{23};$
$x = \mathbf{C}_{31}, \; y = \mathbf{C}_{32}, \; z = \mathbf{C}_{33}.$

This follows from property 8, Section 13–3 and the fact that $|\mathbf{A}| = 0$.

(ii) If all the cofactors of $|\mathbf{A}|$ are zero but not all of the coefficients a_{ij} are zero, then we may also find a nonzero solution. For example, if $a_{22} \neq 0$, we may take $x = a_{22}$, $y = -a_{21}$, $z = 0$ as a nonzero solution. A simple computation using the fact that all $\mathbf{C}_{ij}$ are zero verifies that this is a solution. Similarly, for any other nonzero coefficient, we may find a solution using this coefficient. We leave the details as an exercise.

(iii) If all the coefficients a_{ij} in the equations (2) are zero, clearly any value for x, y, z is a solution.

The following examples illustrate the theorem we have just proved. The determinant of the coefficients in

$$2x - y + 3z = 0$$
$$3x + 2y - 5z = 0$$
$$5x - 6y + 17z = 0$$

is zero. Hence, the equations have a nonzero solution. Since the cofactor

$$\mathbf{C}_{11} = \begin{vmatrix} 2 & -5 \\ -6 & 17 \end{vmatrix} \neq 0$$

we may take $x = \mathbf{C}_{11} = 4$, $y = \mathbf{C}_{12} = -76$, $z = \mathbf{C}_{13} = -28$ as a solution.

We note that for homogeneous systems of linear equations, if x_1, y_1, z_1 is a solution, then so is kx_1, ky_1, kz_1 for any number k. Thus, there is the slightly simpler solution $x = 1$, $y = -19$, $z = -7$ to the above equations and we may say that, for any number t, $x = t$, $y = -19t$, $z = -7t$ is a solution.

The determinant of the coefficients in

$$-3x + 6y - 3z = 0$$
$$2x - 4y + 2z = 0$$
$$5x - 10y + 5z = 0$$

is zero. All the cofactors are zero also. However, $a_{11} = -3 \neq 0$. Hence, one solution is $x = 6$, $y = 3$, $z = 0$. A simpler solution is $x = 2$, $y = 1$, $z = 0$. In fact, for any number t, $x = 2t$, $y = t$, $z = 0$ is a solution. We may obtain other solutions not of this form in a similar way. For example, $x=0$, $y=1$, $z=2$ is a solution and hence, for any number s, $x=0$, $y=s$, $z=2s$ is a solution. We leave to the student (see Exercise 2 below) the verification that for any numbers s and t, $x=2t$, $y=s+t$, $z=2s$ is a solution of the equations.

We sum up our results so far. Cramer's Rule gives us a unique solution if the determinant of the coefficients is not zero. If the system of linear equations is homogeneous, the determinant of coefficients must be zero in order that the equations have a nonzero solution. Clearly, these two results are far from a complete theory of systems of three linear equations in three unknowns. To complete the theory we will take a geometric point of view. A linear equation (with not all coefficients a, b, and c zero)

$$ax+by+cz=d$$

represents a plane, and so the set of solutions of the three linear equations

$$a_{11}x + a_{12}y + a_{13}z = b_1$$
$$a_{21}x + a_{22}y + a_{23}z = b_2$$
$$a_{31}x + a_{32}y + a_{33}z = b_3$$

corresponds geometrically to the set of points common to the three planes represented by the equations. The geometric configurations which three planes may have are as follows.

If the three planes are parallel there is no common solution to the equations.

If two of the planes are parallel and the third plane intersects both there is again no common solution to the equations.

If no two of the planes are parallel but the line of intersection of any two of the planes is parallel to the third plane, there is again no common solution to the equations.

If the three planes have a common line of intersection the equations will have solutions corresponding to each of the infinite number of points on this line.

If the three planes intersect in only one point the three linear equations have a unique solution.

The last case is taken care of algebraically by Cramer's Rule. The determinant of the coefficients in the equations is nonzero, and Cramer's Rule gives the unique solution of the equations.

The first two cases are easily checked by inspection of the equations. In the first example below, all three planes are parallel; in the second example the second and third planes are parallel but the first is not parallel to them.

$$\begin{aligned} x - y + 3z &= 1 \\ 4x - 4y + 12z &= 3 \\ -3x + 3y - 9z &= 2 \end{aligned} \qquad \begin{aligned} x + y + z &= 3 \\ 2x + 5y - 7z &= -4 \\ 4x + 10y - 14z &= 1 \end{aligned}$$

We may perform three operations on a system of linear equations (two or more equations in any number of unknowns) which do not change the set of solutions of the equations. The order in which the equations are listed may be changed; both sides of an equation may be multiplied by the same nonzero number; or an equation may be replaced by the equation obtained by adding to each side of it the same multiple of the corresponding sides of one of the other equations.

We claim that these operations on a system of equations do not change the set of solutions. The third operation is the only one for which this is not obvious, and we leave to the student the verification that the equations

$$a_1x + b_1y + c_1z = d_1$$
$$a_2x + b_2y + c_2z = d_2$$

have the same set of common solutions as the equations

$$a_1x + b_1y + c_1z = d_1$$

$$(a_2 + ka_1)x + (b_2 + kb_1)y + (c_2 + kc_1)z = d_1 + kd_2.$$

(See Exercise 6.)

Geometrically, in this case, if the original equations represent intersecting planes, the new equations represent planes having the same line of intersection as the original planes. If the given planes are parallel, then so are the two planes obtained by the operation.

The use of these operations enables us to obtain from a given system of linear equations a new system of equations whose solution is obvious. We illustrate the procedure.

example 1

Consider the equations

$$2x - 3y + 4z = 1$$
$$3x + 5y - 2z = -2.$$

These equations represent different nonparallel planes with a line of intersection, so we may expect an infinite number of solutions. We solve the equations by obtaining new pairs of equations which have exactly the same solutions. First, we divide both sides of the first equation by two.

$$x - \frac{3}{2}y + 2z = \frac{1}{2}$$
$$3x + 5y - 2z = -2$$

We now subtract three times the sides of the first equation from the corresponding sides of the second equation

$$x - \frac{3}{2}y + 2z = \frac{1}{2}$$
$$\frac{19}{2}y - 8z = -\frac{7}{2}.$$

We may solve these equations easily. Give z any value. Then y is determined for this value of z by the second equation. The first equation now determines the value of x for these values of y and z. In detail

$$z=t \qquad t, \text{any number}$$

$$y=\frac{-7}{19}+\frac{16}{19}t$$

$$x=\frac{1}{2}+\frac{3}{2}\left(\frac{-7}{19}+\frac{16}{19}t\right)+2t$$

$$=\frac{-1}{19}-\frac{14}{19}t.$$

This is the complete solution of the original equations. We may regard this solution as giving, for any t, the coordinates of a point on the line of intersection of the planes $2x-3y+4z=1$ and $3x+5y-2z=-2$.

example 2

Consider the system of linear equations

$$\begin{array}{rrrr} -3x+ & 7y+ & z= & 2 \\ x+ & 3y- & z= & -1 \\ 4x+ & y+ & 2z= & 0. \end{array}$$

We rearrange the order of the equations so that the first equation has a leading coefficient of one, and get

$$\begin{array}{rrrr} x+ & 3y- & z= & -1 \\ -3x+ & 7y+ & z= & 2 \\ 4x+ & y+ & 2z= & 0. \end{array}$$

We now add three times the first equation to the second and subtract four times the first from the third. (We use this abbreviated description instead of the more precise "three times the sides of the first equation from the corresponding sides....")

$$\begin{array}{rrr} x+ & 3y- & z=-1 \\ & 16y- & 2z=-1 \\ & -11y+ & 6z= 4. \end{array}$$

The effect of this is to obtain new second and third equations with no x term. Now we divide both sides of the second equation by sixteen in order to obtain an equation with a leading coefficient of one.

$$\begin{array}{rrr} x+ & 3y- & z=-1 \\ & y- & \frac{1}{8}z=-\frac{1}{16} \\ & -11y+ & 6z= 4 \end{array}$$

Adding eleven times the second to the third gives us

$$\begin{array}{rrr} x+ & 3y- & z=-1 \\ & y- & \frac{1}{8}z=-\frac{1}{16} \\ & & \frac{37}{8}z=\frac{53}{16}. \end{array}$$

These equations have a unique solution which we may read directly. From the third equation, $z = 53/74$. From the second equation, $y = -1/16 + 1/8 \cdot 53/74 = 1/37$. Then, from the first equation, $x = -1 + 53/74 - 3 \cdot 1/37 = -27/74$. Hence, the solution is: $x = -27/74$, $y = 1/37$, and $z = 53/74$. Geometrically the original equations represent three planes with the point of intersection at $(-27/74, 1/37, 53/74)$.

The above example illustrates the general procedure. We operate on the equations so that the first has leading coefficient one. (This need not be the x term.) Then we obtain new second and third equations which do not contain the unknown with leading coefficient one in the first equation. We now repeat this procedure with the second and third equations, eliminating another unknown.

example 3

Consider the system of linear equations

$$2x + 4y - 6z = 1$$
$$2x + 7y - 5z = 4$$
$$3x + 9y - 8z = 2.$$

We divide both sides of the first equation by two.

$$x + 2y - 3z = \frac{1}{2}$$
$$2x + 7y - 5z = 4$$
$$3x + 9y - 8z = 2$$

Subtract two times the first from the second, and three times the first from the third.

$$x + 2y - 3z = \frac{1}{2}$$
$$3y + z = 3$$
$$3y + z = \frac{5}{2}$$

At this stage, we can see that the second and third equations represent parallel planes and that the three equations have no common solution. If we proceed systematically, however, we obtain the final system of equations

$$x + 2y - 3z = \frac{1}{2}$$
$$y + \frac{1}{3}z = 1$$
$$0 = -\frac{1}{2}.$$

Since $0 = -1/2$ is false, no values of x, y, and z can make all three equations true statements. Hence, the set of solutions of these equations is empty, and so the original equations also have an empty solution set.

Geometrically, since no two of the original equations represent parallel planes, the line of intersection of any two of the planes must be parallel to the third plane. The three planes form an "infinite prism."

example 4

To solve

$$4x + 3y - 5z = 2$$
$$2x + 5y + z = 1$$
$$2x + 3y - z = 1$$

we perform the following sequence of operations. We leave the student to fill in the details.

$$\left. \begin{array}{l} 4x + 3y - 5z = 2 \\ 2x + 5y + z = 1 \\ 2x + 3y - z = 1 \end{array} \right\} \rightarrow \left. \begin{array}{l} z + 2x + 5y = 1 \\ -z + 2x + 3y = 1 \\ -5z + 4x + 3y = 2 \end{array} \right\} \rightarrow \left. \begin{array}{l} z + 2x + 5y = 1 \\ 4x + 8y = 2 \\ 14x + 28y = 7 \end{array} \right\} \rightarrow$$

$$\left. \begin{array}{l} z + 2x + 5y = 1 \\ x + 2y = \dfrac{1}{2} \\ x + 2y = \dfrac{1}{2} \end{array} \right\} \rightarrow \begin{array}{l} z + 2x + 5y = 1 \\ x + 2y = \dfrac{1}{2} \\ 0 = 0 \end{array}$$

At the next-to-last step, we see that the second and third equations are the same. This means that we actually have only two distinct equations to solve— a fact emphasized by the last system of equations we obtain, in which the third equation is simply $0 = 0$, automatically satisfied by any values of x, y, and z satisfying the first two equations.

The complete solution of these equations is $y = t$, any number, $x = 1/2 - 2t$, $z = -t$.

Geometrically, this example corresponds to three planes having a common line of intersection, this line also being the line of intersection of the planes $z + 2x + 5y = 1$ and $x + 2y = 1/2$.

The method illustrated in the above examples is in general much more efficient than Cramer's Rule for obtaining the solution of a system of linear equations with nonzero determinant of coefficients. We may use the same procedure in solving homogeneous systems of equations. Our geometric point of view illuminates the situation here also. Three homogeneous equations correspond to three planes through the origin. If the three planes are distinct, there are only two possibilities; either the planes intersect in the origin only or they have a common line of intersection. In the first case, the equations have only the zero solution; in the second case, they have an infinite number of nonzero solutions.

We remark finally that the so-called "diagonalization" procedure used in the above examples is not restricted to solving linear equations in three unknowns. The same technique will give the general solution for any system of linear equations in any number of unknowns. The student may try the procedure on more complicated systems of equations in Exercise 7 below.

exercises

1. Find the complete solution for each of the following systems of linear equations. In each case give the geometric interpretation.

(a) $\begin{aligned} x - 3y + z &= 1 \\ 2x + y + 9z &= 0 \\ -3x + 2y - z &= 4 \end{aligned}$

(b) $\begin{aligned} x + y + z &= 4 \\ 4x - y - 2z &= 1 \\ 3x - 2y - 3z &= -1 \end{aligned}$

(c) $\begin{aligned} 2x + 2y - z &= 1 \\ 2x + 5y - 9z &= 5 \\ 4x - y + 7z &= -3 \end{aligned}$

(d) $\begin{aligned} 2x + y - z &= 4 \\ 4x + 2y - 2z &= 1 \\ x - y + 3z &= 1 \end{aligned}$

(e) $\begin{aligned} x + y - z &= 0 \\ 6x - y + 2z &= 0 \\ 3x + 7y - 4z &= 0 \end{aligned}$

(f) $\begin{aligned} x + y - z &= 0 \\ -3x - 3y + 3z &= 0 \\ 2x + 2y - 2z &= 0 \end{aligned}$

(g) $\begin{aligned} 4x + y + z &= 0 \\ 2x - y - z &= 0 \\ x + y + z &= 0 \end{aligned}$

(h) $\begin{aligned} 4x + y + z &= 2 \\ 2x - y - z &= 0 \\ x + y + z &= 1 \end{aligned}$

(i) $\begin{aligned} 2x + y - z &= 3 \\ -4x - 2y + 2z &= 1 \\ x + y - z &= 4 \end{aligned}$

(j) $\begin{aligned} 2x + y - z &= 3 \\ -4x - 2y + 2z &= 6 \\ x + y - z &= 4 \end{aligned}$

2. Prove that if $x = x_1$, $y = y_1$, $z = z_1$ and $x = x_2$, $y = y_2$, $z = z_2$ are two solutions of a homogeneous system of linear equations in unknowns x, y, and z, then $x = x_1 + x_2$, $y = y_1 + y_2$, $z = z_1 + z_2$ is also a solution. What is the geometric significance of this?

3. Let $x = x_1$, $y = y_1$, $z = z_1$ be a fixed solution of the system of linear equations (1) in this section. Prove that every solution of the equations is of the form $x = x_1 + u$, $y = y_1 + v$, $z = z_1 + w$ where $x = u$, $y = v$, $z = w$ are solutions of the homogeneous system (2).

4. A homogeneous system of three linear equations in three unknowns has determinant zero but one of the cofactors C_{ij} of the determinant is not zero. Interpret this situation geometrically and show that the complete solution of the system of equations is given by

$$x = C_{1j}t, \quad y = C_{2j}t, \quad z = C_{3j}t$$

where t is any real number.

5. A homogeneous system of three linear equations in three unknowns (with at least one coefficient in each equation nonzero) has determinant zero and also every cofactor zero but with one entry not zero. Interpret this situation geometrically and give a complete solution to the system of equations.

6. Prove that, for any number k, the two equations

$$\begin{aligned} a_1x + b_1y + c_1z &= d_1 \\ a_2x + b_2y + c_2z &= d_2 \end{aligned}$$

have the same set of solutions as the two equations

$$\begin{aligned} a_1x + b_1y + c_1z &= d_1 \\ (a_2 + ka_1)x + (b_2 + kb_1)y + (c_2 + kc_1)z &= d_2 + kd. \end{aligned}$$

Give the details of the geometric interpretation of this.

7. Find the general solution of the following systems of linear equations.

(a)
$$\begin{aligned} x + y + z + t &= 1 \\ x + y - z &= 3 \\ 2x + 3z - t &= -1 \\ 2y - 3z + 2t &= 5 \end{aligned}$$

(b)
$$\begin{aligned} 3y - z &= 1 \\ x + 2y + z &= 4 \\ 2x - 3y - 2z &= -3 \\ -x + 5y + 3z &= 7 \end{aligned}$$

(c)
$$\begin{aligned} 4x - 2y + z - t &= 0 \\ 3x + y - z + 3t &= 0 \\ 2x + 4y - 3z + 7t &= 0 \end{aligned}$$

(d)
$$\begin{aligned} x_1 + x_2 + x_3 + x_4 + x_5 &= 0 \\ x_1 - x_2 \qquad - x_4 &= 1 \\ x_2 - x_3 \qquad - x_5 &= -1 \\ x_1 \qquad + x_3 \qquad + x_5 &= 2 \end{aligned}$$

13–5   determinants of order n

The method we used to define the determinant of a 3×3 matrix in terms of determinants of 2×2 matrices can be extended to give a definition of determinants of $n \times n$ matrices for any positive integer n. Let A be a *square matrix of order* n—that is, an n by n array of n^2 numbers arranged in n rows and n columns. The *entry* in the ith row, jth column of A will be denoted by a_{ij}.

$$A = \begin{bmatrix} a_{11} & a_{12} & \cdots & a_{1n} \\ a_{21} & a_{22} & \cdots & \\ a_{31} & \cdots & \cdots & \\ \cdots & \cdots & & \\ \cdots & \cdots & & \\ a_{n1} & \cdots & \cdots & a_{nn} \end{bmatrix}$$

The $(n-1)$ by $(n-1)$ matrix obtained by omitting the ith row, jth column of A will be called the *minor* of a_{ij} in A and will be denoted by A_{ij}. We now define the determinant of A to be the number given by

$$|A| = a_{11}|A_{11}| - a_{21}|A_{21}| + a_{31}|A_{31}| - \cdots (-1)^{n+1}|A_{n1}|$$

where for $n = 2$, as in Section 13–1,

$$\begin{vmatrix} a_{11} & a_{12} \\ a_{21} & a_{22} \end{vmatrix} = a_{11}a_{22} - a_{12}a_{21}.$$

Note that this definition does, in fact, assign a number as the determinant of a square matrix of any order since it defines, successively, determinants of order 3 in terms of determinants of order 2, determinants of order 4 in terms of determinants of order 3, and so on. The principle of mathematical induction guarantees that our definition assigns a number as the determinant of an $n \times n$ matrix, for any n greater than or equal to 2. Of course, our definition agrees with that of Section 13–2 for the case $n = 3$.

Some examples of the use of this definition are:

(i)
$$\begin{vmatrix} 1 & -4 & 0 & 1 \\ 2 & 0 & 3 & 1 \\ -4 & 2 & 0 & 0 \\ -3 & 1 & 1 & 5 \end{vmatrix} = 1\begin{vmatrix} 0 & 3 & 1 \\ 2 & 0 & 0 \\ 1 & 1 & 5 \end{vmatrix} - 2\begin{vmatrix} -4 & 0 & 1 \\ 2 & 0 & 0 \\ 1 & 1 & 5 \end{vmatrix}$$

$$+ (-4)\begin{vmatrix} -4 & 0 & 1 \\ 0 & 3 & 1 \\ 1 & 1 & 5 \end{vmatrix} - (-3)\begin{vmatrix} -4 & 0 & 1 \\ 0 & 3 & 1 \\ 2 & 0 & 0 \end{vmatrix}$$

$$= 1(-28) - 2(2) + (-4)(-59) - (-3)(-6)$$

$$= 186$$

(ii)
$$\begin{vmatrix} 1 & 0 & 0 & \cdots & 0 \\ 0 & 1 & 0 & \cdots & 0 \\ 0 & 0 & 1 & \cdots & \\ \vdots & & \cdots & \ddots & \vdots \\ 0 & 0 & 0 & \cdots & 1 \end{vmatrix}$$ ($n \times n$ with 1's on the main diagonal, 0's elsewhere.)

$$= 1\begin{vmatrix} 1 & 0 & \cdots & 0 \\ 0 & 1 & \cdots & 0 \\ \vdots & \vdots & \ddots & 0 \\ 0 & & 0 & 1 \end{vmatrix}$$ (where this determinant is $n-1$ by $n-1$.)

Applying the definition $n-2$ times, we see that

$$\begin{vmatrix} 1 & 0 & \cdots & 0 \\ 0 & 1 & 0 \cdot\cdot & 0 \\ \vdots & \vdots & \ddots & \\ 0 & \cdots & 0 & 1 \end{vmatrix} = \begin{vmatrix} 1 & 0 \\ 0 & 1 \end{vmatrix} = 1.$$

We define the *cofactor* of an entry a_{ij} in $\mathbf{A}$ to be the number $(-1)^{i+j}|\mathbf{A}_{ij}|$ and we will denote it by $\mathbf{C}_{ij}$. Our definition of $|\mathbf{A}|$ now takes the form

$$|\mathbf{A}| = a_{11}\,\mathbf{C}_{11} + a_{21}\,\mathbf{C}_{21} + a_{31}\,\mathbf{C}_{31} + \cdots + a_{n1}\,\mathbf{C}_{n1}.$$

Both this and our original definition of $|\mathbf{A}|$ are called the *expansion of $\mathbf{A}$ by its first column*. For example, the minor of a_{32} in

$$\mathbf{A} = \begin{bmatrix} 1 & -4 & 0 & 1 \\ 2 & 0 & 3 & 1 \\ -4 & 2 & 0 & 0 \\ -3 & 1 & 1 & 5 \end{bmatrix}$$

is the 3×3 matrix

$$\mathbf{A}_{32} = \begin{bmatrix} 1 & 0 & 1 \\ 2 & 3 & 1 \\ -3 & 1 & 5 \end{bmatrix}$$

and the cofactor of a_{32} is $(-1)^5 |\mathbf{A}_{32}|$ —that is,

$$\mathbf{C}_{32} = - \begin{vmatrix} 1 & 0 & 1 \\ 2 & 3 & 1 \\ -3 & 1 & 5 \end{vmatrix} = -25.$$

We now list (without proof) the main properties of determinants of order n. These are the same as those we have already met in the cases $n = 2, 3$. As before, $\mathbf{A}$ is an $n \times n$ matrix.

1. If $\mathbf{A}$ has a row of zeros or a column of zeros, then $|\mathbf{A}| = 0$.

2. If the matrix $\mathbf{B}$ is obtained from $\mathbf{A}$ by multiplying the entries in one row (or in one column) by the number k, then $|\mathbf{B}| = k|\mathbf{A}|$.

3. If the matrix $\mathbf{B}$ is obtained from $\mathbf{A}$ by interchanging two rows (or two columns), then $|\mathbf{B}| = -|\mathbf{A}|$.

4. If $\mathbf{A}$ has two rows (or two columns) identical, then $|\mathbf{A}| = 0$.

5. If the matrix $\mathbf{B}$ is obtained from $\mathbf{A}$ by adding some multiple, k, of the entries in one row (column) to the corresponding entries in another row (column), then $|\mathbf{B}| = |\mathbf{A}|$.

As before, we define the *transpose* of $\mathbf{A}$ to be the $n \times n$ matrix having the rows of $\mathbf{A}$ as its columns, the columns of $\mathbf{A}$ as its rows. That is, the entry in the ith row, jth column of the transpose of $\mathbf{A}$ is a_{ji}. We have the following property of the transpose.

6. The determinant of the transpose of $\mathbf{A}$ is equal to the determinant of $\mathbf{A}$.

We called our definition of $|\mathbf{A}|$ the expansion of $|\mathbf{A}|$ by its first column. We may also expand $|\mathbf{A}|$ by any other column.

7. $$|\mathbf{A}| = a_{1j} \mathbf{C}_{1j} + a_{2j} \mathbf{C}_{2j} + \cdots + a_{nj} \mathbf{C}_{nj}; \ j = 1, 2, \ldots, n$$
(expansion by the jth column)

In terms of minors, this expansion may be written as

$$|\mathbf{A}| = (-1)^{1+j} a_{1j} |\mathbf{A}_{1j}| + (-1)^{2+j} |\mathbf{A}_{2j}| + \cdots + (-1)^{n+j} a_{nj} |\mathbf{A}_{nj}|.$$

8. $$|\mathbf{A}| = a_{i1} \mathbf{C}_{i1} + a_{i2} \mathbf{C}_{i2} + \cdots + a_{in} \mathbf{C}_{in}; \ i = 1, 2, \ldots, n$$
(expansion by the ith row)

In terms of minors, this expansion may be written as

$$|\mathbf{A}| = (-1)^{i+1} |\mathbf{A}_{i1}| + (-1)^{i+2} |\mathbf{A}_{i2}| + \cdots + (-1)^{i+n} |\mathbf{A}_{in}|.$$

We illustrate how these properties are used in the computation of determinants. To compute $|\mathbf{A}|$, where

$$\mathbf{A} = \begin{bmatrix} 4 & 2 & 0 & 1 \\ 10 & -5 & 0 & 15 \\ 6 & 1 & -1 & 3 \\ 2 & 0 & 4 & 1 \end{bmatrix}$$

we use property 2 on the first column and then again on the second row.

$$|\mathbf{A}| = 2 \begin{vmatrix} 2 & 2 & 0 & 1 \\ 5 & -5 & 0 & 15 \\ 3 & 1 & -1 & 3 \\ 1 & 0 & 4 & 1 \end{vmatrix} = 10 \begin{vmatrix} 2 & 2 & 0 & 1 \\ 1 & -1 & 0 & 3 \\ 3 & 1 & -1 & 3 \\ 1 & 0 & 4 & 1 \end{vmatrix}$$

Now expand by the third column.

$$|\mathbf{A}| = 10 \left\{ 0 \,|\cdots \quad \cdots| - 0 \,|\cdots \quad \cdots| + (-1) \begin{vmatrix} 2 & 2 & 1 \\ 1 & -1 & 3 \\ 1 & 0 & 1 \end{vmatrix} - 4 \begin{vmatrix} 2 & 2 & 1 \\ 1 & -1 & 3 \\ 3 & 1 & 3 \end{vmatrix} \right\}$$

$$= 10 \left\{ -3 - 4(4) \right\} = -190$$

To compute

$$\begin{vmatrix} 1 & 1 & -1 & 2 \\ 4 & 0 & 1 & 1 \\ 2 & 11 & 5 & 7 \\ 1 & 3 & -1 & 2 \end{vmatrix}$$

first add column 2 to column 3, then subtract three times column 2 from column 1 and subtract twice column 2 from column 4.

$$\begin{vmatrix} 1 & 1 & -1 & 2 \\ 4 & 0 & 1 & 1 \\ 2 & 11 & 5 & 7 \\ 1 & 3 & -1 & 2 \end{vmatrix} = \cdots = \cdots = \cdots \begin{vmatrix} 0 & 1 & 0 & 0 \\ 4 & 0 & 1 & 1 \\ -9 & 11 & 16 & -15 \\ -2 & 3 & 2 & -4 \end{vmatrix}.$$

Expand by the first row. We get

$$- \begin{vmatrix} 4 & 1 & 1 \\ -9 & 16 & -15 \\ -2 & 2 & 4 \end{vmatrix}.$$

We leave the computation of this 3×3 determinant to the student. Consider the determinant equation

$$\begin{vmatrix} x & x_1 & x_2 & x_3 \\ y & y_1 & y_2 & y_3 \\ z & z_1 & z_2 & z_3 \\ 1 & 1 & 1 & 1 \end{vmatrix} = 0.$$

If we expand by the first column we see that the left-hand side is a linear expression in x, y, and z, so the equation represents a plane in three-dimensional coordinate geometry. Now putting x_1 for x, y_1 for y, and z_1 for z, the resulting determinant has two columns identical and so equals zero. Hence, x_1, y_1, and z_1 satisfy the equation and the point (x_1, y_1, z_1) lies on the plane represented by the equation. Similarly, the points (x_2, y_2, z_2) and (x_3, y_3, z_3) lie on this plane. It follows that provided (x_1, y_1, z_1), (x_2, y_2, z_2), and (x_3, y_3, z_3) do not lie on a line the determinant equation is the equation of the plane through the three points.

$$\begin{vmatrix} 1 & a & a^2 & a^3 \\ 1 & b & b^2 & b^3 \\ 1 & c & c^2 & c^3 \\ 1 & d & d^2 & d^3 \end{vmatrix} = \begin{vmatrix} 1 & a & a^2 & a^3 \\ 0 & b-a & b^2-a^2 & b^3-a^3 \\ 0 & c-a & c^2-a^2 & c^3-a^3 \\ 0 & d-a & d^2-a^2 & d^3-a^3 \end{vmatrix}$$ (subtracting row 1 from rows 2, 3, and 4)

$$= \begin{vmatrix} b-a & b^2-a^2 & b^3-a^3 \\ c-a & c^2-a^2 & c^3-a^3 \\ d-a & d^2-a^2 & d^3-a^3 \end{vmatrix}$$ (expanding by column 1)

$$= (b-a)(c-a)(d-a) \begin{vmatrix} 1 & b+a & b^2+ba+a^2 \\ 1 & c+a & c^2+ca+a^2 \\ 1 & d+a & d^2+da+a^2 \end{vmatrix}$$

(taking factors $b-a$, $c-a$, and $d-a$ from rows 1, 2, and 3 respectively)

$$= (b-a)(c-a)(d-a) \begin{vmatrix} 1 & b+a & b^2+ba+a^2 \\ 0 & c-b & c^2-b^2+ca-ba \\ 0 & d-b & d^2-b^2+da-ba \end{vmatrix}$$

(subtracting row 1 from rows 2 and 3)

$$= (b-a)(c-a)(d-a) \begin{vmatrix} c-b & c^2-b^2+ca-ba \\ d-b & d^2-b^2+da-ba \end{vmatrix}$$

(expanding by the first column)

$$= (b-a)(c-a)(d-a)(c-b)(d-b) \begin{vmatrix} 1 & c+b+a \\ 1 & d+b+a \end{vmatrix}$$

(factoring rows 1 and 2)

$$= (b-a)(c-a)(d-a)(c-b)(d-b)(d-c)$$

exercises

1. Use the definition of a 4×4 determinant in terms of 3×3 determinants to compute:

(a) $\begin{vmatrix} 1 & 0 & 1 & -1 \\ 1 & -1 & 0 & 0 \\ 1 & 0 & 1 & 1 \\ 1 & 1 & 0 & 0 \end{vmatrix}$,

(b) $\begin{vmatrix} 1 & 2 & 3 & 4 \\ 2 & 0 & -1 & 1 \\ 0 & 0 & 1 & 2 \\ 3 & -1 & 0 & 1 \end{vmatrix}$,

(c) $\begin{vmatrix} 1 & 0 & 0 & 0 \\ 0 & 1 & -3 & 0 \\ 0 & 0 & 1 & 0 \\ 0 & 0 & 0 & 1 \end{vmatrix}$.

Compute (a) and (b) also, using the general properties of determinants described in this section.

2. Compute

(a)
$$\begin{vmatrix} 2 & 3 & 2 & 1 & -1 \\ 7 & 1 & 0 & 4 & 0 \\ -1 & 2 & -1 & 2 & 5 \\ 4 & 1 & 6 & 1 & 1 \\ 2 & 3 & 3 & -1 & 1 \end{vmatrix},$$

(b)
$$\begin{vmatrix} 4 & -4 & 3 & 7 \\ 2 & -3 & 4 & 1 \\ 1 & 0 & -5 & 2 \\ 3 & 5 & 1 & 1 \end{vmatrix}.$$

3. Use the properties of $n \times n$ determinants to show that

$$\begin{vmatrix} 1 & a & a^2 & a^3 & a^4 \\ 1 & b & b^2 & b^3 & b^4 \\ 1 & c & c^2 & c^3 & c^4 \\ 1 & d & d^2 & d^3 & d^4 \\ 1 & e & e^2 & e^3 & e^4 \end{vmatrix} = (a-b)(a-c)(a-d)(a-e)(b-a)(b-d)$$
$$(b-e)(c-d)(c-e)(d-e).$$

4. Use the properties of $n \times n$ determinants to show that

$$\begin{vmatrix} a & b & c & d \\ b & c & d & a \\ c & d & a & b \\ d & a & b & c \end{vmatrix} = (a+b+c+d)(a-b+c-d) \times \{\text{a polynominal of degree 2 in } a, b, c, \text{ and } d\}.$$

5. Compute
$$\begin{vmatrix} b+c & c+d & d+a & a+b \\ e+a & c+d & d+b & a+b \\ b+c & a+d & d+a & b+c \\ a+d & a+b & b+c & c+d \end{vmatrix}.$$

6. Prove, assuming the properties of determinants listed in this section, that

$$\begin{vmatrix} x^2+y^2 & x & y & 1 \\ x_1^2+y_1^2 & x_1 & y_1 & 1 \\ x_2^2+y_2^2 & x_2 & y_2 & 1 \\ x_3^2+y_3^2 & x_3 & y_3 & 1 \end{vmatrix} = 0$$

is an equation of the circle through the points (x_1,y_1), (x_2,y_2), and (x_3,y_3) in a coordinate plane.

7. A skew-symmetric matrix is one in which for all i, j, $a_{ij}=-a_{ji}$. Prove that if $\mathbf{A}$ is an $n \times n$ skew-symmetric matrix where n is odd, then $|A|=0$.

8. State Cramer's Rule for n equations in n unknowns. Prove it, assuming the properties of determinants listed in this section.

vector algebra

14

14-1 introduction

A *vector* may be defined either geometrically or analytically. Geometrically, a vector is a *directed line segment* with points P and Q as endpoints. When we say that the segment is "directed" we mean that one endpoint, say P, is considered to be the initial point and the other endpoint Q is the terminal point. A vector with initial point P and terminal point Q is denoted by $\overline{PQ}$ and is represented

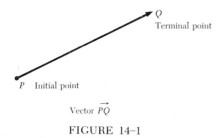

Vector $\overrightarrow{PQ}$

FIGURE 14-1

by an arrow with tip at Q. (See Figure 14-1.) The length of the arrow is called the *magnitude* of the vector. In physics, vectors are used to represent quantities with magnitude and direction—such as velocity, force, and acceleration. The arrow indicates the direction in which the force is applied, and the length of the vector indicates the magnitude of the force.

Our approach to the study of vectors will be to discuss two- and three-dimensional vectors both geometrically and analytically. We allow ourselves the latitude of using either analytic or geometric arguments to justify any theorems discussed for two and three dimensions.

14–2   two-dimensional vectors

A two-dimensional vector may be denoted by an ordered pair of real numbers $[a,b]$. We use brackets in vector notation, while parentheses are used in point notation. Two vectors $[a,b]$ and $[c,d]$ are equal if and only if $a=c$ and $b=d$. We also denote a vector $[a,b]$ by $\vec{A}$; thus, $\vec{A}=[a,b]$. Geometrically, if P and Q are any two points in the coordinate plane with coordinates (a_1,b_1) and (a_2,b_2), respectively, the ordered pair $[a_2-a_1, b_2-b_1]$ represents the vector with P as initial point and Q as terminal point; it is denoted by $\overrightarrow{PQ}$. If P is the origin with coordinates $(0,0)$ and Q is the point with coordinates (a,b), the directed segment PQ from the origin to (a,b) represents the vector $[a,b]$.

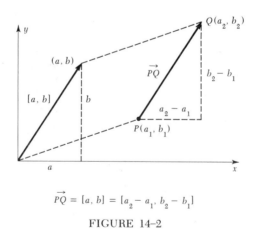

$$\overrightarrow{PQ} = [a, b] = [a_2 - a_1, b_2 - b_1]$$

FIGURE 14–2

It should be apparent from studying Figure 14–2 that two vectors $\overrightarrow{PQ}$ and $\overrightarrow{RS}$ in the plane are equal if and only if they have the same length and direction. The student should note that the *geometric equality of vectors is not one of identity*. Since vectors having the same length and direction are equal, it is possible to consider any vector as having its initial point at the origin.

The length of a vector $[a,b]$ is defined to be $\sqrt{a^2+b^2}$. If $\vec{A}=[a,b]$, the length of $\vec{A}$ is denoted by $|\vec{A}|$. Geometrically, if P and Q are two points with coordinates (a_1,b_1) and (a_2,b_2), respectively, $\overrightarrow{PQ}=[a_2-a_1, b_2-b_1]$ and by definition

$$|\overrightarrow{PQ}| = \sqrt{(a_2-a_1)^2+(b_2-b_1)^2}.$$

Notice that $|\overrightarrow{PQ}|$ is the distance between points P and Q by the distance formula.

definition: If $\vec{A}=[a_1,b_1]$ and $\vec{B}=[a_2,b_2]$, the sum of vectors $\vec{A}$ and $\vec{B}$, denoted by $\vec{A}+\vec{B}$, is defined by

$$\vec{A}+\vec{B}=[a_1+a_2, b_1+b_2].†$$

The sum of two vectors is a vector by definition. Geometrically, if vectors $\vec{A}$ and $\vec{B}$ have their initial points at the origin, the sum vector $\vec{A}+\vec{B}$ is the vector with initial point at the origin and the

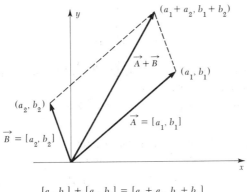

$$[a_1, b_1] + [a_2, b_2] = [a_1+a_2, b_1+b_2]$$

FIGURE 14–3

terminal point at the vertex opposite the origin in the parallelogram with $\vec{A}$ and $\vec{B}$ as adjacent sides.

If $\vec{A}=[a,b]$ and $\vec{0}=[0,0]$, then

$$\vec{A}+\vec{0}=[a+0, b+0]=[a,b]=\vec{A}.$$

The vector $\vec{0}$ is called the *zero vector*. The length of the zero vector is 0; it is not assigned any direction. The vector $[-a,-b]$ is denoted

† It would be more appropriate to write $\vec{A}\oplus\vec{B}=[a_1+a_2, b_1+b_2]$ since $\vec{A}\oplus\vec{B}$ is the sum of two vectors while a_1+a_2 is the sum of two real numbers.

by $-\vec{A}$ and is called the *negative vector of* $\vec{A}$. It is obvious that $\vec{A} + (-\vec{A}) = \vec{0}$.

definition: The *difference* of two vectors $\vec{A}$ and $\vec{B}$, denoted by $\vec{A} - \vec{B}$, is defined as follows: $\vec{A} - \vec{B} = \vec{A} + (-\vec{B})$

Thus, the difference $\vec{A}$ subtract $\vec{B}$ is the sum of $\vec{A}$ and the negative of $\vec{B}$. Geometrically, the vector $-\vec{B}$ points in the opposite direction of $\vec{B}$ and has the same length as $\vec{B}$. The vector $\vec{A} - \vec{B}$ is not only represented by the arrow from the origin to the opposite vertex of the parallelogram having $\vec{A}$ and $-\vec{B}$ as sides but it is also represented by

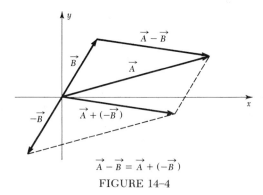

FIGURE 14–4

the arrow with initial point the tip of $\vec{B}$ and terminal point the tip of $\vec{A}$. In other words, vector $\vec{A} - \vec{B}$ is the vector from the terminal point of $\vec{B}$ to the terminal point of $\vec{A}$. (See Figure 14–4.)

definition: If $\vec{A} = [a,b]$, and c is a real number, *multiplication of a vector by a scalar* is defined in the following manner:

$$c\vec{A} = c[a,b] = [ca,cb].$$

Geometrically, if $c > 0$ the vector $[ca,cb]$ has the same direction as $[a,b]$. If $c = 0$, then $[ca,cb]$ is the zero vector. If $c < 0$, $[ca,cb]$ has the opposite direction of $[a,b]$. Since length of $[ca,cb]$ is

$$\sqrt{(ca)^2 + (cb)^2} = \sqrt{c^2(a^2 + b^2)} = |c| \sqrt{a^2 + b^2},$$

then length of $[ca,cb]$ is different from the length of $[a,b]$ by a factor of $|c|$. Thus, $3\vec{A}$ is a vector three times as long as $\vec{A}$. If the initial points of vectors $\vec{A}$ and $c\vec{A}$ are at the origin and if $c > 1$, we can consider that c "stretches" $\vec{A}$ by a factor of c.

Multiplication of a vector by a scalar (real number) has the following important properties.

1. $c(\vec{A}+\vec{B})=c\vec{A}+c\vec{B}$
2. $(cd)\,\vec{A}=c(d\vec{A})$
3. $1\vec{A}=\vec{A}$
4. $0\vec{A}=\vec{0}$
5. $-1\vec{A}=-\vec{A}$

We prove Property 1 and leave the others as exercises for the student. If $\vec{A}=[a_1,b_1]$ and $\vec{B}=[a_2,b_2]$, then

$$
\begin{aligned}
c(\vec{A}+\vec{B}) &= c([a_1,b_1]+[a_2,b_2]) \\
&= c[a_1+a_2,b_1+b_2] \\
&= [c(a_1+a_2),c(b_1+b_2)] \\
&= [ca_1+ca_2,cb_1+cb_2] \\
&= [ca_1,cb_1]+[ca_2,cb_2] \\
&= c[a_1,b_1]+c[a_2,b_2] \\
&= c\vec{A}+c\vec{B}.
\end{aligned}
$$

definition: If $\vec{A}=[a_1,b_1]$ and $\vec{B}=[a_2,b_2]$ are two vectors, the *dot product* of the two vectors is defined as follows:

$$\vec{A}\cdot\vec{B}=a_1a_2+b_1b_2.$$

We should take special note that the dot product of two vectors is a real number and *not* a vector. The dot product has some of the properties of multiplication of real numbers.

1. $\vec{A}\cdot\vec{B}=\vec{B}\cdot\vec{A}$ commutative law
2. $\vec{A}\cdot(\vec{B}+\vec{C})=\vec{A}\cdot\vec{B}+\vec{A}\cdot\vec{C}$ distributive law
3. $c(\vec{A}\cdot\vec{B})=(c\vec{A})\cdot\vec{B}$ c a real number

We prove the distributive property for the dot product and leave the other two properties as exercises for the student. If $\vec{A}=[a_1,b_1]$, $\vec{B}=[a_2,b_2]$, and $\vec{C}=[a_3,b_3]$, then

$$
\begin{aligned}
\vec{A}\cdot(\vec{B}+\vec{C}) &= [a_1,b_1]\cdot([a_2,b_2]+[a_3,b_3]) \\
&= [a_1,b_1]\cdot[a_2+a_3,b_2+b_3] \\
&= a_1(a_2+a_3)+b_1(b_2+b_3) \\
&= a_1a_2+a_1a_3+b_1b_2+b_1b_3 \\
&= (a_1a_2+b_1b_2)+(a_1a_3+b_1b_3) \\
&= [a_1,b_1]\cdot[a_2,b_2]+[a_1,b_1]\cdot[a_3,b_3] \\
&= \vec{A}\cdot\vec{B}+\vec{A}\cdot\vec{C}
\end{aligned}
$$

examples

Let $\vec{A}=[2,3]$, $\vec{B}=[3,8]$, and $\vec{C}=[-2,7]$.

1. $|\vec{A}|=\sqrt{2^2+3^2}=\sqrt{13}$

2. $\vec{A}+\vec{C}=[2,3]+[-2,7]=[0,10]$

3. $7\vec{A}=7[2\cdot3]=[14,21]$

4. $\vec{A}\cdot\vec{B}=[2,3]\cdot[3,8]=6+24=30$

5. $[2,3]\cdot([3,8]+[-2,7])=[2,3]\cdot[1,15]=2+45=47$

6. $[2,3]\cdot[3,8]+[2,3]\cdot[-2,7]=(6+24)+(-4+21)=47$

exercises

1. Let $\vec{A}=[2,3]$ and $\vec{B}=[-7,5]$. Find each of the following.
   (a) $\vec{A}+\vec{B}$ (b) $\vec{A}-\vec{B}$
   (c) $|\vec{A}|$ (d) $|\vec{B}|$

2. Let $\vec{A}=[-5,8]$ and $\vec{B}=[3,7]$. Find each of the following.
   (a) $3\vec{A}$ (b) $0\vec{B}$
   (c) $6(\vec{A}+\vec{B})$ (d) $6\vec{A}+6\vec{B}$

3. Let $\vec{A}=[a_1,b_1]$ and $\vec{B}=[a_2,b_2]$. Prove that $\vec{A}+\vec{B}=\vec{B}+\vec{A}$.

4. Let $\vec{A}=[3,5]$. Prove that $3|\vec{A}|=|3\vec{A}|$.

5. Let $\vec{A}=[a_1,b_1]$ and let c be a positive real number. Prove that $c|\vec{A}|=|c\vec{A}|$. What can you conclude if $c=0$? $c<0$?

If $\vec{A}=[a_1,b_1]$, then $|\vec{A}|=\sqrt{a_1^2+b_1^2}$ and $\vec{A}\cdot\vec{A}=[a_1,b_1]\cdot[a_1,b_1]$ $=a_1^2+b_1^2$. Thus, $|\vec{A}|^2=\vec{A}\cdot\vec{A}$. We use this fact and the properties of the dot product to give a geometric interpretation of the dot product. If $\vec{A}$ and $\vec{B}$ are two vectors with the same initial point, then $\vec{A}-\vec{B}$ is the vector from the tip of $\vec{B}$ to the tip of $\vec{A}$, and $|\vec{A}|$, $|\vec{B}|$, and $|\vec{A}-\vec{B}|$

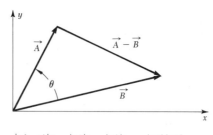

$$|\vec{A}-\vec{B}|^2 = |\vec{A}|^2 + |\vec{B}|^2 - 2|\vec{A}||\vec{B}| \cos \theta$$

Law of cosines

FIGURE 14–5

are the lengths of each side of the triangle formed. (See Figure 14–5.) If θ is the measure of the angle between $\vec{A}$ and $\vec{B}$, then by the *law of cosines*

$$|\vec{A}-\vec{B}|^2=|\vec{A}|^2+|\vec{B}|^2-2|\vec{A}||\vec{B}|\cos\theta.$$

Since

$$|\vec{A}-\vec{B}|^2 = (\vec{A}-\vec{B}) \cdot (\vec{A}-\vec{B}) = \vec{A} \cdot \vec{A} - 2\vec{A} \cdot \vec{B} + \vec{B} \cdot \vec{B}$$
$$= |\vec{A}|^2 - 2\vec{A} \cdot \vec{B} + |\vec{B}|^2,$$
$$|\vec{A}|^2 + |\vec{B}|^2 - 2|\vec{A}||\vec{B}| \cos \theta = |\vec{A}|^2 - 2\vec{A} \cdot \vec{B} + |\vec{B}|^2.$$

Hence,

$$\vec{A} \cdot \vec{B} = |\vec{A}||\vec{B}| \cos \theta.$$

Therefore, the dot product $\vec{A} \cdot \vec{B}$ is the product of the length of $\vec{A}$, the length of $\vec{B}$, and the cosine of the measure of the angle between $\vec{A}$ and $\vec{B}$.

If the dot product of two vectors $\vec{A}$ and $\vec{B}$ is zero, then $|\vec{A}||\vec{B}| \cos \theta = 0$. If neither $\vec{A}$ nor $\vec{B}$ is the zero vector, then $|\vec{A}| \neq 0$, $|\vec{B}| \neq 0$, and $\cos \theta = 0$. Hence, $\theta = 90°$ and the two vectors are perpendicular. Conversely, if $\theta = 90°$, then $\cos \theta = 0$ and $\vec{A} \cdot \vec{B} = 0$. Thus, two nonzero vectors are perpendicular if and only if their dot product is zero.

examples

1. (a) Let $P(-4,6)$, $Q(3,14)$, and $R(4,-1)$ be three points in the coordinate plane. By vector methods, prove that the line segment PQ is perpendicular to the line segment RP.

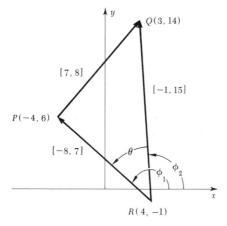

FIGURE 14–6

Solution: $\overrightarrow{PQ} = [7,8]$ and $\overrightarrow{RP} = [-8,7]$. Now

$$\overrightarrow{PQ} \cdot \overrightarrow{RP} = [7,8] \cdot [-8,7] = -56 + 56 = 0.$$

Since the dot product is zero, $\overrightarrow{PQ}$ is perpendicular to $\overrightarrow{RP}$ and the two line segments are perpendicular.

(b) Find the measure θ of the angle PRQ in the triangle formed by the three points given in part (a).

Solution: Part 1. $\overrightarrow{RP} = [-8,7]$ and $\overrightarrow{RQ} = [-1,15]$. Thus $|\overrightarrow{RP}| = \sqrt{64+49} = \sqrt{113}$ and $|\overrightarrow{RQ}| = \sqrt{1+225} = \sqrt{226}$.

$$\begin{aligned} \cos\theta &= \frac{\overrightarrow{RP}\cdot\overrightarrow{RQ}}{|\overrightarrow{RP}||\overrightarrow{RQ}|} \\ &= \frac{[-8,7]\cdot[-1,15]}{\sqrt{113}\,\sqrt{226}} \\ &= \frac{8+105}{\sqrt{113}\,\sqrt{2}\,\sqrt{113}} \\ &= \frac{113}{\sqrt{2}\,(113)} \\ &= .7071 \end{aligned}$$

Part 2. We check the result in Part 1 using the trigonometric identity for $\tan(\phi_1 - \phi_2)$ and the fact that $\tan\phi_1 = -7/8$, the slope of the line containing P and R, and $\tan\phi_2 = -15$, the slope of the line containing R and Q.

Since

$$\begin{aligned} \theta &= \phi_1 - \phi_2, \\ \tan\theta &= \tan(\phi_1 - \phi_2) \\ &= \frac{\tan\phi_1 - \tan\phi_2}{1 + \tan\phi_1\,\tan\phi_2} \\ &= \frac{-7/8 - (-15)}{1 + \dfrac{105}{8}} \\ &= \frac{-7 + 120}{8 + 105} \\ &= 1. \end{aligned}$$

Since $\tan 45° = 1$ and $\cos 45° = .7071$, our solutions check.

Part 3. As a further check, we notice that $|\overrightarrow{RP}| = |\overrightarrow{PQ}|$. Hence, the triangle is an isosceles right triangle. The two acute angles have measure 45°.

2. Let O, P, Q, and R be the vertices of a parallelogram. Let $\vec{A} = \overrightarrow{OP}$ and $\vec{B} = \overrightarrow{OR}$. Since the opposite sides of a parallelogram are equal in length and parallel, $\vec{A} = \overrightarrow{OP} = \overrightarrow{RQ}$ and $\vec{B} = \overrightarrow{OR} = \overrightarrow{PQ}$.

$$\vec{A} + \vec{B} = \overrightarrow{OQ}$$

and

$$\vec{B} - \vec{A} = \overrightarrow{PR}.$$

Subtracting,

$$2\vec{A} = \overrightarrow{OQ} - \overrightarrow{PR};$$

thus,

$$2\vec{A} + \overline{PR} = \overline{OQ}.$$

Hence,

$$\vec{A} + \frac{1}{2}\,\overline{PR} = \frac{1}{2}\,\overline{OQ}.$$

This proves that the midpoint of the diagonal $\overline{PR}$ is the same as the midpoint of the diagonal $\overline{OQ}$. In other words, the diagonals of a parallelogram bisect each other.

3. Prove by vector methods that one half the sum of the squares of the lengths of the diagonals of a parallelogram is the sum of the squares of two adjacent sides. (See Figure 14–7.)

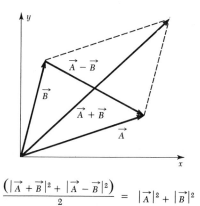

$$\frac{\left(|\vec{A} + \vec{B}|^2 + |\vec{A} - \vec{B}|^2\right)}{2} = |\vec{A}|^2 + |\vec{B}|^2$$

FIGURE 14–7

Solution: We need to prove that

$$1/2\ (|\vec{A} + \vec{B}|^2 + |\vec{A} - \vec{B}|^2) = |\vec{A}|^2 + |\vec{B}|^2.$$

Since

$$
\begin{aligned}
|\vec{A} + \vec{B}|^2 &= (\vec{A} - \vec{B}) \cdot (\vec{A} + \vec{B}) \\
&= \vec{A} \cdot \vec{A} + 2\,\vec{A} \cdot \vec{B} + \vec{B} \cdot \vec{B} \\
&= |\vec{A}|^2 + 2\,\vec{A} \cdot \vec{B} + |\vec{B}|^2
\end{aligned}
$$

and

$$|\vec{A} - \vec{B}|^2 = |\vec{A}|^2 - 2\,\vec{A} \cdot \vec{B} + |\vec{B}|^2,$$
$$|\vec{A} + \vec{B}|^2 + |\vec{A} - \vec{B}|^2 = 2\,|\vec{A}|^2 + 2\,|\vec{B}|^2.$$

Thus, $1/2\ (|\vec{A} + \vec{B}|^2 + |\vec{A} - \vec{B}|^2) = |\vec{A}|^2 + |\vec{B}|^2.$

exercises

1. Let $P(2,7)$, $Q(-3,11)$, and $R(1,-5)$ be three points in the coordinate plane.

   (a) Find $|\overline{PQ}|$.   (b) Find $|\overline{PR}|$.

   (c) If θ is the measure of angle QPR, find $\cos\theta$.

   (d) Find $\overline{RQ}\cdot\overline{RP}$.

2. Draw vectors $\vec{A}=[2,5]$ and $\vec{B}=[7,3]$ with initial points at the origin. On the same graph, draw $\vec{C}=\vec{A}+t\vec{B}$ with initial point at the origin for the following values of t: $t=-5$, $t=-4$, $t=-3$, $t=-2$, $t=-1$, $t=1/3$, $t=1/2$, $t=2/3$, $t=3/4$, $t=1$, $t=2$, $t=3$, $t=4$, $t=5$.

3. Let $\vec{A}=[2,5]$, $\vec{B}=[7,3]$, and $\vec{C}=[x,y]$ be vectors with initial points at the origin. Let t be any real number and let $[x,y]=[2,5]+t[7,3]$. Use vector properties to find two equations in x, y, and t. Eliminate t by solving one equation for t and substituting in the second equation. Describe the graph of pairs of real numbers (x,y) satisfying the resulting equation.

4. Let $\vec{A}$, $\vec{B}$, and $\vec{C}$ be vectors with initial points at the origin. Describe the collection of points in the coordinate plane that are terminal points of the vectors $\vec{C}=\vec{A}+t\vec{B}$ where t is any real number. (See Exercises 2 and 3.)

5. Let $\vec{A}$, $\vec{B}$, and $\vec{C}$ be vectors with initial points at the origin. Describe the collection of points in the coordinate plane that are terminal points of the vectors $\vec{C}=\vec{A}+t\vec{B}$ where $0\leqslant t\leqslant 1$. (See Exercises 2, 3, and 4.)

6. Let $\vec{A}=[2,5]$ and $\vec{B}=[7,3]$ be two vectors with initial points at the origin. Let s and t be real numbers such that $s+t=1$. Draw the graph of $\vec{C}=s\vec{A}+t\vec{B}$ with initial point at the origin for the following values of t: -5, -4, -3, -2, -1, $1/3$, $1/2$, $2/3$, $3/4$,1, 2, 3, 4, and 5.

7. Let $\vec{A}$ and $\vec{B}$ be two vectors with initial points at the origin. Describe the graph of the collection of terminal points of vectors $\vec{C}=s\vec{A}+t\vec{B}$ with initial point at the origin where s and t are real numbers such that $s+t=1$.

8. Let $\vec{A}$ and $\vec{B}$ be two vectors with initial points at the origin. Describe the graph of the collection of terminal points of $\vec{C}=s\vec{A}+t\vec{B}$ with initial points at the origin where s and t are real numbers such that $0\leqslant s\leqslant 1$, $0\leqslant t\leqslant 1$.

9. Let $\vec{A}=[3,8]$, $\vec{B}=[5,-2]$, and $\vec{C}=[1,3]$. Prove there are real numbers s and t such that $\vec{C}=s\vec{A}+t\vec{B}$.

10. Let $\vec{A}$ and $\vec{B}$ be two nonzero vectors such that $\vec{B}$ is not a scalar multiple of $\vec{A}$. Prove there are real numbers s and t such that $\vec{C}=s\vec{A}+t\vec{B}$ for any vector $\vec{C}$. (Hint: Let $\vec{A}=[a_1,b_1]$, $\vec{B}=[a_2,b_2]$, and $\vec{C}=[a_3,b_3]$. Solve for s and t.)

11. Find a vector of unit length that is perpendicular to the vector $\vec{A} = [3,7]$. (There are two answers.)

12. Find a vector of unit length that is perpendicular to a nonzero vector. $\vec{A} = [a_1,b_1]$. (See Exercise 11.)

13. Let $\vec{A}$ and $\vec{B}$ be two vectors with same initial point. Draw the graph and indicate the vector $\vec{A} - \vec{B}$ from the tip of $\vec{B}$ to the tip of $\vec{A}$.
    (a) In the triangle formed, show that the medians of the triangle are $\frac{1}{2}\vec{A} + \frac{1}{2}\vec{B}$, $\frac{1}{2}\vec{A} - \vec{B}$, and $\frac{1}{2}\vec{B} - \vec{A}$.
    (b) Show that the square of the length of each median is $\frac{1}{4}|\vec{A}|^2 + \frac{1}{2}\vec{A} \cdot \vec{B} + \frac{1}{4}|\vec{B}|^2$, $\frac{1}{4}|\vec{A}|^2 - \vec{A} \cdot \vec{B} + |\vec{B}|^2$, and $\frac{1}{4}|\vec{B}|^2 - \vec{A} \cdot \vec{B} + |\vec{A}|^2$, respectively.

    (c) Prove that the sum of the squares of the lengths of the medians is three-fourths the sum of the squares of the lengths of the sides of the triangle.

14-3 three-dimensional vectors

An ordered triple of real numbers $[a_1,b_1,c_1]$ denotes a *three-dimensional vector*. Geometrically, if points P and Q have coordinates (p_1,q_1,r_1) and (p_2,q_2,r_2), respectively, $[p_2 - p_1, q_2 - q_1, r_2 - r_1]$ is the vector from P to Q. Thus, $[a_1,b_1,c_1]$ can be considered as a vector from the origin of the three-dimensional rectangular coordinate system to the point (a_1,b_1,c_1). If $\vec{A} = [a_1,b_1,c_1]$ the length of $\vec{A}$, denoted by $|\vec{A}|$, is given by

$$|\vec{A}| = \sqrt{a_1{}^2 + b_1{}^2 + c_1{}^2}.$$

Consequently,

$$|\overrightarrow{PQ}| = \sqrt{(p_2 - p_1)^2 + (q_2 - q_1)^2 + (r_2 - r_1)^2}.$$

Let $\vec{A} = [a_1,b_1,c_1]$. Consider the vector with the origin as initial point and (a_1,b_1,c_1) as the terminal point. (See Figure 14-8.) The vector $\vec{A}$ and the *positive* x-axis determine a plane, since two intersecting lines determine a plane in three-space. The angle in this plane with positive x-axis as one side and vector $\vec{A}$ as the other side is assigned measure α where $0° < \alpha < 180°$. If $\vec{A}$ is coincident with the positive x-axis $\alpha = 0°$, and if $\vec{A}$ is coincident with the negative x-axis $\alpha = 180°$. Similarly, β and γ are the measures of the angles the vector makes with the positive y-axis and z-axis, respectively. The three angles with measures α, β, *and* γ are called *direction angles*. Essentially, direction angles determine the direction in which the vector points. The three real numbers $\cos \alpha$, $\cos \beta$, and $\cos \gamma$ are called *direction cosines* of the vector.

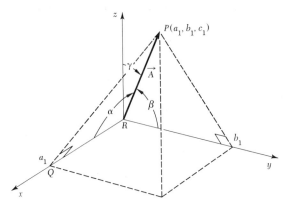

FIGURE 14–8

Consider the right triangle PQR. (See Figure 14–8.) It is evident that $\cos \alpha = a_1/|\vec{A}|$. Similarly, $\cos \beta = b_1/|\vec{A}|$ and $\cos \gamma = c_1/|\vec{A}|$. Hence,

$$\cos^2\alpha + \cos^2\beta + \cos^2\gamma = \frac{a_1{}^2 + b_1{}^2 + c_1{}^2}{|\vec{A}|^2} = \frac{|\vec{A}|^2}{|\vec{A}|^2} = 1.$$

The scalar product $c\vec{A}$ and the dot product $\vec{A} \cdot \vec{B}$ are defined for three-dimensional vectors in a way analogous to the two-dimensional definitions. The proofs of the various theorems,—such as if $\vec{A}$ and $\vec{B}$ are vectors with θ as the measure of the angle between them, then

$$\vec{A} \cdot \vec{B} = |\vec{A}||\vec{B}| \cos \theta$$

—are the same for three-dimensional vectors as for two-dimensional vectors.

exercises

1. Let $\vec{A} = [2,1,3]$ and $\vec{B} = [-2,-1,2]$.
   (a) Find $\vec{A} \cdot \vec{B}$.
   (b) Find the direction cosines of vector $\vec{A}$.
   (c) Find the measure of the direction angles of vector $\vec{B}$.
   (d) If $\vec{A}$ and $\vec{B}$ have initial points at the origin, find the measure of the angle having $\vec{A}$ and $\vec{B}$ as sides.

2. Let $\vec{A} = [3,4,5]$ and $\vec{B} = [1,1,2]$ be vectors with initial points at the origin.
   (a) Describe the locus of the terminal points of the vectors kB with initial points at the origin and $k > 0$.
   (b) Find the vector $k\vec{B}$ such that $k\vec{B}$ and $k\vec{B} - \vec{A}$ are perpendicular.
   (c) Find the area of the triangle with $\vec{A}$, $\vec{B}$ and $\vec{A} - \vec{B}$ as sides.

3. Let $(0,0,0)$, $(1,3,8)$, and $(2,5,1)$ be vertices of a triangle. Find the measure of each of the interior angles.

4. Let $(1,2,3)$, $(4,5,6)$, and $(7,8,9)$ be three points.
(a) Are the three points collinear? Justify.
(b) If the points are not collinear, find the area of the triangle formed.

5. Prove that if $\vec{A} \cdot \vec{B} = 0$, then $|\vec{A} - \vec{B}|^2 = |\vec{A}|^2 + |\vec{B}|^2$. Interpret geometrically.

6. Prove that if $|\vec{A} - \vec{B}|^2 = |\vec{A}|^2 + |\vec{B}|^2$, then $\vec{A} \cdot \vec{B} = 0$. (See Exercise 5.)

7. Prove that vector $[a,b,c]$ is perpendicular to the plane $ax + by + cz = d$.

8. Find two perpendicular vectors of length 3, each of which is perpendicular to $\vec{A} = [2,1,2]$.

14–4   cross product

definition: Let $\vec{A} = [a_1, b_1, c_1]$ and $\vec{B} = [a_2, b_2, c_2]$ be two vectors. The *cross product* of the two vectors *(which is a vector)* is defined as follows:

$$\vec{A} \times \vec{B} = \left[\begin{vmatrix} b_1 & b_2 \\ c_1 & c_2 \end{vmatrix}, \begin{vmatrix} c_1 & c_2 \\ a_1 & a_2 \end{vmatrix}, \begin{vmatrix} a_1 & a_2 \\ b_1 & b_2 \end{vmatrix} \right]$$

or

$$\vec{A} \times \vec{B} = [b_1 c_2 - c_1 b_2, \ c_1 a_2 - a_1 c_2, \ a_1 b_2 - b_1 a_2] .\dagger$$

Notice that

$$\vec{B} \times \vec{A} = \left[\begin{vmatrix} b_2 & b_1 \\ c_2 & c_1 \end{vmatrix}, \begin{vmatrix} c_2 & c_1 \\ a_2 & a_1 \end{vmatrix}, \begin{vmatrix} a_2 & a_1 \\ b_2 & b_1 \end{vmatrix} \right].$$

Although the cross product is not a commutative operation, since

$$\begin{vmatrix} a & b \\ c & d \end{vmatrix} = - \begin{vmatrix} b & a \\ d & c \end{vmatrix}$$

we have $\vec{A} \times \vec{B} = -\vec{B} \times \vec{A}$. Geometrically, the vectors $\vec{A} \times \vec{B}$ and $\vec{B} \times \vec{A}$ have the same length but opposite directions.

Since a determinant is zero if two rows are the same, we have that $\vec{A} \times \vec{A} = \vec{0}$. Four more important properties of the cross product are stated in the following theorems.

theorem 14–1:   If k is a real number and if $\vec{A}$ and $\vec{B}$ are three-dimensional vectors, then $k(\vec{A} \times \vec{B}) = (k\vec{A}) \times \vec{B}$.

$\dagger$Notice that $\vec{A} \times \vec{B} = \left[\begin{vmatrix} b_1 & c_1 \\ b_2 & c_2 \end{vmatrix}, \begin{vmatrix} c_1 & a_1 \\ c_2 & a_2 \end{vmatrix}, \begin{vmatrix} a_1 & b_1 \\ a_2 & b_2 \end{vmatrix} \right]$

proof: Let $\vec{A} = [a_1, b_1, c_1]$ and $\vec{B} = [a_2, b_2, c_2]$.

$$k([a_1, b_1, c_1] \times [a_2, b_2, c_2]) = k[b_1 c_2 - b_2 c_1, \; c_1 a_2 - c_2 a_1, \; a_1 b_2 - a_2 b_1]$$
$$= [(kb_1)c_2 - b_2(kc_1), \; (kc_1)a_2 - c_2(ka_1), \; (ka_1)b_2 - a_2(kb_1)]$$
$$= [ka_1, kb_1, kc_1] \times [a_2, b_2, c_2]$$
$$= (k\vec{A}) \times \vec{B}$$

theorem 14–2: Let $\vec{A}$, $\vec{B}$, and $\vec{C}$ be three-dimensional vectors. Then $\vec{A} \times (\vec{B} + \vec{C}) = (\vec{A} \times \vec{B}) + (\vec{A} \times \vec{C})$.

proof: Left as an exercise for the student.

theorem 14–3:   Let $\vec{A}$ and $\vec{B}$ be three-dimensional vectors. Then $\vec{A} \cdot (\vec{A} \times \vec{B})$ $= 0$ and $\vec{B} \cdot (\vec{A} \times \vec{B}) = 0$.

proof: *Part* 1. Let $\vec{A} = [a_1, b_1, c_1]$ and $\vec{B} = [a_2, b_2, c_2]$.

$$\vec{A} \cdot (\vec{A} \times \vec{B}) = [a_1, b_1, c_1] \cdot \left[\begin{vmatrix} b_1 & c_1 \\ b_2 & c_2 \end{vmatrix}, \begin{vmatrix} c_1 & a_1 \\ c_2 & a_2 \end{vmatrix}, \begin{vmatrix} a_1 & b_1 \\ a_2 & b_2 \end{vmatrix} \right]$$

$$= a_1 \begin{vmatrix} b_1 & c_1 \\ b_2 & c_2 \end{vmatrix} + b_1 \begin{vmatrix} c_1 & a_1 \\ c_2 & a_2 \end{vmatrix} + c_1 \begin{vmatrix} a_1 & b_1 \\ a_2 & b_2 \end{vmatrix}$$

$$= a_1 \begin{vmatrix} b_1 & c_1 \\ b_2 & c_2 \end{vmatrix} - b_1 \begin{vmatrix} a_1 & c_1 \\ a_2 & c_2 \end{vmatrix} + c_1 \begin{vmatrix} a_1 & b_1 \\ a_2 & b_2 \end{vmatrix}$$

$$= \begin{vmatrix} a_1 & b_1 & c_1 \\ a_1 & b_1 & c_1 \\ a_2 & b_2 & c_2 \end{vmatrix} \qquad \text{(expanding by the first row)}$$

$$= 0 \qquad \text{(since two rows are the same).}$$

Part 2. Left as an exercise for the student.

Geometrically, since $\vec{A} \cdot (\vec{A} \times \vec{B})$ and $\vec{B} \cdot (\vec{A} \times \vec{B})$ are zero, vector $(\vec{A} \times \vec{B})$ is perpendicular to both $\vec{A}$ and $\vec{B}$. Thus, $\vec{A} \times \vec{B}$ is a vector perpendicular to the plane determined by vectors $\vec{A}$ and $\vec{B}$ if they are nonparallel.

theorem 14–4: Let $\vec{A}$ and $\vec{B}$ be two three-dimensional vectors. Then,

$$|\vec{A} \times \vec{B}| = \sqrt{|\vec{A}|^2 |\vec{B}|^2 - (\vec{A} \cdot \vec{B})^2}.$$

proof: Left as an exercise for the student.

Since $\vec{A} \cdot \vec{B} = |\vec{A}||\vec{B}| \cos \theta$ where θ is the measure of the angle between vectors $\vec{A}$ and $\vec{B}$,

$$(\vec{A} \cdot \vec{B})^2 = |\vec{A}|^2 |\vec{B}|^2 \cos^2\theta.$$

Thus,

$$|\vec{A} \times \vec{B}| = \sqrt{|\vec{A}|^2|\vec{B}|^2 - (\vec{A} \cdot \vec{B})^2}$$
$$= \sqrt{|\vec{A}|^2|\vec{B}|^2 - |\vec{A}|^2|\vec{B}|^2 \cos^2 \theta}$$
$$= \sqrt{|\vec{A}|^2|\vec{B}|^2 (1 - \cos^2 \theta)}$$
$$= |\vec{A}||\vec{B}| \sqrt{\sin^2 \theta}$$
$$= |\vec{A}||\vec{B}| \sin \theta \qquad \text{since } 0 \leqslant \theta \leqslant 180° \text{ and } \sin \theta \geqslant 0.$$

Consequently, the length of $\vec{A} \times \vec{B}$ is the product of the length of $\vec{A}$, the length of $\vec{B}$, and the sine of the measure of the angle between the two given vectors.

Since there are two vectors of equal length, both of which are perpendicular to $\vec{A}$ and $\vec{B}$, we now describe geometrically in which direction $\vec{A} \times \vec{B}$ points from the plane containing $\vec{A}$ and $\vec{B}$. If we look toward the plane containing $\vec{A}$ and $\vec{B}$ and if the measure θ of the angle from $\vec{A}$ counterclockwise to $\vec{B}$ is $0 < \phi < 180°$, vector $\vec{A} \times \vec{B}$ points toward us. If $180 < \phi < 360°$, vector $\vec{A} \times \vec{B}$ points away from us. Of course, this assumes that the coordinate axes are oriented on a right-hand system.

Consider the three vectors $\vec{A} = [a_1, b_1, c_1]$, $\vec{B} = [a_2, b_2, c_2]$, and $\vec{C} = [a_3, b_3, c_3]$. Since

$$\vec{B} \times \vec{C} = \left[\begin{vmatrix} b_2 & c_2 \\ b_3 & c_3 \end{vmatrix}, \begin{vmatrix} c_2 & a_2 \\ c_3 & a_3 \end{vmatrix}, \begin{vmatrix} a_2 & b_2 \\ a_3 & b_3 \end{vmatrix} \right]$$

$$\vec{A} \cdot (\vec{B} \times \vec{C}) = a_1 \begin{vmatrix} b_2 & c_2 \\ b_3 & c_3 \end{vmatrix} + b_1 \begin{vmatrix} c_2 & a_2 \\ c_3 & a_3 \end{vmatrix} + c_1 \begin{vmatrix} a_2 & b_2 \\ a_3 & b_3 \end{vmatrix}$$

$$= a_1 \begin{vmatrix} b_2 & c_2 \\ b_3 & c_3 \end{vmatrix} - b_1 \begin{vmatrix} a_2 & c_2 \\ a_3 & c_3 \end{vmatrix} + c_1 \begin{vmatrix} a_2 & b_2 \\ a_3 & b_3 \end{vmatrix}$$

$$= \begin{vmatrix} a_1 & a_2 & a_3 \\ b_1 & b_2 & b_3 \\ c_1 & c_2 & c_3 \end{vmatrix}.$$

Consider the following system of linear equations.

$$a_1 x + a_2 y + a_3 z = d_1$$
$$b_1 x + b_2 y + b_3 z = d_2$$
$$c_1 x + c_2 y + c_3 z = d_3$$

If $\vec{A} = [a_1, b_1, c_1]$, $\vec{B} = [a_2, b_2, c_2]$, $\vec{C} = [a_3, b_3, c_3]$, and $\vec{D} = [d_1, d_2, d_3]$, then the system can be written as the vector equation

$$x\vec{A} + y\vec{B} + z\vec{C} = \vec{D}.$$

Multiplying both sides by $\vec{B} \times \vec{C}$, we obtain

$$x(\vec{A} \cdot (\vec{B} \times \vec{C})) + y(\vec{B} \cdot (\vec{B} \times \vec{C})) + z(\vec{C} \cdot (\vec{B} \times \vec{C})) = \vec{D} \cdot (\vec{B} \times \vec{C}).$$

Thus,

$$x(\vec{A} \cdot (\vec{B} \times \vec{C})) = \vec{D} \cdot (\vec{B} \times \vec{C})$$

$$x = \frac{\vec{D} \cdot (\vec{B} \times \vec{C})}{\vec{A} \cdot (\vec{B} \times \vec{C})} \qquad \text{provided } \vec{A} \cdot (\vec{B} \times \vec{C}) \neq 0.$$

Consequently,

$$x = \frac{\begin{vmatrix} d_1 & a_2 & a_3 \\ d_2 & b_2 & b_3 \\ d_3 & c_2 & c_3 \end{vmatrix}}{\begin{vmatrix} a_1 & a_2 & a_3 \\ b_1 & b_2 & b_3 \\ c_1 & c_2 & c_3 \end{vmatrix}}.$$

This is a vector derivation of Cramer's Rule discussed in Chapter 13.

exercises

1. Let $\vec{A} = [2,1,3]$ and $\vec{B} = [3,-1,-2]$.
   (a) Find $\vec{A} \times \vec{B}$.
   (b) Find $|\vec{A} \times \vec{B}|$ using Theorem 14–4.
   (c) Find $\vec{A} \times \vec{B}$ by using part (a) and the definition of length of a vector.

2. Let $\vec{A} = [1,2,3]$, $\vec{B} = [-2,-1,4]$, and $\vec{C} = [2,0,5]$.
   (a) Find $\vec{A} \times (\vec{B} \times \vec{C})$.
   (b) Find $(\vec{A} \times \vec{B}) \times \vec{C}$.
   (c) Find $(\vec{C} \times \vec{A}) \times \vec{B}$.
   (d) Find $(\vec{A} \times \vec{B}) \cdot \vec{C}$.
   (e) Find $(\vec{B} \times \vec{C}) \cdot \vec{A}$.
   (f) Find $(\vec{C} \times \vec{A}) \cdot \vec{B}$.

3. Prove if $\vec{A} \times \vec{B} = \vec{0}$ and $\vec{A} \cdot \vec{B} = 0$, then either $\vec{A} = \vec{0}$ or $\vec{B} = \vec{0}$. Is the converse true?

4. Let $\vec{A} = [1,3,4]$ and $\vec{B} = [3,5,9]$ be vectors with initial points at the origin.
   (a) Find the area of the parallelogram with $\vec{A}$ and $\vec{B}$ as two adjacent sides.
   (b) Find $|\vec{A} \times \vec{B}|$.

5. Generalize your results in Exercise 4 and prove your resulting conjectures.

6. Write the system $2x + 3y - 5z = 11$, $3x + y - 6z = 2$, $x + 5y - 8z = 4$ as a vector equation. Use vector methods to solve for y. (Hint: Let $\vec{A} = [2,3,1]$, $\vec{B} = [3,1,5]$, $\vec{C} = [-5,-6,-8]$, and $\vec{D} = [11,2,4]$.)

7. Prove Theorem 14–2.

8. Prove Part 2 of Theorem 14–3.

9. Prove Theorem 14–4.

10. Let $\vec{A}$, $\vec{B}$, and $\vec{C}$ be three-dimensional vectors. Prove that $(\vec{A} \times \vec{B}) \cdot \vec{C} = (\vec{B} \times \vec{C}) \cdot \vec{A} = (\vec{C} \times \vec{A}) \cdot \vec{B}$.

introduction to differential calculus

15

15–1   Velocity

Let us consider the concept of velocity as related to a free-falling object. Neglecting air resistance, the distance s in feet that a body falls from rest is directly proportional to the square of the time t in seconds for which it falls. In fact, the distance function s is defined by $s(t) = 16t^2$. Thus, in 2 seconds a body falling from rest would fall $s(2) = 64$ feet.

Since $s(3) = 144$, the distance the object falls in 3 seconds is 144 feet. Thus, $s(3) - s(2) = 80$ feet is the distance the object falls during the one-second time lapse from 2 to 3 seconds. When the distance a body travels is divided by the time, a number, called *average speed*, is assigned to the motion; thus, the average speed during the one-second time interval considered is 80 feet per second. The average speed of the object in the tenth of a second from 2 to 2.1 seconds is less than 80 feet per second; in fact, it is 65.6 feet per second, as demonstrated by the following computations.

$$\left.\begin{array}{l}\text{Average speed in 2 to 2.1 second}\\ \text{time interval:}\end{array}\right\} = \frac{s(2.1) - s(2)}{2.1 - 2}$$

$$= \frac{16(2.1)^2 - 16(2)^2}{0.1}$$

$$= \frac{16[(2.1)^2 - 2^2]}{0.1}$$

$$= \frac{16(2.1 + 2)(2.1 - 2)}{0.1}$$

$$= \frac{16(4.1)(0.1)}{0.1}$$

$$= 65.6 \text{ feet per second.}$$

If there is to be any meaning to the question "How fast is the object falling at the end of 2 seconds?" something more sophisticated than average speed must be defined. It is clear that a reasonable answer to the proposed question should be less than 65.6 feet per second; in fact, as the following computations indicate, it should be less than 64.16 feet per second.

Average speed in 2 to 2.01 second time interval: $\left. \right\} = \dfrac{s(2.01) - s(2)}{2.01 - 2}$

$$= \frac{16(2.01)^2 - 16(2)^2}{0.01}$$

$$= \frac{16(4.01)(0.01)}{0.01}$$

$$= 64.16 \text{ feet per second.}$$

Two things are clear: (1) for better approximations, the time interval should be shortened; and (2) instead of further considering numerical examples, a symbol such as "x" should be used to represent time (such as 2.1, 2.01, etc.), and the average speed should be computed for the time interval from 2 to x seconds where x is a positive real number greater than 2.

Average speed in 2 to x second time interval: $\left. \right\} = \dfrac{s(x) - s(2)}{x - 2}$

$$= \frac{16x^2 - 16(2)^2}{x - 2}$$

$$= \frac{16(x + 2)(x - 2)}{x - 2}$$

$$= 16(x + 2), \text{ provided } x > 2 .$$

(We note that if $x = 2.1$ or $x = 2.01$, this result agrees with our previous computations.)

It is obvious that the number $16(x + 2)$ can be made "arbitrarily close" to 64 by choosing x "close" to 2. Thus, the velocity of the body at the end of 2 seconds is *defined* to be 64 feet per second. (*Note*: From both

mathematical and physical considerations, it would be incorrect to let
$x = 2$ in the average speed formula.)

As a final generalization, let us consider defining the velocity of a
free-falling body at the end of t seconds, where t is any positive real
number. In t seconds, the object falls $s(t) = 16t^2$ feet, and in x seconds,
where $x > t$, the object falls $s(x) = 16x^2$ feet. Hence, the average speed A
in the time interval between t and x seconds is

$$A = \frac{x(x) - s(t)}{x - t}$$

$$= \frac{16x^2 - 16\ t^2}{x - t}$$

$$= \frac{16(x + t)(x - t)}{x - t}$$

$$= 16(x + t) \text{ feet per second.}$$

By an argument similar to the one above, we are led to *define* the
velocity of a free-falling body at the end of t seconds to be $32t$ feet per
second. Notice that from the distance function s we have derived a new
function v, defined by $v(t) = 32t$, called the *velocity function*.

15–2   slope

Let us consider the geometric problem of finding the slope of the
tangent line to the graph of a function at some point on its graph. Let s
be the function defined by $s(x) = 16x^2$. For the points $(2, s(2))$ and
$(2.1, s(2.1))$, the slope m of the line containing these two points is

$$m = \frac{s(2.1) - s(2)}{2.1 - 2}$$

$$= \frac{16(2.1)^2 - 16(2)^2}{0.1}$$

$$= \frac{16(4.1)(0.1)}{0.1}$$

$$= 65.6\ .$$

If we choose a point closer to $(2, s(2))$, such as $(2.01, s(2.01))$, we obtain a better approximation of the slope of the tangent line at $(2, s(2))$.
The slope of the line containing the points $(2, s(2))$ and $(2.01, s(2.01))$
is 64.16, as the reader may verify.

The slope of the line through the points $(2, s(2))$ and $(x, s(x))$, where
x is any real number other than 2, is given by

$$m = \frac{16x^2 - 16(2)^2}{x - 2}$$

$$= \frac{16(x + 2)(x - 2)}{x - 2}$$

$$= 16(x + 2), \text{ provided } x \neq 2.$$

Since the line containing the two points "becomes" the tangent line as the two points become coincident (see Figure 15–1), the slope of the

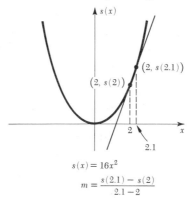

$$s(x) = 16x^2$$

$$m = \frac{s(2.1) - s(2)}{2.1 - 2}$$

FIGURE 15–1

tangent line at $(2, s(2))$ is approximated by $16(x + 2)$, where x is a real number "close" to 2. Geometrically, it is evident that the slope of the tangent line to the curve at $(2, s(2))$ is 64.

If $(x, s(x))$ and $(t, s(t))$ are any two points on the graph of s, then the slope of the line containing these two points is

$$m = \frac{16x^2 - 16t^2}{x - t}$$

$$= \frac{16(x + t)(x - t)}{x - t}$$

$$= 16(x + t), \text{ provided } x \neq t.$$

By an argument similar to the one above, we conclude that the slope of the tangent line to the curve at $(t, s(t))$ is $32t$. It should be noted that this process defines a slope function, since for any real number t the slope m of the tangent line at t is given by $m(t) = 32t$.

15–3   the derivative

An examination of the methods for finding the velocity function in our physical example and the slope function in our geometric example reveals that in each case the process is the same. The mathematical approach to such a situation is to abstract and to generalize by using the process involved on any given function f. Not only will velocity and

slope be applications of this newly defined process but this generalization will also lead to an interesting theory and to other (unexpected)
applications.

Let f be a function with the real number t in its domain. If there is an
open interval in the domain of f containing t, consider the quotient

$$\frac{f(x) - f(t)}{x - t},$$

where x is any real number in the interval other than t. This is sometimes called the *Newton quotient of f at t*, in honor of Sir Isaac Newton
(1643–1727), one of the first persons to develop differential and integral
calculus. If there exists an interval containing t such that for every real
number x different from t in the interval the Newton quotient is "arbitrarily close" to one and only one real number, then the number is
called the *derivative of f at t* and is denoted by $f'(t)$. The process for
finding this number is called *differentiation*. The function defined by
the ordered pairs $\{(t, f'(t))\}$ is called the *derived function of f*, or the
derivative of f; it is denoted by f'. If f' exists, then f is said to be a *differentiable* function.

If f is given by $f(x) = 16x^2$, then, as indicated in our examples, the
derivative of f at 2 is given by $f'(2) = 64$. Furthermore, since $f'(t)$
$= 32t$ for every number t in the domain of f, the function $f' = \{(t, f'(t))\}$
is the derived function of f; thus, f' is defined by $f'(x) = 32x$.

We would like to obtain a routine method, if one exists, to find the
derivative of any given differentiable function f. But before this can be
accomplished, it is necessary to give a more precise definition of the
derivative. Such terminology as "arbitrarily close" in our preceding
definition is not exact enough to permit proofs of theorems. In attempting to clear up this difficulty, we are led to define what is meant
by the limit of a function f at t. The limit concept is one of the most
fundamental ideas of calculus; when the student has gained an understanding of the limit concept, he will have cleared a major "hurdle"
necessary to a complete understanding of the subject.

Let f be a function and let t be some given number in the domain of f.
Define the function g by

$$g(x) = \frac{f(x) - f(t)}{x - t}$$

where x is in the domain of f and $x \neq t$. Then, although g is not defined
at $x = t$, we say that the function g has a limit L at t if for any positive
real number ϵ there exists an open interval $(t - \delta, t + \delta)$ such that the
absolute value of the difference between L and the value of the g function for every $x \neq t$ in the open interval is less than ϵ. Roughly speaking,
we mean that there exists an open interval containing t such that the
function values of g for every number different from t in the interval
are at a distance less then ϵ from L. Symbolically, $\lim_{x \to t} g(x) = L$—read

"the limit of g at t is L" or "the limit of g of x as x approaches t is L." Of course, if this limit L exists, then $f'(t) = L$ by our previous remarks.

definition: Let f be a function defined in some interval containing a real number t. The derivative of f at t is

$$f'(t) = \lim_{x \to t} \frac{f(x) - f(t)}{x - t}.$$

provided the limit exists.

We have taken a first step toward the understanding of the limit concept by considering the derivative of a function. Let us consider a few examples in this setting before giving a more extensive discussion of limits in the next section.

examples

1. If f is the constant function defined by $f(x) = 6$ and g is defined by $g(x) = \frac{f(x) - f(3)}{x - 3}$, find $\lim_{x \to 3} g(x)$.

    Solution:

    Since

    $$g(x) = \frac{6 - 6}{x - 3},$$

    $$g(x) = 0 \text{ for all } x \neq 3.$$

    Thus, $|g(x) - 0|$ is less than any positive real number ϵ for every $x \neq 3$ in *any* open interval containing 3. Therefore, $\lim_{x \to 3} g(x) = 0$, and the derivative of the constant function f at 3 is $f'(3) = 0$.

2. (a) If f is defined by $f(x) = x^2$ and if g is defined by

    $$g(x) = \frac{f(x) - f(5)}{x - 5},$$

    graph f and g.

    (b) What is $\lim_{x \to 5} g(x)$?

    (c) Find an open interval $(5 - \delta, 5 + \delta)$ such that the absolute value of the difference between this number (limit) and the function values of g for every number in the interval $(5 - \delta, 5 + \delta)$, except 5, is less than $1/10$.

    (d) Find a positive number δ such that for every x in $(5 - \delta, 5 + \delta)$, except $x = 5$, it is true that $|g(x) - 10| < \epsilon$ where ϵ is any positive number.

    Solution:

    (a) Since

    $$g(x) = \frac{x^2 - 25}{x - 5} = x + 5,$$

provided $x \neq 5$, the graph of g is all of the points on the graph of the linear
function $g(x) = x + 5$ except $(5, 10)$.

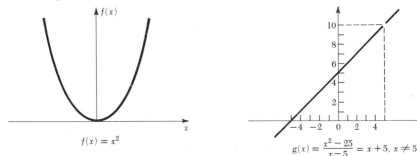

FIGURE 15-2

(b) Now, $\lim_{x \to 5} g(x) = \lim_{x \to 5} (x + 5)$ since the function value at 5 is not
considered in finding the limit of a function at 5. Hence, $\lim_{x \to 5} g(x) = 10$.

(c) If

$$\left| \frac{x^2 - 25}{x - 5} - 10 \right| < 1/10$$

for all x in an interval $(5 - \delta, 5 + \delta)$, except $x = 5$, then

$$\left| \frac{(x - 5)^2}{x - 5} \right| < 1/10 \ .$$

Now, for $\qquad x \neq 5, \ \left| \dfrac{(x - 5)^2}{x - 5} \right| < 1/10$

if $|(x - 5)| < 1/10$. Hence, $|g(x) - 10| < 1/10$ for all x in the open interval
$(5 - 1/10, 5 + 1/10)$, except $x = 5$.

(d) Referring to part (c), it is evident that for any positive number ϵ we can
choose $\delta = \epsilon$; that is, $|g(x) - 10| < \epsilon$ whenever $0 \neq |x - 5| < \epsilon$.

3. If f is defined by $f(x) = x^3$, find $f'(t)$ where t is any real number in the domain of f.

Solution:

By definition,

$$f'(t) = \lim_{x \to t} \frac{f(x) - f(t)}{x - t} \ .$$

Thus,

$$f'(t) = \lim_{x \to t} \frac{x^3 - t^3}{x - t}$$

$$= \lim_{x \to t} \frac{(x - t)(x^2 + xt + t^2)}{x - t}$$

$$= \lim_{x \to t} (x^2 + xt + t^2)$$

$$= 3t^2.$$

It should be noted that there is considerable difference between "finding" limits and proving they exist. To prove that $\lim_{x \to t} (x^2 + xt + t^2) = 3t^2$, it would be necessary to find for any $\epsilon > 0$ a positive number δ such that

$$|(x^2 + xt + t^2) - 3t^2| < \epsilon$$

whenever $0 \neq |x - t| < \delta$ — not an easy task.

4. If g is defined by $g(x) = |x|/x$ for $x \neq 0$, explain why $\lim_{x \to 0} g(x)$ does not exist.

Solution:

If $x > 0$, then $|x| = x$ and $|x|/x = 1$. If $x < 0$, then $|x| = -x$ and $|x|/x = -1$. Since $|x|/x$ has values 1 and -1 in *any* open interval $(-\delta, \delta)$ containing 0, no real number L could exist for, say, 1/2 such that $||x|/x - L| < 1/2$ for all x satisfying $0 \neq |x| < \delta$.

5. If f is defined by $f(x) = x^2/x$ where $x \neq 0$ and $f(0) = 7$, find $\lim_{x \to 0} f(x)$.

Solution:

Since $x^2/x = x$ where $x \neq 0$, f is the same as F defined $F(x) = x$, except at $x = 0$; thus, $\lim_{x \to 0} x^2/x = \lim_{x \to 0} x = 0$. *Note:* $\lim_{x \to 0} f(x) \neq f(0)$.

exercises

1. If f is the identity function defined by $f(x) = x$, what is $\lim_{x \to 0} f(x)$? Justify your answer.

2. (a) If f is the constant function defined by $f(x) = c$, what is $\lim_{x \to 0} f(x)$? Justify your answer.
   (b) Find $f'(7)$ from the definition of derivative.

3. From the distance function, it was found that the velocity v of a free-falling body at the end of t seconds is given by $v(t) = 32t$. Give a physical interpretation for the quotient

$$\frac{v(x) - v(t)}{x - t},$$

where $x > t$. If v is the velocity function, what would be the physical interpretation of

$$v'(t) = \lim_{x \to t} \frac{v(x) - v(t)}{x - t}?$$

4. If f is defined by $f(x) = x^4$, find $f'(3)$ by using the definition of derivative.

5. If f is defined by

$$f(x) = \frac{x + 1}{x},$$

find $f'(5)$ by using the definition of derivative.

6. If f is defined by $f(x) = (x + 1)^4$, consider the graph of f to conjecture the value $f'(-1)$. Use the definition of derivative to check your conjecture.

7. Use the definition of derivative to find f' for each function f defined by the following.

(a) $f(x) = x^3$

(b) $f(x) = x^{1/2}$ where $x > 0$. Hint: $(x^{1/2} - t^{1/2})/(x - t) = 1/(x^{1/2} + t^{1/2})$.

(c) $f(x) = x^{1/3}$ where $x \neq 0$. Hint: $(x^{1/3} - t^{1/3})/(x - t) = 1/(x^{2/3} + x^{1/3}t^{1/3} + t^{2/3})$.

8. Use the definition of derivative to find f' for each function f defined by the following.
   (a) $f(x) = x^{3/2}$ where $x > 0$.

   (b) $f(x) = x^{-1/2}$ where $x > 0$.

   (c) $f(x) = x^{-2/3}$ where $x \neq 0$.

   (d) What conjecture could you make concerning f' if $f(x) = x^r$ where r is a rational number. (See Exercise 7.)

*9. Consider the function f defined by $f(x) = (1 + x)^{1/x}$ where $x > -1$. Use at least seven-place logarithm tables to find the following values. (a) $f(0.01)$ (b) $f(0.001)$ (c) $f(0.0001)$ (d) $f(0.00001)$ (e) $f(-0.01)$ (f) $f(-0.001)$ (g) $f(-0.0001)$ (h) Would you assume that this function has a limit at 0? (i) If so, guess a two-place decimal approximation of the limit.

10. Graph the function g given by $g(x) = 3x/x$ where $x \neq 0$. What is $\lim_{x \to 0} g(x)$?

11. If f is the function defined by $f(x) = x^3 - x$, find the slope of the tangent line to the graph of f at $x = 1$.

12. If f is the function defined by $f(x) = 2x^3 - 3x^2 - 36x$, what are the coordinates of the points on the graph of g where the tangent line is parallel to the x-axis?

*13. For a body rising vertically, if the distance s from the ground at time t is given by $s(t) = 73t - 16t^2$, what is the initial velocity $s'(0)$?

*14. For a body rising vertically, if the distance s in feet from the ground at time t seconds is given by $s(t) = 90t - 16t^2$, what is the greatest height reached by the object? How many seconds is the object in the air?

15–4   limit of a function

Two long-range objectives are to find techniques for differentiating functions and to study the applications of the derivative. Since the limit concept is basic to the development of this theory, a more detailed study of limit is important if a clear understanding of calculus is to be attained.

As we found in our previous discussion of the limit of a function f at t, the value of f at t was immaterial to the limit; in fact, f was often not defined at t. If t is any real number and if δ is a positive number, then the open interval $(t - \delta, t + \delta)$ with the real number t removed is called a *deleted δ-neighborhood of t*.

If f is a function defined in a deleted δ-neighborhood of the real number t, the following is a definition of the limit of f at t.

definition: A function f has a limit L at t if for any $\epsilon > 0$ *there exists* a deleted δ-neighborhood of t such that $|f(x) - L| < \epsilon$ for every x in the deleted δ-neighborhood of t. Symbolically, $\lim_{x \to t} f(x) = L$.

From this definition, we conclude that if we want to *prove* that $\lim_{x \to t}$ $(3x + 2) = 14$, it is necessary to find for any $\epsilon > 0$ a deleted δ-neighborhood of 4 such that $|(3x - 2) - 14| < \epsilon$ for every x satisfying $0 \neq |x - 4| < \epsilon$. This can be accomplished by noting that

$$|(3x + 2) - 14| < \epsilon \quad \text{if and only if}$$

$$|3x - 12| < \epsilon \quad \text{if and only if}$$

$$|x - 4| < \epsilon/3 .$$

Thus, if x is in the deleted $\left(\dfrac{\epsilon}{3}\right)$-neighborhood of 4, then

$$|(3x + 2) - 14| < \epsilon ;$$

hence, we choose δ to be $\epsilon/3$. Of course, δ could be chosen to be any positive number less than $\epsilon/3$. Although δ depends on the ϵ chosen, it is not uniquely determined by ϵ.

If we consider the graph of f defined by $f(x) = 3x + 2$, it is geometrically obvious how close numbers in the domain of f must be to 4 so that the function values are within ϵ of 14. Draw lines parallel to the x-axis from $14 + \epsilon$ and $14 - \epsilon$ on the y-axis to the graph of f and drop perpendiculars from these intersection points to the x-axis. (See Figure 15–3.)

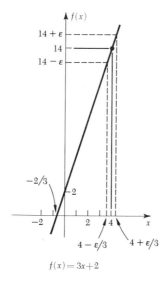

$$f(x) = 3x + 2$$

FIGURE 15–3

Since the graph of f is a straight line with slope 3, the foot of each perpendicular on the x-axis will be $\epsilon/3$ on each side of 4. The function values for all numbers in the interval $(4 - \epsilon/3, 4 + \epsilon/3)$ will be within ϵ of 14.

At first, the limit concept may seem extremely complex; but although the proofs of basic limit theorems are rather difficult, these theorems make much of our subsequent work easier (not only by comparison but also in fact). Thus, we turn our attention to the theorems that make the road of progress easier.

Let us begin by speculating on what might be limit theorems and consider their consequences. If a function f has limit a at t and if g has limit b at t, we know that $f(x)$ is close to a for each x in some deleted neighborhood of t and that $g(x)$ is close to b for each x in some (other) deleted neighborhood of t. It seems reasonable to expect that a deleted neighborhood of t could be found so that $f(x) + g(x)$ is arbitrarily close to $(a + b)$ for each x in the neighborhood; that is, we anticipate that

I. $$\lim_{x \to t} [f(x) + g(x)] = \lim_{x \to t} f(x) + \lim_{x \to t} g(x) .$$

In other words, it seems reasonable to expect the limit of the sum of two functions to be equal to the sum of the limits of each of the functions, provided each limit exists. Similarly, we are led to speculate on the validity of the following.

II. $$\lim_{x \to t} [f(x) - g(x)] = \lim_{x \to t} f(x) - \lim_{x \to t} g(x) .$$

III. $$\lim_{x \to t} [f(x) \cdot g(x)] = [\lim_{x \to t} f(x)] \cdot [\lim_{x \to t} g(x)] .$$

The statements I, II, and III are indeed valid limit theorems; their proofs are beyond the scope of this text.

It is easy to prove from the definition of limit that for the identity function f defined by $f(x) = x$ and for the constant function g defined by $g(x) = k$ that $\lim_{x \to t} f(x) = t$ and $\lim_{x \to t} g(x) = k$. It is important to note that the limits of f and g at t are $f(t)$ and $g(t)$, respectively.

Assuming that I, II, and III express valid limit theorems, consider the polynomial function P defined by

$$P(x) = 3x^2 + 7x + 5 .$$

Since $\lim_{x \to t} x = t$ and since $x^2 = x \cdot x$, by the limit theorem for the product of two functions

$$\lim_{x \to t} x^2 = (\lim_{x \to t} x)(\lim_{x \to t} x) = t \cdot t = t^2 ;$$

furthermore,

$$\lim_{x \to t} 3x^2 = 3t^2 .$$

Since $\lim_{x \to t} 7x = 7t$ and $\lim_{x \to t} 5 = 5$, it follows by the theorem for the limit of a sum that

$$\lim_{x \to t} P(x) = 3t^2 + 7t + 5 ;$$

that is,

$$\lim_{x \to t} P(x) = P(t) \ .$$

If we accept the limit theorems without proof, it should be apparent from this example that it is not very difficult to prove that the limit of any polynomial function P exists at any real number t and that

$$\lim_{x \to t} P(x) = P(t) \ .$$

Thus, the limit theorems make it possible to prove that the limit at t of any polynomial function is the value of the function at t.

The student may have wondered whether or not there is a limit theorem for the quotient f/g of two functions. In fact, there is; but if a function f has limit a at t and if g has limit b at t, the limit of the quotient f/g might not exist if $b = 0$. Although the limit of f/g could exist even though $b = 0$ it is obvious that the limit is *not* a/b since division by 0 is not defined. However, if $b \neq 0$ then it should seem reasonable that $f(x)/g(x)$ could be made arbitrarily close to a/b. It can be proved that if $\lim_{x \to t} f(x)$ exists, $\lim_{x \to t} g(x)$ exists, and if $\lim_{x \to t} g(x) \neq 0$, then

IV.
$$\lim_{x \to t} \frac{f(x)}{g(x)} = \frac{\lim_{x \to t} f(x)}{\lim_{x \to t} g(x)} \ .$$

If P and Q are polynomial functions and $Q(t) \neq 0$, then it follows from the quotient theorem and the previous remarks on polynomials that

$$\lim_{x \to t} \frac{P(x)}{Q(x)} = \frac{P(t)}{Q(t)} \ .$$

Thus,

$$\lim_{x \to 1} \frac{3x + 7}{5x - 2} = \frac{10}{3}$$

as a consequence of the foregoing theorems.

To find $\lim_{x \to 2} \sqrt{4x + 1}$, a natural approach would be to notice that $\lim_{x \to 2} (4x + 1) = 9$ and assert that $\lim_{x \to 2} \sqrt{4x + 1} = \sqrt{9} = 3$; however, no theorem has been stated to justify the correctness of this procedure. What we need to justify is that $\lim_{x \to 1} \sqrt{4x + 1} = \sqrt{\lim_{x \to 1} (4x + 1)}$. Let us consider what is involved. If F is given by $F(x) = \sqrt{4x + 1}$, then F is the composition $f \circ g$ where $f(x) = \sqrt{x}$ and $g(x) = 4x + 1$. Thus, we would like to prove that $\lim_{x \to t} f(g(x)) = f(\lim_{x \to t} g(x))$. Obviously this statement is not true unless we place some restrictions on f and g. For example, if $\lim_{x \to t} g(x)$ exists but is not in the domain of f, then $f(\lim_{x \to t} g(x))$ is undefined. A more careful scrutiny shows that assuming the limit of g at t to be in the domain of f is still not enough to make the statement true. For example, let f be defined by

$$f(x) = \frac{x^2 - 4}{x - 2}$$

where $x \neq 2$ and $f(2) = 10$, and let g be defined by $g(x) = 5x - 13$ for all real numbers. Now, $\lim_{x \to 3} (5x - 13) = 2$ and 2 is in the domain of f; furthermore, $f(2) = 10$. Hence, $f(\lim_{x \to 3} g(x)) = 10$. Now,

$$f(g(x)) = \frac{(5x - 13)^2 - 4}{(5x - 13) - 2} = \frac{(5x - 11)(5x - 13)}{(5x - 15)} = 5x - 11$$

for $x \neq 3$; thus, $\lim_{x \to 3} f(g(x)) = 4$ and

$$f(\lim_{x \to 3} g(x)) \neq \lim_{x \to 3} f(g(x)) .$$

What makes this a counterexample to what we want to prove is the fact that $\lim_{x \to 2} f(x) \neq f(2)$; that is, the limit of f at 2 is not the value of f at 2. Making the two restrictions indicated on f and g is sufficient to make our conjecture a proper theorem on limits.

Following are precise statements of the limit theorems discussed in this section; their proofs are omitted.

theorem 15-1: Assume that $\lim_{x \to t} f(x) = a$ and $\lim_{x \to t} g(x) = b$.

(a) $\lim_{x \to t} \{f(x) + g(x)\} = a + b$

(b) $\lim_{x \to t} \{f(x) \cdot g(x)\} = ab$

(c) $\lim_{x \to t} \{f(x) - g(x)\} = a - b$

(d) $\lim_{x \to t} \{f(x)/g(x)\} = a/b$, provided $b \neq 0$.

(e) $\lim_{x \to t} f(g(x)) = f(\lim_{x \to t} g(x)) = f(b)$ provided b is in the domain of f and $\lim_{x \to b} f(x) = f(b)$.

As we have seen, many functions — such as the polynomial functions — have the important property that $\lim_{x \to t} f(x) = f(t)$; that is, t is in the domain of f, the limit f at t exists, and the limit at t is $f(t)$. This ensures that for real numbers "near" t the function values are "near" $f(t)$; geometrically, the point $(x, f(x))$ on the graph of f is "close" to $(t, f(t))$ if x is "close" to t.

definition: A function f is said to be *continuous* at t in its domain if and only if $\lim_{x \to t} f(x) = f(t)$. A function is continuous *on an interval* if it is continuous at each number in the interval.

If f and g are polynomial functions, then $\lim_{x \to t} f(x) = f(t)$ and $\lim_{x \to t} g(x) = g(t)$. If $g(t) \neq 0$,

$$\lim_{x \to t} \frac{f(x)}{g(x)} = \frac{\lim_{x \to t} f(x)}{\lim_{x \to t} g(x)}$$

$$= \frac{f(t)}{g(t)} \; .$$

Thus, any rational function is continuous at each number in its domain. In fact, if f and g are any two continuous functions, it is an immediate consequence of the limit theorems that $f + g$, fg, and $f - g$ are continuous, and f/g is continuous at t if $g(t) \neq 0$.

theorem 15–2: Let f and g be continuous functions at t. Then $f + g$, $f - g$, and fg are continuous at t and f/g is continuous at t provided $g(t) \neq 0$.

If a function is not continuous at t, it is said to be discontinuous. For a function to be discontinuous in an interval, it is only necessary to have one point of discontinuity in the interval.

examples

1. If f is defined by $f(x) = (x^2 - 4)/(x - 2)$ for $x \neq 2$, then f is not continuous at 2 since 2 is not in the domain of f. f is continuous for every other real number.

2. If
$$f(x) = \frac{x^2 - 4}{x - 2}$$

   for $x \neq 2$ and $f(2) = 7$, then

$$\lim_{x \to 2} \frac{x^2 - 4}{x - 2}$$

   exists and 2 is in the domain of f. However,

$$\lim_{x \to 2} \frac{x^2 - 4}{x - 2} = 4 \neq f(2) \; ;$$

   thus, f is not continuous at 2.

3. If f is defined by $f(x) = 1/x$ where $x \neq 0$, then f is discontinuous at 0 since it is not in the domain of f. However, since $\lim_{x \to t} 1/x = 1/t$ where $0 < t < 1$, f is continuous in the open interval $(0, 1)$. In fact, f is continuous at every real number in its domain.

If f is the function defined by $f(x) = x^{1/3}$, then, as a consequence of the limit theorems, $\lim_{x \to t} f(x) = f(t)$. Hence, f is continuous for all real numbers. If one considers the graph of f carefully, it appears that there is a vertical tangent at $(0, 0)$. That is, the graph would suggest that $f'(0)$ does not exist. Let us exhibit this.

By the definition of the derivative of f at 0,

$$f'(0) = \lim_{x \to 0} \frac{f(x) - f(0)}{x - 0}$$

if the limit exists. That is,

$$f'(0) = \lim_{x \to 0} \frac{x^{1/3}}{x}$$

$$= \lim_{x \to 0} \frac{1}{x^{2/3}} \; .$$

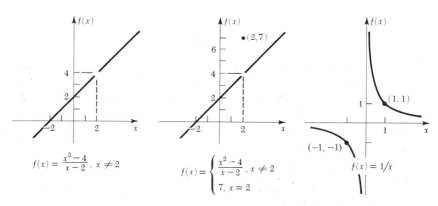

$$f(x) = \frac{x^2 - 4}{x - 2}, \ x \neq 2$$

$$f(x) = \begin{cases} \dfrac{x^2 - 4}{x - 2}, \ x \neq 2 \\ 7, \ x = 2 \end{cases}$$

$$f(x) = 1/x$$

FIGURE 15–4

Since $1/x^{2/3}$ can be made greater than any number M for x "near" zero, the limit does not exist; hence, $f'(0)$ does not exist.

Although a continuous function need not be differentiable, we can prove, using the limit theorems, that every differentiable function is continuous.

theorem 15–3:   Let f be a differentiable function at t. Then, f is continuous at t.

proof: Since f is differentiable at t,

$$f'(t) = \lim_{x \to t} \frac{f(x) - f(t)}{x - t}$$

exists. Now,

$$f(x) - f(t) = (x - t) \left[\frac{f(x) - f(t)}{x - t} \right].$$

Thus,

$$\lim_{x \to t} [f(x) - f(t)] = \lim_{x \to t} (x - t) \left[\frac{f(x) - f(t)}{x - t} \right]$$

$$= \lim_{x \to t} (x - t) \left[\lim_{x \to t} \frac{f(x) - f(t)}{x - t} \right]$$

$$= 0[f'(t)]$$

$$= 0 .$$

Since $\lim_{x \to t} [f(x) - f(t)] = 0$, $\lim_{x \to t} f(x) = f(t)$ and f is continuous at t.

We conclude this section with two theorems which, though geometrically obvious, are not easy to prove.

theorem 15–4:   Let f be a continuous function at t and assume $f(t) > 0$. Then there exists an interval containing t such that $f(x) > 0$ for every x in the interval.

Essentially, Theorem 15–4 states that if the graph of a continuous function f is above the x-axis at some number t in the domain of f, then the graph must be above the x-axis in some interval containing t.

Our final theorem in this section is what is sometimes referred to as the *Mean Value Theorem of Differential Calculus*. Geometrically, the Mean Value Theorem states that if the graph of a continuous function on a closed interval $[a, b]$ has a non-vertical tangent at each point in the open interval (a, b), then at least one tangent line is parallel to the line containing $(a, f(a))$ and $(b, f(b))$. See Figure 15–5. Since the slope of

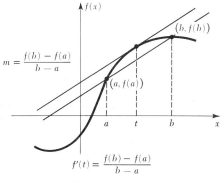

Mean value theorem

FIGURE 15–5

the line containing $(a, f(a))$ and $(b, f(b))$ is $(f(b) - f(a))/(b - a)$, the Mean Value Theorem asserts that there exists a $t \in (a, b)$ such that

$$f'(t) = \frac{f(b) - f(a)}{b - a}.$$

theorem 15–5 (Mean Value Theorem): Let f be a differentiable function on (a, b). Assume f is continuous at a and b. Then there exists a $t \in (a, b)$ such that

$$f'(t) = \frac{f(b) - f(a)}{b - a}.$$

Note two things: (1) the Mean Value Theorem only assures the existence of a number t; it does not provide a method for determining such a t; and (2) the number t need not be unique in the interval.

One of the important uses for the Mean Value Theorem is to prove other theorems. For example, assume f is a differentiable function on $[a, b]$ such that $f'(x) = 0$ for every $x \in [a, b]$. For any $x \neq b$, we have by the Mean Value Theorem that there exists a t between x and b such that

$$f'(t) = \frac{f(b) - f(x)}{b - x}.$$

But since $f'(t) = 0$, we concluded that $f(b) - f(x) = 0$, or $f(x) = f(b)$. That is, f is the constant function with $\{f(b)\}$ as its range set.

Earlier we proved that if f is a constant function then $f'(x) = 0$ for every x in the domain. Now, we have used the Mean Value Theorem to prove the converse of this theorem; that is, if $f'(x) = 0$ for every x in the domain of f, f is a constant function. We shall see the importance of this converse theorem in Section 15–11.

exercises

Find each limit, if it exists, in Exercises 1–8.

1. $\lim\limits_{x \to 2} (x^3 - 2x + 13)$

2. $\lim\limits_{x \to -1} \dfrac{x^2 + 1}{3x - 5}$

3. $\lim\limits_{x \to 5} \dfrac{x^2 - 25}{x - 5}$

4. $\lim\limits_{x \to 0} \dfrac{1}{\sqrt{2 + x} - \sqrt{2}}$

5. $\lim\limits_{x \to 3} \dfrac{x^3 - 27}{x - 3}$

6. $\lim\limits_{x \to 2} \left(\dfrac{1}{2x^2 - x - 6} - \dfrac{1}{3x^2 - x - 10} \right)$

7. $\lim\limits_{x \to 7} \dfrac{3x - 6}{x - 2}$

8. $\lim\limits_{x \to t} \dfrac{x^n - t^n}{x - t}$

9. Using the definition of limit, prove that $\lim_{x \to 2}(3x + 2) = 11$.

°10. Using the definition of limit, prove that
$$\lim_{x \to 2} \frac{x + 5}{x} = \frac{7}{2}.$$

11. Find $\lim_{x \to -2}(x^5 + 5)^{1/3}$. Justify your answer.

°12. If f is defined by
$$f(x) = \frac{\sqrt{x + 1}}{\sqrt[5]{x + 8}},$$
use limit theorems to prove that $\lim_{x \to 24} f(x) = f(24)$.

13. If
$$f(x) = \frac{x^2 - 16}{x - 4},$$
$x \neq 4$, and $f(4) = 8$, is f continuous for all real numbers?

14. If f defined by $f(x) = \sqrt{x^2 + 1}$, is f continuous for all real numbers?

15. List the points of discontinuity of f defined by
$$f(x) = \frac{x^2 + 2x + 5}{x^2 - x - 20}.$$

16. List the points of discontinuity of f defined by
$$f(x) = \frac{x^2 + 3x + 6}{x^3 - x^2 - 6x}.$$

In Exercises 17 through 21, find a t in the open interval (a, b) that satisfies the conditions of the Mean Value Theorem.

17. $f(x) = x^3$, $[a, b] = [2, 3]$

18. $f(x) = x^2 + 6x - 3$, $[a, b] = [1, 3]$

19. $f(x) = x^2 + 4x + 2$, $[a, b] = [-1, 3]$

20. $f(x) = 3x + 1$, $[a, b] = [2, 5]$

21. $f(x) = x^3 - 2x + 5x - 6$, $[a, b] = [0, 2]$

°22. Let $\lim_{x \to t} f(x) = L_1$ and $\lim_{x \to t} f(x) = L_2$ exist. Prove $L_1 = L_2$.

　　In other words, prove that the limit of a function f at t is unique if it exists.

°23. Assume $\lim_{x \to t} f(x)/g(x)$ exists and assume that $\lim_{x \to t} g(x) = 0$.

　　Prove that $\lim_{x \to t} f(x) = 0$. *Hint:* $[f(x)/g(x)] \cdot g(x) = f(x)$.

15–5 derivative of the sum of two functions

By working through the examples and exercises in the last chapter, it should be clear that finding the derivative of a function by direct use of the definition can be tedious and complicated. We turn our attention now to stating and proving differentiation theorems that will simplify the task for finding derivatives by providing routine procedures for differentiation.

In Section 15–3, we proved that if f is defined by $f(x) = c$ then $f'(t) = 0$; furthermore, if $f(x) = x$, then $f'(t) = 1$. We now prove that if $f(x) = x^n$ for any positive integer n, then $f'(t) = nt^{n-1}$.

theorem 15–6: If f is defined by $f(x) = x^n$ for any positive integer n, then $f'(t) = n\, t^{n-1}$.

proof:

$$f'(t) = \lim_{x \to t} \frac{f(x) - f(t)}{x - t}$$

$$= \lim_{x \to t} \frac{x^n - t^n}{x - t}$$

$$= \lim_{x \to t} \frac{(x - t)(x^{n-1} + x^{n-2} + x^{n-3}t^2 + \cdots + xt^{n-2} + t^{n-1})}{(x - t)}$$

$$= \lim_{x \to t} (x^{n-1} + x^{n-2}\, t + x^{n-3}t^2 + \cdots + xy^{n-2} + t^{n-1})$$

$$= \underbrace{(t^{n-1} + t^{n-1} + t^{n-1} + \cdots + t^{n-1} + t^{n-1})}_{n \text{ terms}}$$

$$= nt^{n-1}$$

example:

If f is defined by $f(x) = x^6$, then $f'(t) = 6t^5$ for any real number t. Since the letter used to define a function is immaterial, f' could be defined by $f'(u) = 6u^5$, $f'(y) = 6y^5$, or $f'(x) = 6x^5$. For 2 in the domain of f, we have $f'(2) = 6(2)^5 = 192$.

Let g be the function defined by $g(x) = 8x^3$. We would like to use Theorem 15–6 to find the derivative of g in the following manner. Since the derivative of f defined by $f(x) = x^3$ is given by $f'(x) = 3x^2$, we would like to assert that the following procedure for finding g' is valid:

$$g'(x) = 8f'(x) = 8(3x^2) = 24x^2 \ .$$

More precisely, we want to prove that the derivative of $g(x) = cf(x)$ — where c is a given real number (constant) — is given by $g'(x) = cf'(x)$, provided f is a differentiable function. This fact is often stated by saying that the derivative of a constant times a function is the constant times the derivative of the function.

theorem 15–7: Let f be a differentiable function. If g is a function defined by $g(x) = cf(x)$ where c is a real number, then $g'(t)$.

proof:

$$g'(t) = \lim_{x \to t} \frac{g(x) - g(t)}{x - t}$$

$$= \lim_{x \to t} \frac{cf(x) - cf(t)}{x - t}$$

$$= \lim_{x \to t} \frac{c[f(x) - f(t)]}{x - t}$$

$$= c \lim_{x \to t} \frac{f(x) - f(t)}{x - t} \quad \text{[The limit of a constant times a function is the constant times the limit of the function.]}$$

$$= cf'(t) \quad \text{[The limit of the Newton quotient at t is $f'(t)$ since it was given that f is differentiable.]}$$

example:

Let $h(x) = 9x^5$. Then, $h'(x) = 45x^4$ and $h'(1) = 45$. Notice that $h'(1)$ is the value of the derivative at 1 and not the derivative of $h(1)$.

We would next like to prove that Theorems 15–6 and 15–7 can be used in a rather trivial way to find the derivative of a polynomial function. If h is defined by $h(x) = x^4 + 6x^3$, then $h'(x) = 4x^3 + 18x^2$. More precisely, if h is the sum of two differentiable functions f and g ($h = f + g$), then h is differentiable and $h' = f' + g'$; that is, $h'(t) = f'(t) + g'(t)$, for each $t \in D_f \cap D_g$. It is often stated that the derivative of the sum of two functions is the sum of the derivatives. Occasionally, we do not choose to introduce a letter, such as h, to represent the sum of f and g; in this case, the symbolism $(f + g)'$ is used to denote the derivative of the sum of f and g. In this symbolsim, the theorem is stated as follows:

$$(f + g)' = f' + g' \ .$$

theorem 15–8: Let h be the sum of two differentiable functions f and g. Then, $h'(t) = f'(t) + g'(t)$.

proof:

$$h'(t) = \lim_{x \to t} \frac{h(x) - h(t)}{x - t}$$

$$= \lim_{x \to t} \frac{[f(x) + g(x)] - [f(t) - g(t)]}{x - t}$$

$$= \lim_{x \to t} \frac{[f(x) - f(t)] + [g(x) - g(t)]}{x - t}$$

$$= \lim_{x \to t} \frac{f(x) - f(t)}{x - t} + \lim_{x \to t} \frac{g(x) - g(t)}{x - t}$$

$$= f'(t) + g'(t)$$

If h is the sum of three differentiable functions u, v, and w, then h can be defined by $h = u + (v + w)$. Thus, $h' = u' + (v + w)'$ and by the repeated use of Theorem 15–8, $h' = u' + v' + w'$. More generally, the derivative of the sum of a given number of functions is the sum of the derivatives of the functions. Consequently, if $F(x) = 7x^4 + 11x^3 + 3x^2 + x + 13$, then $F'(x) = 28x^3 + 33x^2 + 6x + 1$.

Let f and g be two differentiable functions. If $h = f - g$, then $h' = f' - g'$. The proof of this is similar to the proof of Theorem 15–8. We say that the derivative of a difference is the difference of the derivatives. If $h(x) = 3x^5 - x^2$, then $h'(x) = 15x^4 - 2x$.

exercises

In Exercises 1 through 13 find $f'(x)$.

1. $f(x) = 12x^3 + 5x - 3$ 2. $f(x) = 14x^2 - 6x + 8$

3. $f(x) = 5x^4 - 13x^2$ 4. $f(x) = x^3/3 + 11x$

5. $f(x) = x^5/2 - 42x$ 6. $f(x) = 19x + 3$

7. $f(x) = x^3 - 6x^2 + 7x - 11$ 8. $f(x) = 2x$

9. $f(x) = 7$ 10. $f(x) = (2x + 3)^2$

11. $f(x) = (5x + 1)^3$ 12. $f(x) = (x^2 + 1)^3$

13. $f(x) = (x^2 + 4)^2$

In Exercises 14 through 20, solve the following:

(a) $f'(x) = 0$,   (b) $f'(x) < 0$, and   (c) $f'(x) > 0$.

14. $f(x) = x^3 - 3$ 15. $f(x) = 3x + 11$

16. $f(x) = 2x^3 - 15x^2 - 36x + 11$ 17. $f(x) = 11$

18. $f(x) = x^2 + 4$ 19. $f(x) = x^3 - 6x$

20. $f(x) = x^3 - 3x^2 + 2x - 1$

*21. Let f and g be differentiable functions and let $h = f - g$. Prove $h' = f' - g'$.

15–6   derivative of the product of two functions

Although the derivative of a constant times a function is the constant times the derivative of the function and the derivative of the sum of two functions is the sum of the derivatives, it is *not* generally true that the derivative of the product of two functions is the product of the derivatives. This fact is easy to illustrate. Let h be defined by $h(x) = x^7$. From Theorem 15–6, we have that $h'(x) = 7x^6$. Now, h can be expressed as fg where $f(x) = x^3$ and $g(x) = x^4$. Since $f'(x) = 3x^2$ and $g'(x) = 4x^3$ and since $(3x^2)(4x^3) \neq 7x^6$, it is obvious that $h' \neq f'g'$. We now state and prove the product theorem.

theorem 15–9:   Let f and g be differentiable functions and let h be the product function defined by $h(x) = f(x)g(x)$. Then,

$$h'(t) = f(t)g'(t) + f'(t)g(t) .$$

proof:

$$h'(t) = \lim_{x \to t} \frac{h(x) - h(t)}{x - t} \tag{1}$$

$$= \lim_{x \to t} \frac{f(x)g(x) - f(t)g(t)}{x - t} \tag{2}$$

$$= \lim_{x \to t} \frac{f(x)g(x) - f(x)g(t) + f(x)g(t) - f(t)g(t)}{x - t} \tag{3}$$

$$= \lim_{x \to t} f(x) \frac{[g(x) - g(t)]}{x - t} + \lim_{x \to t} g(t) \frac{[f(x) - f(t)]}{x - t} \tag{4}$$

$$= \lim_{x \to t} f(x) \lim_{x \to t} \frac{g(x) - g(t)}{x - t} + g(t) \lim_{x \to t} \frac{f(x) - f(t)}{x - t} \tag{5}$$

$$= f(t)g'(t) + g(t)f'(t)$$

Let us review each step in the proof of Theorem 15–9 to be certain the proof is clear. Step (1) follows from the definition of the derivative of h at t. Step (2) follows from the definition of h. In step (3), we added $f(x)g(t) - f(x)g(t)$—that is, zero—to the numerator of the fraction. In step (4), we used some elementary algebraic identities and the fact that the limit of a sum is the sum of the limits. (Of course, we must prove that the individual limits exist.) In step (5), we use the fact that the limit of a product is the product of the limits; again, we must show that the limits exist. Also in step (5), we use the fact that the limit of a constant ($g(t)$ is a constant) times a function is the constant times the limit of the function to obtain

$$g(t) \lim_{x \to t} \frac{f(x) - f(t)}{x - t}$$

Since it is given that f is differentiable, we conclude that

$$\lim_{x \to t} \frac{f(x) - f(t)}{x - t} = f'(t) .$$

Similarly,

$$\lim_{x \to t} \frac{g(x) - g(t)}{x - t} = g'(t) .$$

We still must justify the fact that $\lim_{x \to t} f(x) = f(t)$; this fact is true because the differentiability of f implies that f is continuous and, by definition, f is continuous if and only if $\lim_{x \to t} f(x) = f(t)$.

Let us take our example where $h(x) = x^7 = f(x)g(x)$, $f(x) = x^3$, and $g(x) = x^4$ to verify the product theorem. Since $f'(x) = 3x^2$ and $g'(x) = 4x^3$,

$$h'(x) = f(x)g'(x) + f'(x)g(x)$$

$$= (x^3)\,(4x^3) + (3x^2)\,(x^4)$$

$$= 4x^6 + 3x^6$$

$$= 7x^6, \text{ the desired result.}$$

If h is the product of three differentiable functions u, v, and w, then h can be defined by $h = u(vw)$. Thus, $h' = u(vw)' + u'(vw)$, and, by repeated use of Theorem 15–9,

$$h' = u(vw' + v'w) + u'(vw) .$$

Thus,

$$h' = uvw' + uv'w + u'vw .$$

It is important to notice that if $u = v = w$, then $h' = 3u^2u'$. For example, if $h(x) = (x^2 + 5x + 2)^3$, h is the product of three equal functions u defined by $u(x) = x^2 + 5x + 2$; hence,

$$h'(x) = 3[u(x)]^2u'(x)$$

$$= 3(x^2 + 5x + 2)^2(2x + 5) .$$

It should be clear that finding the derivative by this method is easier than cubing $(x^2 + 5x + 2)$ and then differentiating the resulting polynomial term by term.

exercises

In Exercises 1 through 12, find $f'(x)$.

1. $f(x) = (x^2 + 3x + 5)(x^2 - 3x + 7)$
2. $f(x) = (x^2 + 3x)(x^3 + 5x^2 - 6x + 1)$
3. $f(x) = (x^3 + 7x^2 + 3x + 11)^2$
4. $f(x) = (x^2 + 3)^2$
5. $f(x) = (3x^5 + 7x^2 - 2)^3$
6. $f(x) = (3x^2 - 2x + 1)^3$
7. $f(x) = (x^3 + 7x - 1)(x^2 + 2x + 5)$
8. $f(x) = (x^3 + 3x)^2(2x + 1)$

9. $f(x) = (x^3 - 5x + 1)^3$

10. $f(x) = (x + 2)(3x + 5)^3$

11. $f(x) = (x - 3)(2x + 1)(5x - 7)$

12. $f(x) = (2x + 7)(5x - 11)(12x + 5)$

13. (a) If u, v, w, and z are differentiable functions and $h = uvwz$, show that
   $h' = u'vwz + uv'wz + uvw'z + uvwz'$.

   (b) Use part (a) to find the derivative of h if $h(x) = (2x + 3)(3x^2 + 11)$ $(5x - 11)(x^3 + 7)$. (Do not simplify your answer.)

   (c) Prove that if y is a differentiable function and $h(x) = [u(x)]^4$, then $h'(x) = 4[u(x)]^3 u'(x)$.

   (d) Use part (c) to find the derivative of $h(x) = (3x^3 + 7x + 2)^4$.

*14. Use the product theorem and mathematical induction to prove that if $f(x) = x^n$ then $f'(x) = nx^{n-1}$ for every positive integer n. (Hint: $x^{k+1} = x^k x$.)

*15. Assume that f is a differentiable function. Use the product theorem and mathematical induction to prove that if $h(x) = [f(x)]^n$, then $h'(x) = n[f(x)]^{n-1}f'(x)$ for every positive integer n. Show the theorem in Exercise 14 is a special case of this theorem.

15–7   derivative of the quotient of two functions

In the last section, we proved that the derivative of the product of two functions is the first factor times the derivative of the second plus the second factor times the derivative of the first. We now prove that the derivative of the quotient of two functions can be found by multiplying the denominator times the derivative of the numerator, subtracting the numerator times the derivative of the denominator, and dividing the difference by the square of the denominator.

theorem 15–10:   Let f and g be differentiable functions and let h be the quotient defined by $h(x) = f(x)/g(x)$. Then

$$h'(t) = \frac{g(t)f'(t) - f(t)g'(t)}{[g(t)]^2}, \qquad \text{provided } g(t) \neq 0.$$

proof:

$$h'(t) = \lim_{x \to t} \frac{h(x) - h(t)}{x - t}$$

$$= \lim_{x \to t} \frac{\dfrac{f(x)}{g(x)} - \dfrac{f(t)}{g(t)}}{x - t}$$

$$= \lim_{x \to t} \frac{g(x)g(t) - g(x)f(t)}{g(x)g(t)(x - t)}$$

$$= \lim_{x \to t} \frac{f(x)g(t) - f(t)g(t) - g(x)f(t) + f(t)g(t)}{g(x)g(t)(x - t)}$$

$$= \lim_{x \to t} \frac{g(t)}{g(x)g(t)} \cdot \frac{f(x) - f(t)}{x - t} - \lim_{x \to t} \frac{f(t)}{g(x)g(t)} \cdot \frac{g(x) - g(t)}{x - t}$$

$$= \frac{g(t)}{[g(t)]^2} f'(t) - \frac{f(t)}{[g(t)]^2} g'(t)$$

$$= \frac{g(t)f'(t) - f(t)g'(t)}{[g(t)]^2}$$

The steps in the proof of this theorem are rather similar to the steps in the proof of the product theorem, with one important exception. Although it is given that $g(t) \neq 0$, it need not be true that $g(x) \neq 0$ for every x in the domain of g, so we must be concerned about $g(x)$ being zero in the denominator in some of the steps of the proof. Actually, we make use of Theorem 15–3. Since g is differentiable, it is continuous; furthermore, since $g(t) \neq 0$, there must exist an interval containing t such that $g(x) \neq 0$ for every x in this interval. We assume in the proof of the theorem that x is in this interval where $g(x) \neq 0$.

We have proved that if $f(x) = x^p$ where p is a positive integer, then $f'(x) = px^{p-1}$. The quotient theorem can be used to prove that this formula is also valid if p is a negative integer. Let $p = -n$ be a negative integer. If $f(x) = x^p = x^{-n}$, then

$$f(x) = \frac{1}{x^n} \text{ , where } n \text{ is a positive integer.}$$

Using the quotient theorem,

$$f'(x) = \frac{x^n(0) - (n)x^{n-1}}{[x^n]^2}$$

$$= \frac{-nx^{n-1}}{x^{2n}}$$

$$= -nx^{-n-1}$$

$$= px^{p-1}.$$

Notice that if $p = 0$, the formula is also valid.

In the next section, we shall prove that if $f(x) = x^p$ where p is any rational, then $f'(x) = px^{p-1}$.

exercises

1. If $f(x) = 1/x$, find $f'(x)$.

2. If $f(x) = \dfrac{x^2 + 7x + 4}{x + 2}$, find $f'(1)$.

3. If $f(x) = \dfrac{1}{x^2}$, find $f'(x)$.

4. If $f(x) = \dfrac{1}{x^2 + 1}$, find $f'(x)$.

5. If $f(x) = \dfrac{1}{x^3 + 2x + 1}$, find $f'(x)$.

6. If g is a differentiable function and $f(x) = 1/g(x)$, find $f'(x)$.

7. If $f(x) = \dfrac{2x}{x^2 + 3x + 1}$, find $f'(2)$.

8. If $f(x) = \dfrac{x^2 + 3x + 4}{x + 3}$, for what x is $f'(x) = 0$? $f'(x) > 0$? $f'(x) < 0$?

9. If $f(x) = \dfrac{2x^2 + 3x - 3}{x + 5}$, for what x is $f'(x) = 0$? $f'(x) > 0$? $f'(x) < 0$?

10. If $f(x) = \dfrac{x^3 + 5x^2 - 7x}{x^2 + 1}$, find $f'(x)$.

*11. Let p be any integer and let g be a differentiable function such that $g(x) \neq 0$. Prove that if $h(x) = [g(x)]^p$, then $h'(x) = p[g(x)]^{p-1}g'(x)$.

12. If $g(x) = \dfrac{x}{x^2 + 1}$, find $g'(x)$.

13. If $f(x) = \dfrac{3x + 5}{2x - 1}$, find $f'(x)$.

14. If $f(x) = \left(\dfrac{3x - 7}{x^2 + 4}\right)^2$, find $f'(x)$.

15. If $f(x) = \left(\dfrac{2x + 1}{x^2 + 2}\right)^2$, find $f'(x)$.

15–8   composite function theorem

For differentiable functions f and g, we have proved the following.
$$(f + g)' = f' + g'$$
$$(f - g)' = f' - g'$$
$$(fg)' = fg' + f'g$$
$$(f/g)' = \frac{gf' - fg'}{g^2}$$

Our final general differentiation theorem is called the Composite Function Theorem; it is stated without proof. The Composite Function Theorem gives us the technique for finding the derivative of the composition of two differentiable functions.*

theorem 15–11:   Let f and g be differentiable functions. If $h(x) = f(g(x))$, then $h'(x) = f'(g(x)) \cdot g'(x)$.

* This is sometimes called the *Chain Rule* for differentiation.

In the composite function theorem, it should be noted that $f'(g(x))$ is the composition of the derivative of f with g. For example, let $h(x) = (x^2 + 2x + 3)^{15}$, $f(x) = x^{15}$, and $g(x) = x^2 + 2x + 3$. Then,

$$h(x) = f(g(x)) = (x^2 + 2x + 3)^{15}.$$

Since $f'(x) = 15x^{14}$,

$$f'(g(x)) = 15(x^2 + 2x + 3)^{14}.$$

Thus,

$$h'(x) = 15(x^2 + 2x + 3)^{14}(2x + 2).$$

The composite function theorem is often stated in the following way:

$$[f(g)]' = f'(g) \cdot g'$$

We now prove three significant consequences of the composite function theorem.

I. Let g be a differentiable function and let $h(x) = [g(x)]^n$ where n is an integer. If we let $f(x) = x^n$, then $f'(x) = nx^{n-1}$ and $h(x) = f(g(x))$. Hence,

$$h'(x) = f'(g(x)) \cdot g'(x)$$
$$= n[g(x)]^{n-1}g'(x) .$$

In other words, the derivative of a function raised to the nth power is n times the function raised to the $(n - 1)$st power times the derivative of the function. (See Section 15–6, Exercise 9, for a different proof of this important result when n is a positive integer. Notice in this proof we used the result proved in Section 15–7 that $f'(x) = nx^{n-1}$ for any *integer n*.)

example

If $h(x) = (2x^3 + 7x - 1)^{-3}$, then $h'(x) = -3(2x^3 + 7x - 1)^{-4}(6x^2 + 7)$.

II. Let g be defined by $g(x) = x^{1/n}$ where $x > 0$. Thus, $[g(x)]^n = x$. Since g^n is the identity function, its derivative is 1; that is,

$$n[g(x)]^{n-1}g'(x) = 1.$$

Consequently,

$$g'(x) = \frac{1}{n[g(x)]^{n-1}}$$

$$= \frac{1}{n[x^{1/n}]^{n-1}}$$

$$= \frac{1}{nx^{1-1/n}}$$

$$= \frac{1}{n}x^{1/n-1} .$$

This proves that for a rational number p of the form $1/n$ where n is an integer if $g(x) = x^p$ then $g'(x) = px^{p-1}$.

III. Let $h(x) = x^{m/n}$ where $x > 0$, m and n are integers. Now,

$$h(x) = (x^{1/n})^m .$$

Combining our results in I and II,

$$h'(x) = m(x^{1/n})^{m-1} \cdot \frac{1}{n} x^{1/n-1}$$

$$= \frac{m}{n} x^{m/n-1/n} \cdot x^{1/n-1}$$

$$= \frac{m}{n} x^{m/n-1} .$$

Thus, if p is any rational number and $h(x) = x^p$, then $h'(x) = px^{p-1}$.

exercises

1. Let $h(x) = [g(x)]^p$, where $g(x) > 0$ and p is any rational number. Prove that if g is differentiable, then $h'(x) = p[g(x)]^{p-1} \cdot g'(x)$.

In Exercises 2 through 15 find the derivative of the functions defined.

2. $h(x) = x^2(x^3 - 7x)^{11}$

3. $t(x) = x(x^2 + 1)^{3/2}$

4. $f(x) = \sqrt{3x + 7}$

5. $f(x) = (2x^2 + 1)^8$

6. $g(x) = x \sqrt{2x - 1}$

7. $h(x) = \sqrt{\dfrac{x+1}{x+2}}$

8. $g(x) = (2x + 1) \sqrt{x^2 + 9}$

9. $h(x) = \dfrac{x^2 + 1}{2x + 1}$

10. $h(x) = \dfrac{(x^2 + 5x + 1)^{1/3}}{5x - 2}$

11. $g(x) = x^2(3x^3 + 1)^{2/3}$

12. $f(x) = \dfrac{3x + 1}{2x - 5}$

13. $f(x) = [(x^2 + 1)^{1/2} + 7x]^2$

14. $h(x) = \sqrt{3x + \sqrt{x^2 + 4}}$

15. $f(x) = (2x + (x^2 + 1)^{1/2})^{4/3}$

15–9   higher derivatives and implicit differentiation

As we shall learn later, it is often quite important to study the derivative of the derivative of some function f. For this reason, the derivative

f' is sometimes called the *first derivative of f*. The derivative of f' is denoted by f'' and is called the *second derivative of f*. For example, if

$$f(x) = x^2,$$

then

$$f'(x) = 2x$$

and

$$f''(x) = 2.$$

The derivative of the second derivative is called the *third derivative of f*; in general, the derivative of the nth derivative of f where n is a positive integer is called the $(n+1)$st derivative of f. The third derivative of f is often denoted by f'''. The nth derivatives of f where $n \geqslant 2$ are called *higher derivatives* of f.

It should be obvious that although the symbol f''''' could be used for the fifth derivative it is not a very good choice of notation. This leads us to discuss some of the other (often used) notations for derivatives. For a function f, if we let $y = f(x)$, then the following are all standard notations for the first derivative:

$$f', \; D_x y, \; D_x f, \; f'(x), \; y', \; \frac{dy}{dx}, \; \text{and} \; \frac{df(x)}{dx}.$$

The most-used notations for the second derivative are the following:

$$f''(x), \; y'', \; \frac{d^2 y}{dx^2} \; \text{and} \; \frac{d^2 f(x)}{dx^2}.$$

The following are all notations for the fourth derivative of f:

$$f^{IV}(x), \; f^{(4)}(x), \; \frac{d^4 y}{dx^4}, \; \text{and} \; \frac{d^4 f(x)}{dx^4}.$$

Although there are several frequently used notations for the first derivative, we have intentionally avoided the introduction of the other notations previously for two reasons: (1) the extra unfamiliar and unnecessary notations are an additional burden tending to interfere with obtaining a firm understanding of the derivative concept and the differentiation theorems; and (2), occasionally, the mnemonic advantages of the dy/dx notation obscure the basic features of the composite function theorem. Let us explain this last remark.

Suppose $y = f(g(x))$ and $u = g(x)$. Then, $y = f(u)$. Now, $dy/dx = [f(g(x))]'$, $du/dx = g'(x)$, and $dy/du = f'(u) = f'(g(x))$. Hence, since

$$[f(g(x))]' = f'(g(x)) \cdot g'(x),$$

$$\frac{dy}{dx} = \frac{dy}{du} \cdot \frac{du}{dx}.$$

If we were allowed to treat dy/dx as a fraction, then the second expression for the composite function theorem is "obviously" valid. Although it is not easy to prove, the notation dy/dx can be treated as a fraction; thus, the notation serves as a memory device for remembering some of the differentiation theorems. For example, if $F(x) = f(g(h(x)))$, then by repeated use of the composite function theorem we can prove that

$$F'(x) = f'(g(h(x))) \cdot g'(h(x)) \cdot h'(x) .$$

If we let $u = h(x)$, $v = g(u)$, and $F = f(v)$, then the formula for $F'(x)$ is equivalent to

$$\frac{dF}{dx} = \frac{dF}{dv} \cdot \frac{dv}{du} \cdot \frac{du}{dx} .$$

Up to this point, we have defined what is meant by "higher derivatives" and discussed derivative notations. Let us now again turn our attention to techniques for finding the derivatives of functions. This is the last "tool" we present for finding derivatives before discussing many of the important applications of differential calculus.

If we consider the equation $x^2 + y^2 = 25$, then the set S of ordered pairs (x, y) satisfying this equation is not a function since, for example, $(3, 4)$ and $(3, -4)$ are in S. See Figure 15–6. However, if we restrict $y \geq 0$, the set of pairs (x, y) satisfying $x^2 + y^2 = 25$ is a function. In fact,

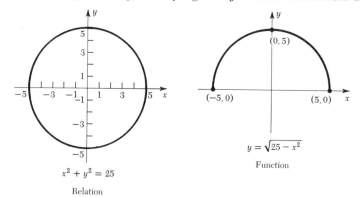

$x^2 + y^2 = 25$

Relation

$y = \sqrt{25 - x^2}$

Function

FIGURE 15–6

the graph of this function is the semicircle defined by $y = \sqrt{25 - x^2}$. The equation $x^2 + y^2 = 25$ is said to define a function *implicitly*. We now discuss a method for differentiating functions implicitly defined by equations; the process is called *implicit differentiation*.

Assume $x^2 + y^2 = 25$ defines a function f with ordered pairs $(x, f(x))$. Then, $x^2 + [f(x)]^2 = 25$ for each $(x, f(x)) \in f$. Differentiating both sides of the equation

$$2x + 2f(x) \cdot f'(x) = 0 .$$

Solving for $f'(x)$:

$$f'(x) = \frac{-x}{f(x)} \, .$$

If $f(x) > 0$, then $f'(x) = -x/\sqrt{25 - x^2}$; this is the same result that would be obtained by differentiating the function defined by $f(x) = \sqrt{25 - x^2}$.

examples

1. Assuming $y^2 + 2xy + x^3 = 25$ defines a function implicitly, we let $f(x)$ be the unique number in the range corresponding to x in the domain. Thus,

$$[f(x)]^2 + 2xf(x) + x^3 = 25.$$

Differentiating, $2f(x) \cdot f'(x) + 2xf'(x) + 2f(x) + 3x^2 = 0$. Thus,

$$f'(x) = \frac{-3x^2 - 2f(x)}{2x + 2f(x)} \, .$$

Notice that $f'(x)$ is given in terms of x and $f(x)$.

2. Find the slope of the tangent line to the curve $x^3 - 2x^2y^2 + 3y = -x$ at $(1, 2)$.

Solution:

Let $f(x)$ be the number in the range paired with x in the domain of the function f defined by the equation. Thus,

$$x^3 - 2x^2[f(x)]^2 + 3f(x) = -x \, .$$

Differentiating,
$$3x^2 - \{2x^2(2)f(x)f'(x) + 4x[f(x)]^2\} + 3f'(x) = -1$$
$$3f'(x) - 4x^2f(x)f'(x) = 4x[f(x)]^2 - 1 - 3x^2$$
$$f'(x) = \frac{4x[f(x)]^2 - 1 - 3x^2}{3 - 4x^2f(x)}$$

Since $f(1) = 2$,

$$f'(1) = \frac{4(2)^2 - 1 - 3}{3 - 4(2)} = -\frac{12}{5} \, .$$

3. If $x^3 + 3xy + y^2 = 7$ defines a function f implicitly, find $f''(x)$.

$$x^3 + 3xf(x) + [f(x)]^2 = 7$$
$$3x^2 + 3xf'(x) + 3f(x) + 2f(x)f'(x) = 0 \qquad \text{(A)}$$

Differentiating again,
$$6x + 3xf''(x) + 3f'(x) + 3f'(x) + 2f(x)f''(x) + 2[f'(x)]^2 = 0 \, .$$
Solving for $f''(x)$,
$$f''(x) = -\frac{6x + 6f'(x) + 2[f'(x)]^2}{3x + 2f(x)} \, . \qquad \text{(B)}$$

The second derivative could be expressed in terms of x and $f(x)$ by solving (A) for $f'(x)$ and substituting in (B).

exercises

Find the first, second, and third derivatives of each function defined in Exercises 1 through 9.

1. $f(x) = x^6 - 5x^3 + 6x^2 - 2x + 11$
2. $F(x) = x^4 - 3x^3 + 7x^2$
3. $y = (x - 1)(x - 2)(x - 3)$
4. $f(x) = \sqrt{3x - 1}$
5. $g(x) = \sqrt[3]{4x + 3}$
6. $f(y) = \dfrac{y - 1}{y + 1}$
7. $G(u) = u\sqrt{u + 1}$
8. $f(x) = x^3$
9. $F(x) = x^n$
10. Let $y = x^n$. Find $\dfrac{d^{n-1}y}{dx^{n-1}}, \dfrac{d^n y}{dx^n},$ and $\dfrac{d^{n+1}y}{dx^{n+1}}$.

Assume functions f are implicitly defined by equations in Exercises 11 through 16 and assume $f'(x)$ and $f''(x)$ exist. Find equations defining $f'(x)$ and $f''(x)$.

11. $y^2 = 4x$
12. $x^3 - y^2 = 3$
13. $xy + y^2 = 4$
14. $x^2 y^2 = 6$
15. $x^2 + 3xy + y = 11$
16. $y^3 x + x = 4$
17. Assume the equation $x^2 + 2xy + y^2 = 4$ defines a function. Find $f'(x)$ for every x in the domain. Graph the equation.

15–10   increasing and decreasing functions

In Chapter 4, we defined what is meant by saying a function is increasing (or decreasing) on a set S. A function f is said to be an increasing function at a point t in its domain if, for some open interval containing t,

$$f(x) < f(t) \quad \text{for} \quad x < t$$

and

$$f(x) > f(t) \quad \text{for} \quad x > t.$$

A function f is said to be decreasing at t if, for some open interval containing t,

$$f(x) > f(t) \quad \text{for} \quad x < t$$

and

$$f(x) < f(t) \quad \text{for} \quad x > t.$$

Assume $f'(t) > 0$. Thus,

$$\lim_{x \to t} \frac{f(x) - f(t)}{x - t}$$

exists and is a positive number. Using the fact that if the limit of a function is positive at some point t in its domain then the function must be positive in some interval containing t (see Theorem 15–4), there exists some interval containing t such that

$$\frac{f(x) - f(t)}{x - t} > 0 .$$

For this quotient to be positive,

$$f(x) - f(t) < 0 \quad \text{for } x - t < 0$$

and

$$f(x) - f(t) > 0 \quad \text{for } x - t > 0 .$$

That is,

$$f(x) < f(t) \qquad \text{for } x < t$$

and

$$f(x) > f(t) \qquad \text{for } x > t .$$

Consequently, if $f'(t) > 0$, then it follows from the definition of increasing that f is an increasing function at t. Geometrically, if the slope of the tangent line is positive, then $f(x)$ "moves up" as x "moves to the right."

Notice we did *not* prove that if the function is increasing and differentiable at t, then $f'(t) > 0$. In fact, this need not be true. Consider f defined by $f(x) = x^3$; then, $f'(x) = 3x^2$. Since $f'(x) > 0$ for all $x \neq 0$, the function is increasing for all $x \neq 0$. Although $f'(0) = 0$, it is obvious that f is also increasing at $x = 0$; if $x < 0$ then $x^3 < 0$ and if $x > 0$ then $x^3 > 0$. See Figure 15–7.

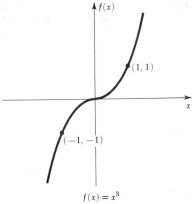

$$f(x) = x^3$$

FIGURE 15–7

It should be obvious that points where the derivative is zero (or undefined) must be considered separately when determining for what subsets of the domain of the function it is either increasing or decreasing.

If $f'(t) < 0$, then f is *decreasing* at t. To prove this statement, we need to use the fact that if the limit of a function at some point t in its domain is negative, then there exists an interval containing t where the function is negative. Since

$$\lim_{x \to t} \frac{f(x) - f(t)}{x - t} < 0 \,,$$

there exists an interval containing t such that

$$f(x) - f(t) > 0 \quad \text{for } x - t < 0$$

and

$$f(x) - f(t) < 0 \quad \text{for } x - t > 0 \,.$$

That is,

$$f(x) > f(t) \qquad \text{for } x < t$$

and

$$f(x) < f(t) \qquad \text{for } x > t \,.$$

examples

1. For the function f given by $f(x) = x^{2/3}$,

$$f'(x) = \frac{2}{3} x^{-1/3} = \frac{2}{3 \sqrt[3]{x}} \,.$$

For any number $t > 0, f'(t) > 0$; thus, the function increases for all positive real numbers. For any number $t < 0, f'(t) < 0$; thus, the function decreases for all negative real numbers. In any interval containing zero, f is positive on both sides of 0; hence, f is neither increasing nor decreasing at 0.

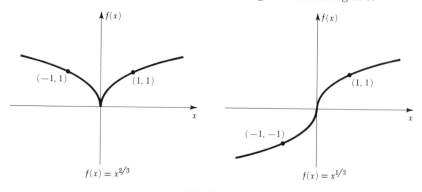

$$f(x) = x^{2/3} \qquad\qquad\qquad f(x) = x^{1/3}$$

FIGURE 15–8

2. For the function given by $f(x) = x^{1/3}$,

$$f'(x) = \frac{1}{3}x^{-2/3} = \frac{1}{3x^{2/3}} = \frac{1}{3\sqrt[3]{x^2}}.$$

Since $f'(x) > 0$ for all $x \neq 0$, the function increases for all real numbers different from zero. As in Example 1, although 0 is not in the domain of f', it is in the domain of f. Furthermore, since $f(x) < f(0)$ when $x < 0$ and $f(x) > f(0)$ when $x > 0$, f is an increasing function at $x = 0$. Consequently, f increases for all real numbers.

15–11 concavity and inflection points

When discussing the graph of a function, not only is it important to know where the graph is "going up," where it is "going down," or where the high and low points are, but it is also important to know how the curve is "bending." In this section, we discuss methods for determining whether the curve "bends up" in some given interval or "bends down" in some interval.

definition: The graph of a function f is said to be *concave upward* at t in its domain if the derivative f' is an increasing function at t. The graph is said to be *concave downward* at t if f' is a decreasing function at t.

Geometrically, the graph of f is concave upward (downward) at t if the tangent at $(t, f(t))$ is below (above) the curve in some interval containing t. Notice that since concavity is defined in terms of the derivative, we have restricted the concept of concavity to points where the function is continuous.

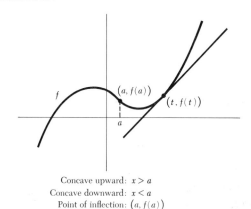

Concave upward: $x > a$
Concave downward: $x < a$
Point of inflection: $(a, f(a))$

FIGURE 15–9

We proved in Section 15–10 that if the derivative of a given function exists and is positive then the function is increasing. Thus, if $f''(t) > 0$ for a function f, then f' is an increasing function at t and the graph of

f is concave upward at t. Similarly, if $f''(t) < 0$, then f' is a decreasing function at t and the graph of f is concave downward at t.

Although in order to define the concavity of the graph of a function at $(t, f(t))$ we have assumed that f' exists, $f''(t)$ need not exist. As we said in the last section, numbers for which the derivative of a function is zero or undefined must be checked separately to find if the function is increasing or decreasing; that is, numbers for which f'' is zero or undefined must be considered separately to determine if f' is increasing or decreasing at t.

examples

1. If f is defined by $f(x) = x^4$, $f'(x) = 4x^3$ and $f''(x) = 12x^2$. If $x \neq 0$, $f''(x) > 0$ and f' is an increasing function; thus, the graph of f is concave upward for $x \neq 0$. Since

$$f'(x) < f'(0) \quad \text{for } x < 0$$

and

$$f'(x) > f'(0) \quad \text{for } x > 0 \, ,$$

f' is an increasing function at 0. Hence, the graph of f is concave upward for every real number.

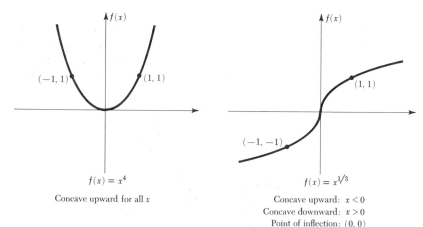

FIGURE 15–10

2. If f is defined by $f(x) = x^{1/3}$, $f'(x) = (1/3)x^{2/3}$, and $f''(x) = -2/9x^{5/3}$. If $x > 0$, $f''(x) < 0$, so the graph of f is concave downward for $x > 0$. If $x < 0$, $f''(x) > 0$, so the graph of f is concave upward for $x < 0$. Since 0 is not in the domain of f'', the graph of f is not concave at 0.

definition: Let $(t, f(t))$ be a point on the graph of a function f. If the graph of f is concave upward on one side of $(t, f(t))$ and concave downward on the other side, then $(t, f(t))$ is called an *inflection point*, or *point of inflection*, of the graph.

Three different conditions sufficient to show that the graph of a function f has an inflection point at $(t, f(t))$ are as follows.

I. If $f''(t) = 0$ and if, in some interval containing t, $f''(x)$ is positive on one side of t and negative on the other, then $(t, f(t))$ is an inflection point. (If f'' changes signs at t, then f must be concave upward on one side of t and concave downward on the other. Thus, $(t, f(t))$ is an inflection point.)

II. If $f''(t) = 0$ and if $f'''(t) \neq 0$, then $(t, f(t))$ is an inflection point. (If $f'''(t) \neq 0$, f'' is either increasing or decreasing at t. Since $f''(t) = 0$, f'' must have a different sign on each side of t; thus, it is concave upward on one side and concave downward on the other.)

III. Assume t is in the domain of f but not in the domain of f''. If $f''(x)$ exists in some deleted interval containing t and has opposite signs on each side of t, then $(t, f(t))$ is an inflection point.

exercises

For each of the functions, determine the following.
(a) The subsets of the domain where the function is increasing.
(b) The subsets of the domain where the function is decreasing.
(c) The coordinates of any inflection points on the graph of the function.
(d) The subsets of the domain where the graph of the function is concave upward.
(e) The subsets of the domain where the graph of the function is concave downward.

1. $f(x) = x^{2/3}$

2. $f(x) = x^{4/3}$

3. $f(x) = x^3 - 3x^2$

4. $f(x) = x/(x + 1)$

5. $f(x) = 2x^3 + 5x^2 - 8x + 1$

6. $f(x) = x^3 + 4x^2 - 3x + 1$

7. $f(x) = 4x^3 - 7x^2$

8. Let g be the inverse of f as defined in Exercise 4. Find $g'(3)$.

9. Make the restriction $-1/2 < x < 1/2$ on the domain of f in Exercise 5 and find $g'(1)$ where g is the inverse function of f.

10. Make the restriction $-1/4 < x < 1/4$ on the domain of f in Exercise 6 and find $g'(1)$ where g is the inverse function of f.

11. Make the restriction $3/4 < x < 7/6$ on the domain of f in Exercise 7 and find $g'(-3)$ where g is the inverse function.

15–12 maxima and minima

definition: A function f is said to have $f(a)$ as a *relative maximum* (or *local maximum*) at a if there is some interval containing a in the domain of f such that

$f(x) \le f(a)$ for every x in the interval. Similarly, function f is said to have $f(a)$ as a *relative minimum* (or *local minimum*) at a if there is some interval containing a in the domain of f such that $f(x) \ge f(a)$.

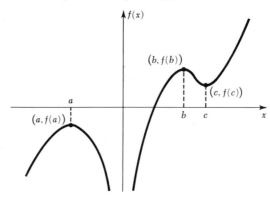

Relative maxima: $f(a)$ and $f(b)$
Relative minimum: $f(c)$

FIGURE 15-11

As defined in Chapter 4, if $f(a) \ge f(x)$ for every x in the domain of f, then $f(a)$ is the absolute maximum of the function. Similarly, if $f(a) \le f(x)$ for every x in the domain of f, then $f(a)$ is absolute minimum.

As shown in Figure 15-11, a relative maximum for a given function may be less than a relative minimum for the function. However, if a function has both an absolute maximum and absolute minimum, then the absolute maximum is greater than or equal to the absolute minimum.

examples

1. Let f be given by $f(x) = 2 + (x - 3)^2$. Since $(x - 3)^2 \ge 0$ for every real number x, the function has an absolute minimum at $x = 3$; the absolute minimum is $f(3) = 2$.

2. Let f be given by $f(x) = \sqrt{x^2 - 1}$. The domain of f is $\{x \mid x \ge 1 \text{ or } x \le -1\}$. Since $f(x) \ge f(1)$ for all $x \ge 1$, we have that $f(1) = 0$ is a relative minimum for f. Similarly, since $f(x) \ge f(-1)$ for all $x \ge -1$, f also has 0 as a relative minimum at $x = -1$. Furthermore, 0 is the absolute minimum for f. Notice that for, say, $x > 7$, $y \approx \sqrt{x^2}$; likewise, if $x < -7$, $y \approx \sqrt{x^2}$. Consequently, $y \approx x$ for $x > 7$ and $y \approx -x$ for $x < -7$. See Figure 15-12. It is geometrically obvious that f does not have any local maxima.

3. Let f be given by $f(x) = 6$. At any point a in the domain of f, there always exists an interval containing a such that $f(x) \ge f(a)$ and $f(x) \le f(a)$ for every x in the interval. Hence, every point in the domain of f is a relative minimum and every point is a relative maximum; both are 6. In fact, 6 is also the absolute maximum and absolute minimum.

We are interested in using techniques of calculus to find local maxima and minima. The following remarks will pertain to *continuous functions*

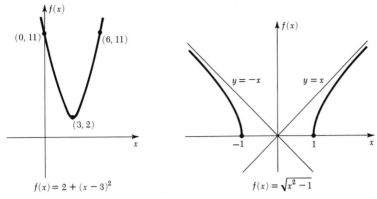

$$f(x) = 2 + (x - 3)^2 \qquad\qquad f(x) = \sqrt{x^2 - 1}$$

FIGURE 15-12

where the domain is some open interval (a, b). If the domain of a function f is a closed interval $[a, b]$, the endpoint values $f(a)$ and $f(b)$ are considered separately in finding maximum and minimum values; these are sometimes called *endpoint extrema*.

If f is a differentiable function and $f'(t) \neq 0$, then f is either an increasing function or a decreasing function at t. Thus, if a number t is in the domain of f such that either $f'(t) = 0$ or if t is not in the domain of f' then $(t, f(t))$ is a "candidate" for a relative maximum or relative minimum point. At a local maximum $(t, f(t))$, there exists an interval containing t such that the function is increasing for $x < t$ and decreasing for $x > t$. Hence, if $f'(t) = 0$, or $f'(t)$ is undefined and if $f'(x)$ is positive for $x < t$ and $f'(x)$ is negative for $x > t$, then $f(t)$ is a local maximum value of the function. By a similar argument, we see that if $f'(t) = 0$, or $f'(t)$ is undefined, and if f' "changes signs" from negative to the left of t to positive to the right of t, then f "changes" from a decreasing function to an increasing function at $(t, f(t))$ and $f(t)$ is a local minimum value of f.

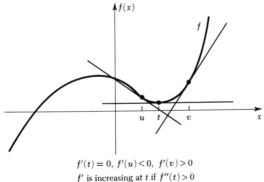

$$f'(t) = 0, \ f'(u) < 0, \ f'(v) > 0$$
$$f' \text{ is increasing at } t \text{ if } f''(t) > 0$$
Relative minimum: $f(t)$

FIGURE 15-13

Another test to determine the relative maxima and minima of a function f is the following. If $f'(t) = 0$ and $f''(t) < 0$, then $f(t)$ is a relative maximum for the function f at t. Notice that if $f''(t) < 0$ the graph is concave downward at $(t, f(f))$. If $f'(t) = 0$ and if $f''(t) > 0$, then $f(t)$ is a relative minimum value of f.

At the endpoint of a closed interval that is the domain of a function, or at points of discontinuity, the techniques previously discussed for finding maxima and minima are not applicable. For example, let f be the function defined as follows.

$$f(x) = \begin{cases} \dfrac{x^2-4}{x-2} & x \neq 2 \\ 16 & x = 2 \end{cases} \quad \text{and} \quad x \in [-1, 6] .$$

Notice that since $(x^2 - 4)/(x - 2) = x + 2$ for $x \neq 2$, the graph of f is the point $(2, 16)$ plus the line segment of the graph of $y = x + 2$ where $-1 \leqslant x \leqslant 6$ except for a "hole" at $x = 2$.

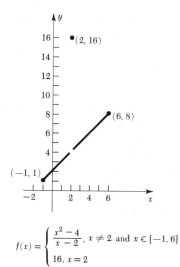

$$f(x) = \begin{cases} \dfrac{x^2-4}{x-2}, & x \neq 2 \text{ and } x \in [-1, 6] \\ 16, & x = 2 \end{cases}$$

FIGURE 15–14

It is obvious that $f(2) \geqslant f(x)$ for every x in an interval containing 2; in fact, $f(2) \geqslant f(x)$ for every x in the domain of the function. Therefore, 16 is not only a relative maximum value of f; it is also the absolute maximum of the function. Since f is increasing in $(-1, 0)$, and since -1 is an endpoint in the domain of the function, $f(x) \geqslant f(-1)$ for every $x \in [-1, 0]$; hence, $f(-1) = 1$ is a relative minimum for the function. In fact, $f(-1) \leqslant f(x)$ for every x in the domain of f; thus, $f(-1)$ is the absolute minimum of the function. If we consider the function value at the other endpoint, we see that there is an interval containing 6 such that $f(x) \leqslant f(6)$ for every x in the interval and in the domain of f. Thus, $f(6) = 8$ is a relative maximum for f.

examples

1. Let f be the function defined by $f(x) = x^3 - 15x^2/2 - 18x + 3/2$. Then, $f'(x) = 3x^2 - 15x - 18$ and $f''(x) = 6x - 15$. Since f is differentiable for every number in its domain, the only possible maximum or minimum points are the function values $f(x)$ such that $3x^2 - 15x - 18 = 0$.

   Since $f'(-1) = 0$ and $f''(-1) = -21$, there is a relative maximum at -1. The relative maximum is $f(-1) = 11$.

   Since $f'(6) = 0$ and $f''(6) = 21$, a positive number, there is a relative minimum at $x = 6$. The relative minimum is $f(6) = -321/2$.

2. Let h be the function defined by $h(x) = x + 4/x$. Then, $h'(x) = 1 - 4/x^2$ and $h''(x) = 8/x^3$. Although $h'(x)$ is undefined at $x = 0$, the function cannot have a maximum or minimum at 0 since h is not defined there. The only possible numbers in the domain for which the function can have a maximum or minimum are those where $h'(x) = 0$; that is, $x = 2$ or $x = -2$.

   Since $h''(2) = 1$, we conclude that $h(2) = 4$ is a relative minimum. Since $h''(-2) = -1$, we conclude that $h(-2) = -4$ is a relative maximum. This is an example of a function whose relative maximum is less than its relative minimum. See Figure 15–15. *Note:* For "large" x, $h(x) \approx x$.

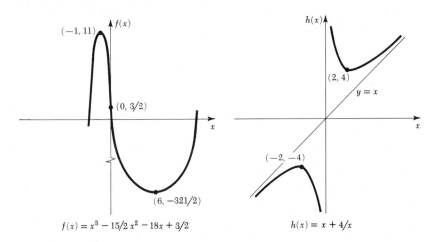

$$f(x) = x^3 - 15/2\, x^2 - 18x + 3/2 \qquad h(x) = x + 4/x$$

FIGURE 15–15

3. Let g be the function defined by $g(x) = \sqrt{x^2 + 4}$. Then, $g'(x) = x/\sqrt{x^2 + 4}$. Since $g'(x) \neq 0$ for $x \neq 0$ and since $g'(0) = 0$, the only possible maximum or minimum point is $(0, g(0))$.

   Although we can find $g''(x)$ and evaluate $g''(0)$ to determine whether or not $g(0)$ is a relative maximum or relative minimum, this is an example of a function where considering the sign of g' is much simpler. Since $\sqrt{x^2 + 4}$ is always positive, we see immediately that $x/\sqrt{x^2 + 4}$ is negative where $x < 0$ and positive where $x > 0$. Hence, since g' "changes" signs from negative to positive, g has a relative minimum at 0; the relative minimum is $g(0) = 2$. *Note:* For "large" $x > 0$, $\sqrt{x^2 + 4} \approx x$, and $x < 0$, $\sqrt{x^2 + 4} \approx -x$.

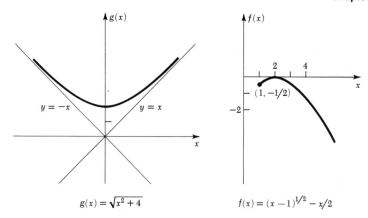

$$g(x) = \sqrt{x^2 + 4} \qquad\qquad f(x) = (x-1)^{1/2} - x/2$$

FIGURE 15–16

4. Let f be defined by $f(x) = (x-1)^{1/2} - x/2$. Then, $f'(x) = 1/2(x-1)^{-1/2} - 1/2$ and $f''(x) = -1/4(x-1)^{-3/2}$. Since $f'(2) = 0$ and since $f''(2) = -1/4$, a negative number, we conclude that $f(2) = 0$ is a relative maximum for f.

To find whether $(1, f(1))$, the endpoint in the domain of f, is a maximum or minimum point, we find for what numbers f' is positive and for what numbers f' is negative.

$$1/2(x-1)^{-1/2} - 1/2 > 0$$

$$\frac{1/2}{(x-1)^{1/2}} > 1/2$$

$$1 > (x-1)^{1/2} .$$

We conclude that $f'(x)$ is positive where $1 < x < 2$. Similarly, $f'(x)$ is negative for all $x > 2$.

Since $f'(x)$ is positive where $1 < x < 2$, f is increasing in the interval. Thus, f has a relative minimum at the endpoint $x = 1$; thus, $f(1) = -1/2$ is a relative minimum. Since $f'(x) < 0$ where $x > 0$, f decreases for all $x > 2$. Thus, $f(2)$ is also the absolute maximum of f; the function has no absolute minimum.

5. A sheet of galvanized tin 28 feet long and 16 inches wide is to be made into a trough by turning up equal "sides" at right angles to the bottom. Find the dimensions that give the maximum volume if the ends are to be closed with some other material. What is the maximum volume?

Solution: Since the length is fixed, it is the maximum cross-sectional area that will make the volume a maximum. If x inches is turned up on each side, the cross-sectional area in square inches is given by

Thus, $A(x) = x(16 - 2x) .$

and $A'(x) = 16 - 4x ,$

$$A''(x) = -4 .$$

Since $A'(4) = 0$ and $A''(4)$ is negative, the area is a maximum when $x = 4$. Since $A''(x)$ is negative for all x in the domain of A, $A(4)$ is not only a relative maximum but also the absolute maximum.

$$A(4) = 32 \text{ square inches} = 2/9 \text{ square feet} .$$

Hence, the maximum volume is $28(2/9) = 56/9$ cubic feet.

6. If a box with a square bottom is open at the top and has a given surface area S, find the ratio of the height to the width of the base so that the volume will be a maximum.
    Solution: If w is the width of the base and h is the height, then the area of the base is w^2 and the area of one of the sides is wh. Therefore, the total surface area is

$$S = w^2 + 4wh ,$$

where S is a constant. Hence, h as a function of w is given by

(1) $$h = \frac{S - w^2}{4w} .$$

If x is the ratio of the height to the width, we have $x = h/w$; that is, $h = wx$. Substituting for h in (1), we get

$$wx = \frac{S - w^2}{4w} ,$$

$$4w^2x = S - w^2 ,$$

$$w^2 = \frac{S}{4x + 1} ,$$

and

(2) $$w = \left(\frac{S}{4x + 1} \right)^{1/2} .$$

Since the volume of the box is $V = hw^2 = xw^3$, from Equation (2) we obtain that the volume V as a function of x is given by

$$V(x) = x \left(\frac{S}{4x + 1} \right)$$

$$= S^{3/2} \frac{x}{(4x + 1)^{3/2}} .$$

Thus,

$$V'(x) = \frac{S^{3/2}[(4x + 1)^{3/2} - x(3/2)\,(4x + 1)^{1/2}(4)]}{(4x + 1)^3}$$

$$= \frac{S^{3/2}[(1 - 2x)]}{(4x + 1)^{5/2}} .$$

Since $V'(1/2) = 0$, and since there is an interval containing $1/2$, namely $0 < x < 1$, such that $V'(x) > 0$ where $x < 1/2$ and $V'(x) < 0$ where $x > 1/2$, $V(x)$ is a maximum for $x = 1/2$.

Therefore, if the ratio of the height to the width is $1/2$, then for a fixed surface area the volume of the box is a maximum.

exercises

For each of the functions in Exercises 1 through 12, determine the following: (a) the subsets of the domain where the function is increasing, (b) the subsets of the domain where the function is decreasing, (c) the coordinates of any inflection points on the graph of the function, (d) the subsets of the domain where the graph of the function is concave upward, (e) the subsets in the domain where the graph of the function is concave downward, (f) relative minimum of the function, (g) relative maximum of the function, (h) absolute maximum, and (i) absolute minimum.

1. $f(x) = x^3 - \dfrac{15}{2} x^2 - 18x + \dfrac{3}{2}$

2. $f(x) = x^3 + x^2 - 8x + 3$

3. $f(x) = 2x^3 + \dfrac{7}{2} x^2 - 5x - \dfrac{7}{2}$

4. $f(x) = 3 + \sqrt{x - 2}$

5. $f(x) = \dfrac{x^2 + 2}{x}$

6. $f(x) = 2x - 2(x - 2)^{3/2}$

7. $f(x) = 4(x - 3)^{1/2} - 2x$

8. $f(x) = \dfrac{3x + 7}{2x - 5}$

9. $f(x) = \dfrac{5x - 6}{3x + 11}$

10. $f(x) = x^{1/3} \sqrt{64 - x^2}$

11. $f(x) = (3x + 1)^2(x - 5)$

12. $f(x) = (x + 3)(2x - 7)^3$

13. A man on an island is 3 miles from a straight shore and he wishes to reach, as soon as possible, a point on the shore 4 miles from the closest point on shore. If he can average 2 mph rowing in a boat and 4 mph walking, what route should he take?

14. A closed cylindrical can is to have a given volume. The cost per square unit of the material for the top and bottom is k times the cost per square unit of the material for the side. Find the most economical ratio of the altitude to the radius.

15. Find the dimensions of the cylinder of maximum volume that can be inscribed in a sphere of fixed radius R.

16. A piece of wire 100 inches long is to be cut. One piece of wire is to be bent into a square and the other into a circle. How should the wire be cut to get a minimum area? How do you get a maximum area?

17. A vertical wall is on level ground three feet away from a building. If the wall is 6 feet high, what is the shortest ladder that can rest on the ground and reach over the wall and lean against the building?

*18. A rod is to be carried (level with the floor) from one corridor to another. If one corridor is 8 feet wide and the other is 11 feet wide, what is the longest rod that can be carried around the corner? (Ignore the cross-sectional dimensions of the rod.)

15–13 differentials

Let us discuss one method for approximating $\sqrt[3]{29}$. If f is defined by $f(x) = x^{1/3}$, we seek an approximation of $f(29)$. It is obvious that

$f(27) = \sqrt[3]{27} = 3$, so if k is the approximate difference in the range values corresponding to 27 and 29 in the domain of f, then $\sqrt[3]{29} \approx 3 + k$.

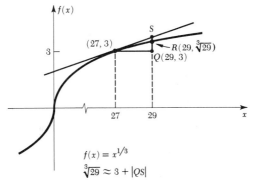

$$f(x) = x^{1/3}$$
$$\sqrt[3]{29} \approx 3 + |QS|$$

FIGURE 15–17

In Figure 5–17, we see that $\sqrt[3]{29} - \sqrt[3]{27} = |QR|$; thus,

$$\sqrt[3]{29} = 3 + |QR| .$$

Furthermore, $|QR| \approx |QS|$ so $\sqrt[3]{29} \approx 3 + |QS|$. The slope of the tangent line at $(27, 3)$ is

$$f'(27) = \frac{1}{3(27)^{2/3}} = \frac{1}{27} ;$$

therefore, the equation of the tangent line is $x - 27y = -54$. Since the x-coordinate of S is 29, the y-coordinate of S is given by

$$-27y = -54 - 29 ,$$

or $y = 83/27 .$

Thus, $|QS| = 83/27 - 3 = 83/27 - 81/27 = 2/27$. Consequently,

$$\sqrt[3]{29} \approx 3 + \frac{2}{27} = 3.074 .$$

A check with cube root tables shows that $\sqrt[3]{29} = 3.0723$ correct to four decimal places.

Let us now generalize this approximation process. See Figure 15–18. If S has x-coordinate $t + h$ we find the y-coordinate of S from the equation of the tangent line. Since the slope of the tangent line is $f'(t)$, the equation of the tangent line at $(t, f(t))$ is

$$y - f(t) = f'(t)(x - t) .$$

Thus, where $x = t + h$,

$$y = f(t) + f'(t)h .$$

Consequently,

$$f(t + h) \approx f(t) + f'(t)h .$$

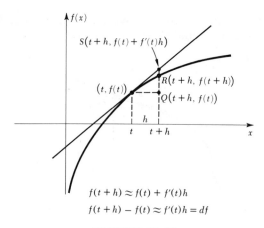

$$f(t+h) \approx f(t) + f'(t)h$$
$$f(t+h) - f(t) \approx f'(t)h = df$$

FIGURE 15–18

example

If f is defined by $f(x) = x^3$ and we wish to approximate $f(2.001) = (2.001)^3$, we let $t = 2$ and $h = 0.001$. Thus,

$$f(2.001) = f(2 + 0.001)$$
$$\approx f(2) + f'(2)\,(0.001)$$
$$= 8 + 3(2)^2(0.001)$$
$$= 8.012.$$

Actually, $f(2.001) = 8.012006001$; thus the error introduced by this method of approximation is 0.000006001.

A non-geometric approach to this method for approximating the value of a differentiable function at x in the domain of f when the value of f at t is known is as follows.

Since

$$f'(t) = \lim_{x \to t} \frac{f(x) - f(t)}{x - t}, \text{ for } x \text{ "close" to } t$$

$$f'(t) \approx \frac{f(x) - f(t)}{x - t}.$$

Thus,

$$f(x) \approx f(t) + f'(t)(x - t) .$$

If we let $x - t = h$, then $x = t + h$, and again we obtain

$$f(t + h) \approx f(t) + f'(t)h .$$

If we are interested in how close $f(t) + f'(t)h$ approximates $f(t + h)$, we can use the fact that

$$f(t + h) = f(t) + f'(t)h + f''(c)h^2 ,$$

where c is some number between t and $t + h$. (This is called a Taylor polynomial with remainder; a proof of its validity can be found in a standard calculus text.) The maximum value of $f''(c)h^2$ for c in the interval $(t, t + h)$ will be an upper bound for the error. See Section 16–4.

We define $f'(x)h$ to be the *differential of the function f at x with increment h*; it is denoted by "dy" or "df." Notice that the differential is a function of two variables since dy depends on t and h. The increment h is more often denoted by "dx" and is sometimes called the *differential of the independent variable*. Consequently, we have

$$dy = f'(x)dx \, ,$$

and

$$\frac{dy}{dx} = f'(x) \, .$$

Thus, we have proved that the derivative of f is equal to the *quotient* of dy divided by dx.

In summary, the differential dy of a function f with increment dx is given by $dy = f'(x)dx$, and, for "suitable" choices of dx,

$$f(x + dx) \approx f(x) + dy \, .$$

15–14 newton's method of root approximation

Let us consider the problem of finding $\sqrt[3]{29}$ from a viewpoint different from that discussed in Section 15–13. Algebraically, we seek the real root of the equation $x^3 = 29$. In other words, we seek the zero of the polynomial

$$f(x) = x^3 - 29 \, ,$$

the number t for which $f(t) = 0$.

For $x = 3$, $f(x) = 27 - 29 = -2$; thus, we take $x_1 = 3$ as a first approximation of the zero of the polynomial. See Figure 15–19. Consider the

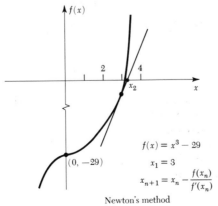

$$f(x) = x^3 - 29$$
$$x_1 = 3$$
$$x_{n+1} = x_n - \frac{f(x_n)}{f'(x_n)}$$

Newton's method

FIGURE 15–19

tangent line to the graph of f at $(3, f(3))$. If we let x_2 be the x-intercept of this tangent line and if we next consider the tangent line to the graph of f at $(x_2, f(x_2))$, then it is geometrically obvious that the x-intercept x_3 of this second tangent line is a better approximation of the zero of the polynomial than x_1. Having established this basic approach, let us now consider the problem in a more general manner and develop formulas for the x-intercepts of the successive tangent lines.

Let f be a polynomial function. Let x_1 be the first approximation of the zero of the function f; that is, $f(x_1) \neq 0$. See Figure 15–19. The slope of the tangent line at $(x_1, f(x_1))$ is $f'(x_1)$ and the equation of the tangent line is

$$y - f(x_1) = f'(x_1)(x - x_1) .$$

Since the x-intercept of this line is where $y = 0$,

$$-f(x_1) = f'(x_1)x - f'(x_1)x_1 ,$$

$$f'(x_1)x = f'(x_1)x_1 - f(x_1) ,$$

and

$$x = x_1 - \frac{f(x_1)}{f'(x_1)}$$

is the x-intercept of the tangent line to the curve at $(x_1, f(x_1))$. (Notice that we pick x_1 so that $f'(x_1) \neq 0$.)

Let the x-intercept of this first tangent line to the curve be our second approximation for the zero of f; then let

$$x_2 = x_1 - \frac{f(x_1)}{f'(x_1)} .$$

Similarly, it can be shown that the x-intercept of the tangent line to the curve at $(x_2, f(x_2))$ is

$$x_3 = x_2 - \frac{f(x_2)}{f'(x_2)} .$$

Continuing, we get that x_n is given by the following formula:

$$x_n = x_{n-1} - \frac{f(x_{n-1})}{f'(x_{n-1})} .$$

Using the sequence $x_1, x_2, x_3, \ldots$ to approximate the zeros of the polynomial f and, thus, the roots of the equation $f(x) = 0$ is called *Newton's method* of root approximation.

Let us return to our original example and use Newton's method to approximate the root of the equation $x^3 - 29 = 0$. We proceed as follows. Let $f(x) = x^3 - 29$. Then, letting $x_1 = 3$ we get

$$x_2 = 3 - \frac{f(3)}{f'(3)}$$

$$= 3 - \frac{(-2)}{27}$$

$$= \frac{83}{27} .$$

Next,

$$x_3 = \frac{83}{27} - \frac{f\left(\frac{83}{27}\right)}{f'\left(\frac{83}{27}\right)}$$

$$= \frac{83}{27} - \frac{(83/27)^3 - 29}{3(83/27)^2}$$

$$= \frac{83}{27} - \frac{83}{81} + \frac{29(27)^2}{3(83)^2}$$

$$= \frac{166}{81} + \frac{21141}{20667}$$

$$\approx 2.049382 + 1.022935$$

$$= 3.072317 .$$

Obtaining $\sqrt[3]{29}$ correct to six decimal places by using the formula only twice should be ample justification of the usefulness here of Newton's method of root approximation.

exercises

In Exercises 1 through 4 find the differential dy in terms of x and dx.

1. $y = x^3$

2. $y = (x + 2)^{3/2}$

3. $y = x \sqrt{x^2 + 3}$

4. $y = \sqrt{1 - 3x}$

5. (a) Use differentials to calculate the approximate volume of a cube that is 3.012 cm on an edge.
   (b) Find the actual volume.

6. Use differentials to approximate $1/10.023$. *Hint:* Find the approximate change in y where $y = 1/x$ when x "changes" from 10 to 10.023.

7. Use differentials to approximate (a) $\sqrt[3]{127}$, (b) $(2.013)^5$.

8. Use Newton's method to approximate the positive real root of $x^4 - 18 = 0$.

9. Use Newton's method to approximate the positive real root of $x^4 - 2x^3 - 8x - 16 = 0$. *Hint:* Let $f(x) = x^4 - 2x^3 - 8x - 16$. Show $f(3) < 0$ and $f(4) > 0$ to choose your first approximation.

10. Use Newton's method to approximate the positive real root of $x^4 - 4x^3 - 4x - 1 = 0$.

15–15   rate of change

We have already discussed that if $s(t) = 16t^2$ is the distance a free-falling body falls from rest in t seconds, then $s'(t) = 32t$ is the velocity at time t and $s''(t) = 32$ is the acceleration at the end of t seconds. In general, if $s(t)$ is the distance a particle moves in rectilinear motion, then $v(t) = s'(t)$ is the velocity function and $a(t) = v'(t) = s''(t)$ is the acceleration function.

If $y = f(x)$ defines a function, then $f'(x)$, or dy/dx, is called the *rate of change* of $f(x)$, or y, with respect to x. For a sphere of radius r, the volume is given by $(4/3)\pi r^3$. Thus, $v'(r) = 4\pi r^2$ is the rate of change of V with respect to r. However, in most applications, we would be interested in the rate of change of V with respect to time t and not with respect to the radius r.

Suppose the radius of a spherical bubble is a function of time t, then $r'(t)$ is the rate of change of r per unit of time t. If the radius is increasing at 2 feet per minute, then $r'(t) = 2$; furthermore,

$$V(t) = \frac{4}{3} \pi [r(t)]^3 \ ;$$

thus the rate of change of V with respect to time t is given by

$$V'(t) = 4\pi [r(t)]^2 r'(t) \ .$$

Hence, the rate of change of the volume with respect to time when the radius $r(t)$ is 3 feet is

$$V'(t) = 4\pi \ [3]^2 (2)$$

$$= 72\pi \text{ cubic feet per minute} \ .$$

Let us consider two more examples of rate-of-change problems. These are sometimes referred to as *related rate* problems.

examples

1. Let a cistern be in the shape of an inverted right circular cone with altitude 15 feet and radius 5 feet. If water is being pumped in at 12 cubic feet per minute, at what rate is the depth h of the water increasing when the depth is 4 feet?

   Solution: Notice that the radii and depths of the cones of water are functions of time t. By similar triangles,

   $$\frac{5}{15} = \frac{r(t)}{h(t)} \ .$$

   Thus,

   $$r(t) = \frac{1}{3} h(t) \ .$$

Since the volume of water $V(t)$ is given by

$$V(t) = \frac{1}{3} \pi [r(t)]^2 h(t)$$

$$= \frac{1}{3} \pi \left[\frac{1}{3} h(t) \right]^2 h(t)$$

$$= \frac{\pi}{3^3} [h(t)]^3$$

we have

$$V'(t) = \frac{\pi}{9} [h(t)]^2 h'(t) .$$

[Consider V as a function of h; thus, $V = 1/3\pi h^3$. Since

$$\frac{dV}{dt} = \frac{dV}{dh} \cdot \frac{dh}{dt}, \quad \frac{dV}{dt} = \frac{1}{9} \pi h^2 \cdot \frac{dh}{dt} ,$$

which is equivalent to Equation (1).]
    It is given that $V'(t) = 12$; therefore,

$$12 = \frac{1}{9} \pi [h(t)]^2 h'(t) .$$

Consequently,

$$h'(t) = \frac{108}{\pi [h(t)]^2} .$$

Where $h(t) = 4$,

$$h'(t) = \frac{108}{\pi (4)^2} = \frac{27}{4\pi} .$$

The depth is increasing at $27/4\pi$ feet per minute.

2. Suppose a boat with a deck 30 feet above the harbor bed is anchored with 90 feet of rope, which is kept taut in a straight line by the current. If rope is hauled in at 5 feet per minute, how fast is the boat moving through the water when there is 50 feet of rope out? Find the acceleration of the boat at this time.
    Solution: See Figure 15–20. We are given that $s'(t) = 5$ and we wish to find $y'(t)$ where $s(t) = 50$. By the Pythagorean Theorem,

$$s^2(t) = y^2(t) + 900 .$$

By implicit differentiation,

$$2s(t)s'(t) = 2y(t)y'(t) .$$

Thus,

(1) $$y(t) = \frac{s(t)s'(t)}{y(t)} .$$

When $s(t) = 50$, $y(t) = 40$. Consequently,

$$y'(t) = \frac{(50)(5)}{40}$$

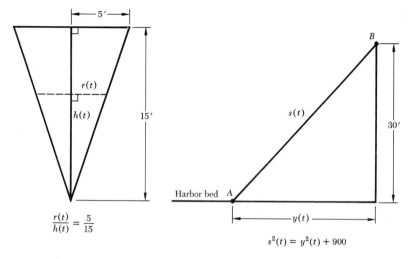

$$\frac{r(t)}{h(t)} = \frac{5}{15}$$

$$s^2(t) = y^2(t) + 900$$

FIGURE 15–20

$$y'(t) = 25/4 \text{ feet per minute}$$

is the velocity of the boat through the water.

Using the fact that if $s'(t) = 5$, Equation (1) can be written

$$y'(t) = \frac{5s(t)}{y(t)} \; ;$$

thus,

$$y''(t) = \frac{5[y(t)s'(t) - s(t)y'(t)]}{y^2(t)}$$

is the acceleration of the boat's movement through the water. When $s(t) = 50$, $y(t) = 40$, and $y'(t) = 25/4$. Hence,

$$y''(t) = \frac{5[(40)(5) - (50)(25/4)]}{(40)^2}$$

$$= -45/128$$

$$= -0.3516 \text{ feet per minute.}$$

The negative sign indicates that the velocity is a decreasing function; thus the ship is slowing down at approximately 0.2516 feet per minute at the given time.

exercises

1. At 9:00 A.M. a boat starts from point A and sails north at the rate of 20 mph. At 11:00 A.M. another boat starts from point A and sails east at the rate of 15 mph. How fast is the distance between the ships increasing at 1:00 P.M. that same day?

2. A cistern in the shape of an inverted right circular cone has altitude 16 feet and radius 4 feet. If water is being pumped in at 13 cubic feet per minute, at what rate is the depth h of the water increasing when the depth is 6 feet?

3. Same as Exercise 3 except the cistern rests on the base of the cone.

4. Water is being pumped into a hemispherical tank, with flat side up and a radius of 12 feet, at the rate of 10 cubic feet per minute. How fast is the water level rising when the water is 4 feet deep at the center? (The volume of a spherical segment is $V = (1/3)\pi h^2(3r - h)$ where h is the altitude of the segment and r is the radius of the sphere.)

5. Assume that a stone dropped into a still pool sends out concentric ripples. If the outermost ripple increases in diameter at the rate of 5 feet per second, how fast is the area of the disturbed surface increasing at the end of 6 seconds?

6. Assume a kite string is kept straight by a kite flying 60 feet above the ground. If the wind blows the kite on a horizontal course at 6 feet per second, how fast will the string be paying out when there is 200 feet of string out?

7. The volume of a cube is increasing at 150 cubic inches per second. How fast is the edge increasing when it is 12 inches?

8. A ship starts from a point A 50 miles directly north of point B and sails east at 15 mph. At the same time that the first ship starts, a second ship sails north from point B at 20 mph. How fast is the distance between them changing at the end of 2 hours? 4 hours?

9. Water is being pumped at 15 cubic feet per second into a right circular cone resting on its base and having altitude 10 feet and radius of base 15 feet. If the depth of water is 4 feet and increasing at 0.05 feet per second, how fast is the water draining through a hole in the bottom of the tank?

15–16   antiderivatives

If we consider the process of finding derivatives as an operation, then it would be natural to consider the "inverse" operation. For example, we know that the derivative of f defined by $f(x) = x^2$ is $f'(x) = 2x$; thus, if $g(x) = 2x$, then one function having g as its derivative is $f(x) = x^2$. Finding a function f having a given function g as its derivative is not always a simple task. For example, if we let $g(x) = 1/x$, it is not trivial to find a function f with g as its derivative.

definition: Let f and g be functions such that $f'(x) = g(x)$ for every x in the domains of f' and g. Then g is the derivative of f and f *is an antiderivative of g.*

For example, $g(x) = 2x$ is the derivative of $f(x) = x^2$ and $f(x) = x^2$ is an anti-derivative of $g(x) = 2x$. Since the derivative of F defined by $F(x) = x^2 + 6$ is also g, F is another antiderivative of g.

Before pursuing any techniques for finding antiderivatives of functions, let us prove that any two antiderivatives of a given function can differ only by a constant. Let $F'(x) = g(x)$ and let $f'(x) = g(x)$ for every x in the domains of F', f', and g. Then, F and f are antiderivatives of g. Let

$$H(x) = F(x) - f(x) ,$$

the difference of F and f. Thus,

$$H'(x) = F'(x) - f'(x)$$
$$= g(x) - g(x)$$
$$= 0 .$$

Since $H'(x) = 0$ for every x, by our theorem on page 287, $H(x) = C$ where C is a constant. Thus,

$$F(x) - f(x) = C ,$$

and

$$F(x) = f(x) + C .$$

A standard notation for an antiderivative of a function g is $\int g$, or $\int g(x)dx$. An antiderivative is often called an *indefinite integral*. Thus,

$$\int 2x \, dx = x^2 + C ,$$

and we say that $x^2 + C$ is *the* indefinite integral of $2x$.

Obviously, if we have differentiated a hundred functions, then we have a hundred antiderivative "formulas" available. However, we are interested in general techniques to find antiderivatives. We postpone most of this task until Chapter 16; at present, we give a few general formulas that are immediate consequences of our differentiation theorems.

I. $\int x^p dx = \dfrac{x^{p+1}}{p+1} + C$, provided $p \neq -1$.

II. $\int kf(x)dx = k \int f(x)dx + C$, k a constant.

III. $\int [f(x) + g(x)]dx = \int f(x)dx + \int g(x)dx$.

IV. $\int [f(x)]^p f'(x)dx = \dfrac{[f(x)]^{p+1}}{p+1} + C$, provided $p \neq -1$.

Each of the theorems above can be verified directly by differentiation. For example, let

$$g(x) = \frac{x^{p+1}}{p+1} + C ;$$

then, $g'(x) = x^p$. Consequently, formula I is verified.

exercises

1. Verify the indefinite integral formula II given above.

2. Verify the indefinite integral formula III given above.

3. Verify the indefinite integral formula IV given above.

In Exercises 4 through 19, find the antiderivative of each of the given functions.

4. $f(x) = x^3$

5. $f(x) = x^{2/3}$

6. $f(x) = 3x^{7/5}$

7. $f(x) = 3x^2 - 6x + 7$

8. $f(x) = 4x^2 + 5x - 11$

9. $f(x) = 8x^3 - 6x^2 + 11$

10. $f(x) = (3x + 5)^3$

11. $f(x) = 3(3x + 5)^3$

12. $f(x) = 2(2x + 1)^{15}$

13. $f(x) = 7(7x - 3)^4$

14. $f(x) = 2x(x^2 + 4)^{3/2}$

15. $f(x) = 3x^2(x^3 - 2)^4$

16. $f(x) = x(3x^2 + 4)^{4/3}$

17. $f(x) = x^2(6x^3 + 11)^{9/5}$

18. $f(x) = (3x^2 + 4x - 13)^5(6x + 4)$

19. $f(x) = (4x^2 + 2x + 11)^{5/3}(4x + 1)$

introduction to integral calculus

16

16–1   area

In Euclidean plane geometry, we learn how area is assigned to polygonal figures in the plane. For example, we learn that a triangle has area $bh/2$ where b is the length of the base and h is the altitude; a rectangle has area lw where l is the length and w is the width; a circle has area πr^2 where r is the radius. In general, since a polygonal figure can be considered to be made up of triangles (see Figure 16–1), area of plane polygonal figures can be found using only the formula for the area of a triangle. We now attempt to discover a method to assign area to regions of irregular shape.

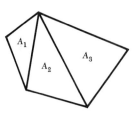

Total area: $A_1 + A_2 + A_3$

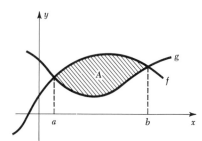

FIGURE 16–1

Suppose we wish to have a method to assign area to a plane region A as in Figure 16–1. If k_1 is the area of the region bounded by the graph of f, the lines $x = a$, $x = b$, and the x-axis, and if k_2 is the area of the region bounded by the graph of g, the lines $x = a$, $x = b$, and the x-axis, then $(k_1 - k_2)$ would be assigned as area of A. Thus, the problem of assigning area to region A is reduced to the method for assigning area to a region between the graph of a function and the x-axis that is between two parallel lines perpendicular to the x-axis. Let us consider a specific example.

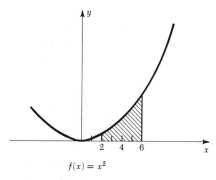

$f(x) = x^2$

FIGURE 16–2

Let f be defined by $f(x) = x^2$. We seek to determine the number (called area) assigned to the region bounded by $x = 2$, $x = 6$, the graph of f, and the x-axis. Suppose we divide the interval into four equal subintervals with $P = \{2, 3, 4, 5, 6\}$ as the set of endpoints of the subintervals. We call this a *partition* of $[2, 6]$. Since f is an increasing function on $[2, 6]$, $f(2) = 4$, $f(3) = 9$, $f(4) = 16$, and $f(5) = 25$ are the minimum values of f on each of the subintervals $[2, 3]$, $[3, 4]$, $[4, 5]$, and $[5, 6]$, respectively. Since the width of each subinterval is 1, the total area of the inscribed rectangles under the graph of f is

$$f(2) + f(3) + f(4) + f(5) = 54 \text{ square units}.$$

We call 54 the *lower sum* of f with respect to partition P of $[2, 6]$ and denote it by "$L(P, f)$." If k is the area of the region in question,

$$L(P, f) < k.$$

If we consider the maximum values on each of the subintervals, we could obtain an approximation of the area by using the circumscribed rectangles. See Figure 16–3. For the given partition P, $f(3) = 9$, $f(4) = 16$, $f(5) = 25$, and $f(6) = 36$ are the maximum values on the subintervals and thus the heights of the circumscribed rectangles. The total area of all of these rectangles is

$$f(3) + f(4) + f(5) + f(6) = 86 \text{ square units}.$$

We call 86 an *upper sum* of f with respect to partition P of $[2, 6]$ and denote it by "$U(P, f)$." It is geometrically obvious that if k is assigned

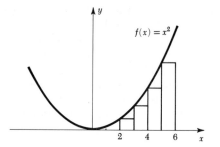

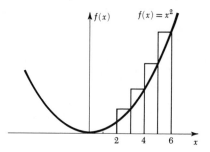

$$P = \{2, 3, 4, 5, 6\}$$

$$L(P, f) = f(2) + f(3) + f(4) + f(5) = 54 \qquad U(P, f) = f(3) + f(4) + f(5) + f(6) = 86$$

FIGURE 16-3

as area of the region, then

$$L(P, f) < k < U(P, f);$$

in particular,

$$54 < k < 86.$$

Knowing that the area of the given region is between 54 and 86 square units is desirable information, but we need to seek closer bounds on the area. Let us insert n equal subintervals with partition points the set

$$P = \{2 = x_0, x_1, x_2, x_3, \ldots, x_n = 6 \text{ where } x_t < x_{t+1}\}.$$

Since the width of $[2, 6]$ is 4, then the width of each of the n equal subintervals is $4/n$. Hence,

$$x_0 = 2, \qquad\qquad f(x_0) = 4$$

$$x_1 = 2 + \frac{4}{n}, \qquad f(x_1) = 4 + \frac{16}{n} + \left(\frac{4}{n}\right)^2$$

$$x_2 = 2 + 2\left(\frac{4}{n}\right), \qquad f(x_2) = 4 + 2\left(\frac{16}{n}\right) + 2^2\left(\frac{4}{n}\right)^2$$

$$x_3 = 2 + 3\left(\frac{4}{n}\right), \qquad f(x_3) = 4 + 3\left(\frac{16}{n}\right) + 3^2\left(\frac{4}{n}\right)^2$$

$$\cdots\cdots$$

$$x_t = 2 + t\left(\frac{4}{n}\right), \qquad f(x_t) = 4 + t\left(\frac{16}{n}\right) + t^2\left(\frac{4}{n}\right)^2$$

Notice that

$$f(x_0) + f(x_1) + f(x_2) + f(x_3) + \cdots + f(x_{n-1})$$

$$= 4n + \frac{16}{n}(1 + 2 + 3 + \cdots + n) + \left(\frac{4}{n}\right)^2(1^2 + 2^2 + 3^2 + \cdots + (n-1)^2).$$

Recall that

$$1 + 2 + 3 + \cdots + n = \frac{n(n+1)}{2}$$

and
$$1^2 + 2^2 + 3^2 + \cdots + n^2 = \frac{n(n+1)(2n+1)}{6}$$

for any integer n; thus the sum of the first $(n-1)$ integers is $\frac{(n-1)n}{2}$ and the sum of the first $(n-1)$ squares is $\frac{(n-1)n(2n-1)}{6}$.

Since
$$L(P, f) = \frac{4}{n} [f(x_0) + f(x_1) + \cdots + f(x_{n-1})] ,$$

we conclude that
$$L(P, f) = \frac{4}{n} \left[4n + \frac{16(n-1)n}{2n} + \frac{16}{n^2} \frac{(n-1)n(2n-1)}{6} \right] ;$$

that is,
$$L(P, f) = 16 + 32(1 - 1/n) + \frac{32}{3}(1 - 1/n)(2 - 1/n) .$$

We leave as an exercise for the reader the proof that the upper sum of f with respect to P is given by
$$U(P, f) = 16 + 32(1 + 1/n) + \frac{32}{3}(1 + 1/n)(2 + 1/n) .$$

As a check on our derivations of $L(P, f)$ and $U(P, f)$, let $n = 4$. Then

$$L(P, f) = 16 + 32(3/4) + \frac{32}{3}(3/4)(7/4)$$
$$= 54$$

and

$$U(P, f) = 16 + 32(5/4) + \frac{32}{3}\left(\frac{5}{4}\right)\left(\frac{9}{4}\right)$$
$$= 86 .$$

Since for "large" n both $(1 + 1/n)$ and $(1 - 1/n)$ are "close" to 1 and $(2 + 1/n)$ and $(2 - 1/n)$ are "close" to 2, both $L(P, f)$ and $U(P, f)$ are "close" to $69^1/_3$. Thus, $69^1/_3$ square units is assigned as the area of the region. It should be noted that $69^1/_3$ is the least upper bound of $\{L(P, f)\}$, the set of lower sums, and that $69^1/_3$ is the greatest lower bound of $\{U(P, f)\}$, the set of upper sums.

The reader should be convinced of one thing: this method for assigning area to the given region is at least tedious. It should be apparent that if the function f did not have such a "well-behaved" graph, the method used might prove extremely difficult. In order to show how the arithmetic can be simplified and to give some real purpose to the next two sections, let us "preview" how the area can be found.

Find an antiderivative of $f(x) = x^2$; one antiderivative is $F(x) = x^3/3$. Evaluate $F(6) - F(2)$; that is, find the difference in the values of the anti-derivative at the endpoints of the interval $[2, 6]$:

$$F(6) - F(2) = \frac{216}{3} - \frac{8}{3}$$

$$= \frac{208}{3}$$

$$= 69\frac{1}{3}.$$

In general, we assert that the area under the graph of a function f that is above the x-axis between $x = a$ and $x = b$ is $F(b) - F(a)$ where $F'(x) = f(x)$.

Let us look at a familiar region to give a better understanding of the technique involved. The area of the trapezoid in Figure 16–4,

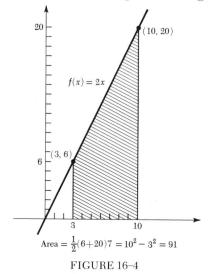

$$\text{Area} = \frac{1}{2}(6+20)7 = 10^2 - 3^2 = 91$$

FIGURE 16–4

using the formula for the area of a trapezoid, is

$$\frac{1}{2}(b_1 + b_2)h = \frac{1}{2}(6 + 20)7$$

$$= 91 \text{ square units.}$$

An antiderivative of $f(x) = 2x$ is $F(x) = x^2$; notice that

$$F(10) - F(3) = 100 - 9$$

$$= 91.$$

In the next two sections we develop the theory necessary to justify the procedures used here.

exercises

1. Let f be defined by $f(x) = 2x$ with domain $[3, 10]$.

   (a) Find $L(P, f)$ for a partition P of 7 equal subintervals.

(b) Find $U(P, f)$ for a partition P of 7 equal subintervals.

(c) Find $L(P, f)$ for a partition P of n equal subintervals.

(d) Find $U(P, f)$ for a partition P of n equal subintervals.

(e) Show that $L(P, f)$ and $U(P, f)$ are "close" to 91 for "large" n.

2. Let f be defined by $f(x) = x^2$ with domain $[0, 4]$.

(a) Find $L(P, f)$ for a partition P of 4 equal subintervals.

(b) Find $U(P, f)$ for a partition P of 4 equal subintervals.

(c) Find $L(P, f)$ for a partition P of n equal subintervals.

(d) Find $U(P, f)$ for a partition P of n equal subintervals.

(e) Show that $L(P, f)$ and $U(P, f)$ are "close" to 64/3 for "large" n.

3. For $f(x) = x^2$, show that

$$U(P, f) = 16 + 32(1 + 1/n) + 32/3(1 + 1/n)(2 + 1/n)$$

for a partition of n equal subintervals of $[2, 6]$.

4. Let f be defined by $f(x) = x^3$ with domain $[0, 4]$.

(a) Find $L(P, f)$ for a partition P of 8 equal subintervals.

(b) Find $U(P, f)$ for a partition P of 8 equal subintervals.

(c) Find $L(P, f)$ for a partition P of n equal subintervals. Recall

$$1^3 + 2^2 + 3^3 + \ldots + n^3 = n^2(n + 1)^n/4.$$

(d) Find $U(P, f)$ for a partition of n equal subintervals.

(e) Find an antiderivative F of f.

(f) Find $F(4) - F(0)$.

(g) Show that both $U(P, f)$ and $L(P, f)$ can be made "close" to $F(4) - F(0)$ for "large" n.

16–2   the riemann integral

In the last section, the functions and the partitions of their domains had the following restrictions: (1) the function values of f throughout the domain $[a, b]$ were non-negative; (2) the function was increasing throughout its domain; (3) the partitions consisted of points dividing the interval into equal subintervals; and (4) the functions were continuous on $[a, b]$. In this section, we generalize the ideas of Section 16–1 and define what is called the *Riemann integral,* or the *definite integral,* of a function f from a to b. Here, we retain only the restriction that f be a continuous function on the closed interval $[a, b]$.

Let f be a continuous function on the closed interval $[a, b]$. Let x_0, $x_1, x_2, \ldots, x_n$ be $n + 1$ numbers in $[a, b]$ such that

$$a = x_0 < x_1 < x_2 < \ldots < x_n = b.$$

The set $P = \{x_0, x_1, x_2, \ldots, x_n\}$ is a partition of $[a, b]$; the numbers in P are the endpoints of n closed subintervals:

$$[x_0, x_1], [x_1, x_2], [x_2, x_3], \ldots, [x_{n-1}, x_n].$$

Since f is continuous on the closed subintervals, it can be proved that f attains a maximum value and a minimum value on each such subinterval; although this is geometrically obvious, it is not easy to prove. Thus, there exists

$$u_i \in [x_{i-1}, x_i], i = 1, 2, 3, \ldots, n,$$

such that

$$f(u_i) \leq f(x) \quad \text{for all} \quad x \in [x_{i-1}, x_i].$$

Notice that although u_i need not be a unique number in the ith subinterval since the minimum value may be attained at more than one point, the minimum value $f(u_i)$ is unique. Thus, $f(u_i)(x_i - x_{i-1})$ is uniquely determined for a given partition P. Similarly, let

$$v_i \in [x_{i-1}, x_i], i = 1, 2, 3, \ldots, n,$$

such that

$$f(v_i) \geq f(x) \text{ for all } x \in [x_{i-1}, x_i].$$

We define the *lower sum* of f on $[a, b]$ with respect to P by

$$L(P, f) = f(u_1)(x_1 - x_0) + f(u_2)(x_2 - x_1) + f(u_3)(x_3 - x_2) + \ldots + f(u_n)(x_n - x_{n-1}).$$

The *upper sum* of f on $[a, b]$ with respect to P is defined by

$$U(P, f) = f(v_1)(x_1 - x_0) + f(v_2)(x_2 - x_1) + f(v_3)(x_3 - x_2) + \ldots + f(v_n)(x_n - x_{n-1}).$$

Since $f(u_i) \leq f(v_i)$ in each subinterval

$$f(u_i)(x_i - x_{i-1}) \leq f(v_i)(x_i - x_{i-1}), i = 1, 2, 3, \ldots, n.$$

Thus, by adding the n inequalities we conclude that

$$L(P, f) \leq U(P, f).$$

Let $f(v)$ be the maximum value of f on $[a, b]$ and let $f(u)$ be the minimum value of f on $[a, b]$; that is, $f(v)$ is the absolute maximum and $f(u)$ is the absolute minimum of f on $[a, b]$. Thus,

$$f(u_i) \leq f(v)$$

and

$$f(u_i)(x_i - x_{i-1}) < f(v)(x_i - x_{i-1}) \text{ for } i = 1, 2, 3, \ldots, n.$$

Thus,

$$L(P, f) \leq f(v)(x_1 - x_0 + x_2 - x_1 + x_3 - x_2 + \ldots + x_n - x_{n-1})$$
$$\leq f(v)(x_n - x_0)$$
$$\leq f(v)(b - a).$$

If the graph of f is above the x-axis, this is equivalent to stating that the area of the inscribed rectangles is never greater than the area of the one circumscribed rectangle. See Figure 16–5.

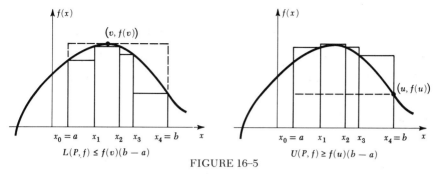

FIGURE 16–5

Similarly,

$$f(v_i) \geqslant f(u)$$

and

$$f(v_i)(x_i - x_{i-1}) \geqslant f(u)(x_i - x_{i-1}).$$

We conclude that $\qquad L(P, f) \geqslant f(u)(b - a).$

Consequently, we have the following theorem.

theorem 16–1: Let f be continuous on $[a, b]$. Let $f(u)$ and $f(v)$, respectively, be the minimum and maximum values of f on $[a, b]$. If P is any partition of $[a, b]$, then

$$f(u)(b - a) \leqslant L(P, f) \leqslant U(P, f) \leqslant f(v)(b - a).$$

For each partition P, a unique number $L(P, f)$ is determined for a continuous function f on $[a, b]$. By Theorem 16–1, $\{L(P, f)\}$ is a set of real numbers having $f(v)(b - a)$ as an upper bound. By the completeness property, the set of lower sums has a least upper bound. Similarly, the set of upper sums $\{U(P, f)\}$ has $f(u)(b - a)$ as a lower bound; thus, it has a greatest lower bound. (See Exercise 4, Section 2–5.) Since f is a continuous function, it can be proved that the least upper bound of the set of lower sums and the greatest lower bound of the set of upper sums are the same number. This number is called the *Riemann integral*, or *definite integral*, *of f from a to b*; it is denoted by

$$\int_a^b f, \text{ or } \int_a^b f(x)dx.$$

theorem 16–2: Let f be a continuous function on $[a, b]$. The least upper bound of $\{L(P, f)\}$ and the greatest lower bound of $\{U(P, f)\}$ exist and are equal.

Geometrically, Theorem 16–2 states that if the graph of f is above the x-axis, we get the same number (area) whether approximating area by inscribed rectangles or circumscribed rectangles.

For a continuous function, we know that $\int_a^b f$ exists where $a < b$. None of our theorems yet provide a technique for finding this number called the Riemann integral of f from a to b. Before considering this problem, let us define $\int_a^b f$ for any real numbers a and b and indicate one immediate consequence.

definition: (1) $\int_a^a f = 0$

(2) $\int_a^b f = -\int_b^a f$ if $a > b$.

theorem 16–3: Let f be a continuous function on a closed interval containing three real numbers $a, b,$ and c. Then,

$$\int_a^b f + \int_b^c f = \int_a^c f.$$

From our usual geometric interpretation, Theorem 16–3 states that if $a < b < c$, then the area under the graph of f from a to b plus the area from b to c is the same as the area under the graph from a to c.

16–3   fundamental theorem of calculus

Let f be a continuous function on $[a, b]$. Then, for any $x \in [a, b]$, $\int_a^x f$ exists. Thus, we can define a new function G by

$$G(x) = \int_a^x f.$$

We would now like to show that not only is the function G a differentiable function but the value of the derivative of G at $t \in [a, b]$ is $f(t)$. That is,

$$G'(t) = f(t).$$

By the definition of the derivative of G at t,

$$G'(t) = \lim_{x \to t} \frac{G(x) - G(t)}{x - t},$$

provided the limit exists. Now, from the definition of G,

$$G'(t) = \lim_{x \to t} \frac{\int_a^x f - \int_a^t f}{x - t}.$$

By Theorem 16–3,

$$G'(t) = \lim_{x \to t} \frac{\int_t^x f}{x - t}.$$

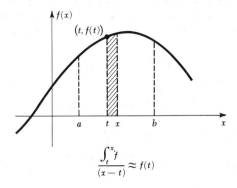

$$\frac{\int_t^x f}{(x-t)} \approx f(t)$$

FIGURE 16-6

If $x > t$, $\int_t^x f$ is the area under the curve in Figure 16-6 where $(x-t)$ is the width of the region. If x is "close" to t, the region is nearly rectangular; thus, the area divided by the width is "close" to the height of the "rectangle," which is the function value of f at t. Thus, $G'(t) = f(t)$. This is a geometric argument to justify the following theorem.

theorem 16-4: Let f be a continuous function on $[a, b]$ and let $G(t) = \int_a^t f$. Then G is a differentiable function on $[a, b]$ and $G'(t) = f(t)$.

Let F be any antiderivative of f. Then $F'(t) = f(t)$. Since if $G(x) = \int_a^x f$ then $G'(t) = f(t)$, the function G is also an antiderivative of f. From Section 15-11, we know that

$$G(x) = F(x) + C$$

where C is a constant. Since $G(a) = \int_a^a f = 0$, $F(a) + C = 0$ and $C = -F(a)$. Thus,

$$G(b) = F(b) - F(a) \text{, or}$$
$$\int_a^b f = F(b) - F(a) .$$

The notation "$F(a) \big|_a^b$" is sometimes used to represent the difference $F(b) - F(a)$. This completes the proof of the Fundamental Theorem of Calculus.

Fundamental Theorem of Calculus: Let f be a function continuous on $[a, b]$. Then an antiderivative F of f exists and

$$\int_a^b f = F(b) - F(a) .$$

Since finding a definite integral by using the Fundamental Theorem entails finding an antiderivative, we have a number of important formulas immediately available for use as a result of our discussion of antiderivatives.

(1) $\displaystyle\int_a^b x^p \, dx = \frac{b^{p+1}}{p+1} - \frac{a^{p+1}}{p+1}$, $p \neq -1$.

(2) $\displaystyle\int_a^b (f(x) + g(x))dx = \int_a^b f(x)dx + \int_a^b g(x)dx.$

(3) $\displaystyle\int_a^b f(g(x))g'(x)dx = f(g(b)) - f(g(a)).$

(4) $\displaystyle\int_a^b [f(x)]^p f'(x)dx = \frac{[f(b)]^{p+1} - [f(a)]^{p+1}}{p+1}$, $p \neq -1.$

(5) $\displaystyle\int_a^b kf(x)dx = k \int_a^b f(x)dx,$ k a constant.

Using our other notation for integrals, formula (2) could be written

$$\int_a^b (f + g) = \int_a^b f + \int_a^b g \, ,$$

formula (3) could be written

$$\int_a^b f(g)g' = f(g(b)) - f(g(a)), \text{ etc.}$$

examples

1. $\displaystyle\int_1^3 (x^2 + 2x)dx = \left[\frac{x^3}{3} + x^2\right] \Big|_1^3 = \left(\frac{27}{3} + 9\right) - \left(\frac{1}{3} + 1\right) = 16\frac{2}{3}$.

2. $\displaystyle\int_0^1 (8x + 1)^{2/3} 8 \, dx = \frac{(8x + 1)^{5/3}}{5/3} \Big|_0^1 = \frac{3}{5} [9^{5/3} - 1^{5/3}]$

$$= \frac{3}{5} (9 \sqrt[3]{81} - 31).$$

Note: We used formula (4) in this example and the next.

3. $\displaystyle\int_0^{\sqrt{15}} (x^2 + 1)^{1/2}x \, dx = \frac{1}{2} \int_0^{\sqrt{15}} (x^2 + 1)^{1/2} 2x \, dx$

$$= \frac{1}{2} \left[\frac{(x^2 + 1)^{3/2}}{3/2}\right] \Big|_0^{\sqrt{15}}$$

$$= \frac{1}{3} [(16)^{3/2} - 1^{3/2}]$$

$$= 21 \, .$$

exercises

1. $\displaystyle\int_{-2}^2 x^3 dx.$ Interpret your answer geometrically.

2. $\displaystyle\int_1^4 (x^2 - x)dx$ 3. $\displaystyle\int_1^3 (x^2 - 2x + 7)dx$

4. $\displaystyle\int_4^1 x\,(\sqrt{x}-1)dx$

5. $\displaystyle\int_1^2 \frac{u+1}{u^3}\,du$

6. $\displaystyle\int_4^7 (x-3)^{1/2}dx$

7. $\displaystyle\int_{-1}^{-27} t(t^{1/3}-1)dt$

8. $\displaystyle\int_0^1 (x^3+2x+1)^4(3x^2+2)dx$

9. $\displaystyle\int_0^2 (4x+1)^{3/2}dx$

10. $\displaystyle\int_0^1 (5x^2+1)^3 x\,dx$

11. $\displaystyle\int_0^1 (x^2+2x+1)^{1/2}(x+1)dx$

12. $\displaystyle\int_{-3}^3 (x^3+x)dx$

13. $\displaystyle\int_{-3}^3 (x+3)^3 dx$

14. Discuss the following:

$$\int_{-1}^3 x^{-2}dx = \frac{x^{-1}}{-1}\Big|_{-1}^3 = (-\frac{1}{3}+1) = \frac{2}{3}$$

Is the answer correct? If not, identify all the errors.

*15. Assume $\displaystyle\int_{-a}^a f$ exists. Prove that if f is an even function,

$$\int_{-a}^a f = 2\int_0^a f\,.$$

*16. Assume $\displaystyle\int_{-a}^a f$ exists. Prove that if f is an odd function,

$$\int_{-a}^a f = 0.$$

Find the area of the regions in the plane bounded by the graphs of the given equations.

17. $y = x^2 - x$ and the x-axis.

18. $y = (x-2)(x-5)$ and the x-axis.

19. $y = (x+4)(x-2)$ and the x-axis.

20. $y = x^3 + 2x$, $x = 1$, $x = 4$, and the x-axis.

21. $y = x$ and $y = x^3$.

22. $y = x$ and $y = x^5$.

23. $y = x^2$ and $y = 2x + 8$.

24. $y = x^2$ and $y = 3x + 10$.

25. $y = x^2 + 1$, $x = -3$, $x = 2$, and the x-axis.

16–4 differentiation and integration of the trigonometric functions

Let us begin by considering a limit of special importance in calculus. We give a geometric proof that

$$\lim_{u\to 0} \frac{\sin u}{u} = 1;$$

this geometric type of proof is in keeping with the geometric definitions of the trigonometric functions given in Chapter 6.

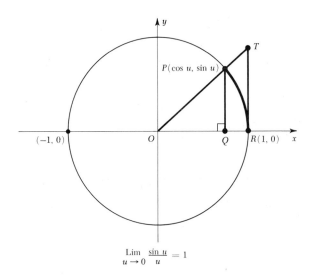

$$\text{Lim}_{u \to 0} \frac{\sin u}{u} = 1$$

FIGURE 16–7

Assume that $0 < u < \pi/2$. See Figure 16–7. By the fact that triangles
OQP and ORT are similar,

$$\frac{|TR|}{|PQ|} = \frac{|OR|}{|OQ|}$$

Thus,

$$\frac{|TR|}{\sin u} = \frac{1}{\cos u}$$

and

$$|TR| = \frac{\sin u}{\cos u}.$$

Furthermore,

$$0 < |PQ| < PR < |TR|;$$

thus,

$$0 < \sin u < u < \frac{\sin u}{\cos u}.$$

Consequently,

$$\frac{1}{\sin u} > \frac{1}{u} > \frac{\cos u}{\sin u}$$

and

$$1 > \frac{\sin u}{u} > \cos u .$$

Now, for u "close" to 0, $\cos u$ is "close" to 1 and $(\sin u)/u$ is even "closer" to 1. Thus, $(\sin u)/u$ can be made arbitrarily "close" to 1 by taking a *positive* u "close" to 0. We leave as an exercise for the reader to prove that $(\sin u)/u$ is "close" to 1 for u "close" to 0 where $-\pi/2 < u < 0$. Thus,

$$\lim_{u \to 0} \frac{\sin u}{u} = 1.$$

Before finding the derivative of the sine function, let us consider the graph of the sine to determine geometrically what might be some of the properties of the derived function. (Although this approach is not es-

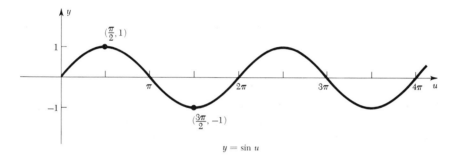

FIGURE 16–8

sential, it is hoped that it will encourage the reader to make similar analyses of similar problems.) Since the sine function has maxima and minima at $\pm\pi/2$, $\pm 3\pi/2$, $\pm 5\pi/2$, etc., the value of the derivative should be zero at each of these points. Since the sine function is increasing where $-\pi/2 < x < \pi/2$, $3\pi/2 < x < 5\pi/2$, etc., the derivative should be positive in these intervals. We leave to the reader a further geometric analysis and the check to see if the solution agrees with the expected results.

By definition of the derivative, if

$$f(x) = \sin x$$

then

$$f'(t) = \lim_{x \to t} \frac{\sin x - \sin t}{x - t},$$

provided the limit exists. Using the trigonometric identity in Exercise 3, page 94,

$$f'(t) = \lim_{x \to t} \frac{2 \sin \dfrac{x-t}{2} \cos \dfrac{x+t}{2}}{x-t}$$

$$= \lim_{x \to t} \frac{2 \sin \dfrac{x-t}{2}}{x-t} \lim_{x \to t} \cos \left(\frac{x+t}{2}\right)$$

$$= \cos t \lim_{x \to t} \left[\frac{\sin \left(\dfrac{x-t}{2}\right)}{\dfrac{x-t}{2}} \right] .$$

If we let $u = \dfrac{x-t}{2}$, then u approaches 0 as x "approaches" t; thus

$$\lim_{x \to t} \frac{\sin \left(\dfrac{x-t}{2}\right)}{\dfrac{x-t}{2}} = \lim_{u \to 0} \frac{\sin u}{u} = 1 .$$

Consequently,

$$f'(t) = \cos t . \qquad\qquad \text{I}$$

Using the fact that the derivative of the sine function is the cosine, we can differentiate the other trigonometric functions.

Let $f(x) = \cos x$, By using the trigonometric identity $\sin (\pi/2 - x) = \cos x$,

$$f(x) = \sin (\pi/2 - x) .$$

By I and the composite function theorem,

$$f'(x) = [\cos (\pi/2 - x)] (-1) .$$

Finally, by using the identity $\cos (\pi/2 - x) = \sin x$,

$$f'(x) = -\sin x . \qquad\qquad \text{II}$$

Let $f(x) = \tan x$. Then

$$f(x) = \frac{\sin x}{\cos x} .$$

Using I, II, and the quotient theorem for differentiation,

$$f'(x) = \frac{(\cos x)(\cos x) - (\sin x)(-\sin x)}{\cos^2 x}$$

$$= \frac{\cos^2 x + \sin^2 x}{\cos^2 x}$$

$$= \frac{1}{\cos^2 x}$$

$$= \sec^2 x . \qquad\qquad \text{III}$$

We leave as an exercise for the reader to prove the following:

$$(\sec x)' = \sec x \tan x \qquad \text{IV}$$
$$(\csc x)' = -\csc x \cot x \qquad \text{V}$$
$$(\cot x)' = -\csc^2 x . \qquad \text{VI}$$

Notice that we have six indefinite integral theorems as a consequence of I, II, III, IV, V, and VI:

$$\int \cos x \, dx = \sin x + C ,$$
$$\int \sin x \, dx = -\cos x + C ,$$
$$\int \sec^2 x \, dx = \tan x + C ,$$
$$\int \sec x \tan x \, dx = \sec x + C ,$$
$$\int \csc x \cot x \, dx = -\csc x + C ,$$

and

$$\int \csc^2 x \, dx = -\cot x + C .$$

Although we have found the derivative of all six trigonometric functions, we have found only the antiderivative of the sine and cosine functions. The reader who takes a course in calculus will learn that the anti-derivatives of the other trigonometric functions involve the logarithm function. The actual derivation of the antiderivatives of the other trigonometric functions is beyond the scope of this text.

exercises

Find the derivative of each function defined in Exercises 1 through 16.

1. $f(x) = \sec x$
2. $f(x) = \csc x$
3. $f(x) = \cot x$
4. $f(x) = \sec^2 x + \sin 2x$
5. $f(x) = \sin^2 x + \sqrt{1 - \sin x}$
6. $f(x) = \dfrac{x^3}{\sin^4 x}$
7. $f(x) = \tan 3x$
8. $f(x) = \cot(1 - 3x) + \sec x^{1/2}$.
9. $f(x) = \cos^2 3x$
10. $f(x) = x^2 \sin x$
11. $f(x) = \cos (\sin x)$.
12. $f(x) = \tan (x^2 + 1)$
13. $f(x) = \csc^2 x - \cot^2 x$
14. $f(x) = \dfrac{\sin x + \cos x}{\tan x}$
15. $f(x) = (\sin x)(\cos^3 x)$
16. $f(x) = (\sec^3 x)(\tan^3 x)$

Find the indicated antiderivative or definite integral in Exercises 17 through 30.

17. $\displaystyle\int_0^{\pi/3} \sin 3x \, dx$
18. $\displaystyle\int \cos 5x \, dx$

19. $\displaystyle\int (\sin x)^3 \cos x \, dx$
20. $\displaystyle\int_0^{\pi/6} \tan x \sec^2 x \, dx$

21. $\displaystyle\int \sec^2 3x \, dx$

22. $\displaystyle\int_0^{\pi/3} \sqrt{1 + \sin^2 x} \, \sin 2x \, dx$

23. $\displaystyle\int \sqrt{1 + \cos^2 x} \cdot \sin 2x \, dx$

24. $\displaystyle\int \frac{\sec^2 x}{\sqrt{1 + \tan x}} \, dx$

25. $\displaystyle\int \frac{\cos x}{\sin^2 x} \, dx$

26. $\displaystyle\int \sec^4 x \tan x \, dx$

27. $\displaystyle\int_{\pi/6}^{\pi/3} \csc^3 x \cot x \, dx$

28. $\displaystyle\int (x + \sin x) \, dx$

29. $\displaystyle\int \frac{2 \sec^2 x \tan x}{\sqrt{1 + \sec^2 x}} \, dx$

30. $\displaystyle\int \frac{\cos x - \sin x}{(\sin x + \cos x)^3} \, dx$

31. Show that if $-\pi/2 < u < 0$, and if u is "close" to 0, then $\dfrac{\sin u}{u}$ is "close" to 1.

16–5   applications using the trigonometric functions

This section is primarily a problems section. It should give the reader an opportunity to apply some of the ideas previously presented and to reinforce the learning of the various concepts involved. Let us first consider four examples.

examples

1. Let P be the point of intersection of the graphs of the sine function and cosine function on the interval $[0, \pi/2]$. Find the measure of the angles between the tangent lines to the curves at point P.

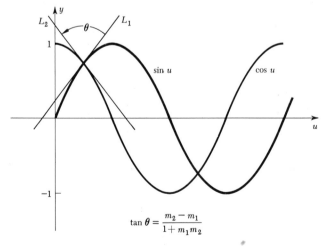

$$\tan \theta = \frac{m_2 - m_1}{1 + m_1 m_2}$$

FIGURE 16–9

Solution: For $x \in [0, \pi/2]$, sin $x = \cos x$ where $x = \pi/4$. Thus P has coordinates $(\pi/4, \sqrt{2}/2)$. Let m_1 be the slope of the tangent line at P to the graph of the sine function, and let m_2 be the slope of the tangent line at P to the graph of the cosine function. Thus, if

$$f(x) = \sin x \text{ and } g(x) = \cos x,$$

then

$$f'(x) = \cos x \text{ and } g'(x) = - \sin x.$$

Furthermore, $m_1 = f'(\pi/4) = \sqrt{2}/2$ and $m_2 = g'(\pi/4) = -\sqrt{2}/2$.
If θ is the measure of the angle from L_1 to L_2,

$$\tan \theta = \frac{m_2 - m_1}{1 + m_1 m_2}$$

$$= 2\sqrt{2}$$

$$\theta \approx 70° \ 32'$$

2. Find maxima, minima, and inflection points, and discuss concavity for the graph of f given by $f(x) = \sin x + \cos x$, $x \in [0, 2\pi]$.

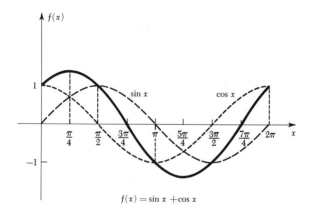

$$f(x) = \sin x + \cos x$$

FIGURE 16–10

Solution: Since

$$f(x) = \sin x + \cos x,$$

$$f'(x) = \cos x - \sin x$$

and

$$f''(x) = - \sin x - \cos x$$

Now, $f'(x) = 0$ where sin $x = \cos x$. Thus, $f'(x) = 0$ for $x = \pi/4$ and $x = 5\pi/4$. Since $f'(\pi/4) = 0$ and $f''(\pi/4) < 0$, $(\pi/4, f(\pi/4))$ is a relative maximum point. Similarly, since $f'(5\pi/4) = 0$ and $f''(5\pi/4) > 0$, $(5\pi/4, f(5\pi/4))$ is a relative minimum point.

The graph of the cosine function is above the graph of the sine function in the open intervals $0 < x < \pi/4$ and $5\pi/4 < x < 2\pi$. In other words, $\cos x > \sin x$ in these intervals; thus, $f'(x) > 0$ where $x \in (0, \pi/4)$ and $x \in (5\pi/4, 2\pi)$. Consequently f increases in these intervals. Furthermore, we conclude that the endpoint extreme $(0, f(0))$ is a relative minimum point and that $(2\pi, f(2\pi))$ is a relative maximum point. The function decreases on the interval $\pi/4 < x < 5\pi/4$.

Since $f''(x) = 0$ where $\sin x = -\cos x$, $f''(3\pi/4) = 0$ and $f''(7\pi/4) = 0$. Furthermore, $f''(x) > 0$ for $x \in (3\pi/4, 7\pi/4)$ and $f''(x) < 0$ for $x \in (0, 3\pi/4)$ and $x \in (7\pi/4, 2\pi)$. Consequently, $(3\pi/4, f(3\pi/4))$ and $(7\pi/4, f(7\pi/4))$ are inflection points. The curve is concave upward on the interval $3\pi/4 < x < 7\pi/4$ and concave downward on the intervals $0 < x < 3\pi/4$ and $7\pi/4 < x < 2\pi$.

3. Approximate $\sin 1$. Find an upper bound on the error.

Solution: If $f(x) = \sin x$, then from page 316

$$f(1) = f(\pi/3) + f'(\pi/3)(1 - \pi/3) + \frac{f''(c)}{21}(1 - \pi/3)^2$$

where $1 < c < \pi/3$.

Since

$$f(x) = \sin x, \quad f(\pi/3) = \frac{\sqrt{3}}{2};$$

since

$$f'(x) = \cos x, \quad f'(\pi/3) = \frac{1}{2};$$

and since

$$f''(x) = -\sin x, \quad f''(c) = -\sin c.$$

Thus,

$$\sin 1 = \frac{\sqrt{3}}{2} + \frac{1}{2}(1 - \pi/3)\frac{\sin c}{2'}(1 - \pi/3)^2,$$

and

$$\sin 1 = \frac{1.7320}{2} + \frac{1}{2}\left(1 - \frac{3.1416}{3}\right)$$

$$= 0.8660 + \frac{1}{2}(1 - 1.0472)$$

$$= 0.8660 - 0.0236$$

$$= 1.8424.$$

The positive error $\left|\frac{\sin c}{2!}(1 - \pi/3)^2\right|$ is less than $\frac{1}{2!}(1 - 1.047197)^2$.

Since

$$\frac{1}{2!}(1 - 1.047197)^2 \leq \frac{1}{2!}(.047197)^2$$

$$< \frac{1}{2!}(5 \times 10^{-2})^2$$

$$\leq \frac{25}{2! \; 100}$$

$$\leq \frac{1}{8}$$

$$\leq 0.0125,$$

$\sin 1 \approx 0.8424$ with an error less than 0.0125.

exercises

In Exercises 1 through 6 find maxima, minima, inflection points, discuss concavity, form the graph of the function, and sketch the graph.

1. $f(x) = \sin x - \cos x, x \in [0, 2]$
2. $f(x) = \sqrt{3} \sin x + \cos x, x \in [0, 2]$
3. $f(x) = x + \sin x, x \in [0, \pi]$
4. $f(x) = \sin^2 x, x \in [0, 2\pi]$
5. $f(x) = \frac{x}{2} - \cos x, x \in [0, \pi]$
6. $f(x) = 2 + \sin x, x \in [0, \pi]$
7. Find the angle between the tangent lines at the point of intersection of the tangent and cotangent functions.
8. Find the angles between the tangent lines at the points of intersection of the graphs of $y = \sin 2x$ and $y = \cos x$ where $-\pi < x < \pi$.
9. Find the area of the region bounded by $y = \sin x$ and the x-axis on the closed interval $[0, \pi]$.
10. Find the area of the region bounded by the graph of $y = x + \sin x$, the x-axis, and the line $x = \pi/2$.
11. Find the area of the region bounded by the graph of $y = \sec^2 x$, the x-axis, the line $x = \pi/4$, and the line $x = \pi/3$.
12. Find the area of the region bounded by the graph of $y = 3 \cos x/2$ on the interval $[0, \pi]$, the y-axis, and the x-axis.
13. Find a decimal approximation of $\sin 1/2$. Give an upper bound on your error. (Let $x = \pi/6$.)

answers to odd-numbered exercises

section 1–1, page 2.

1. True—(c), (d), (h); false—(a), (b), (e), (f), (g).

3. (a)$\{x|x$ is a vowel in the English alphabet$\}$. (b) $\{x|x = 1/n$ where n is a positive integer less than 8$\}$. (c) $\{x|x = 2^n$ where n is a positive integer less than 7$\}$. (d) $\{x|x$ is the square of a positive integer less than 11$\}$. (e) $\{x|x$ served as Vice President of the United States while Franklin Delano Roosevelt was President$\}$. (f) $\{x|x$ is an odd positive integer less than 18$\}$. (g) $\{x|x$ is an odd positive multiple of 3 less than 46$\}$. (h) $\{x|x$ is a Roman numeral$\}$.

5. (a) $\{1\}$. (b) $\{\sqrt{2}, -\sqrt{2}, \sqrt{3}, -\sqrt{3}\}$. (c) $\{0, 1, -1\}$. (d) $\{-11/2\}$.

7. $W = \{1, 2, 2^2, 2^3, \ldots, 2^{p-1}, (2^p - 1), 2(2^p - 1), 2^2(2^p - 1), 2^3(2^p - 1), \ldots, 2^{p-1}(2^p - 1)\}$

section 1–3, page 5.

1. (a) $\{1\}, \{2\}, \{1, 2\}, \emptyset$. (b) $\{1\}, \{2\}, \{3\}, \{1, 2\}, \{1, 3\}, \{2, 3\}, \{1, 2, 3\}, \emptyset$. (c) $\{1\}, \{2\}, \{3\}, \{1, 2\}, \{1, 3\}, \{2, 3\}, \{1, 2, 3\}, \emptyset, \{1, 4\}, \{2, 4\}, \{3, 4\}, \{1, 2, 4\}, \{1, 3, 4\}, \{2, 3, 4\}, \{1, 2, 3, 4\}, \{4\}$. (d) Let $S_1, S_2, S_3, S_4, S_5, S_6, S_7, S_8$ be the eight subsets of $\{1, 2, 3\}$. The subsets of $\{1, 2, 3, 4\}$ are these eight subsets plus the eight subsets obtained by adding the element 4 to each of the subsets $S_1, S_2, S_3, S_4, S_5, S_6, S_7, S_8$. (e) 2^n.

3. True—(a), (d), (e), (f), (h), (i), (k); false—(b), (c), (g), (j).

5. (a)

$$S_2 \sim T_2 \qquad S_2 \sim T_2$$
$$1 \leftrightarrow a \qquad\qquad 1 \leftrightarrow b$$
$$2 \leftrightarrow b \qquad\qquad 2 \leftrightarrow a$$

(b)

$$S_3 \sim T_3 \qquad S_3 \sim T_3 \qquad S_3 \sim T_3$$
$$1 \leftrightarrow a \qquad\quad 1 \leftrightarrow a \qquad\quad 1 \leftrightarrow b$$
$$2 \leftrightarrow b \qquad\quad 2 \leftrightarrow c \qquad\quad 2 \leftrightarrow a$$
$$3 \leftrightarrow c \qquad\quad 3 \leftrightarrow b \qquad\quad 3 \leftrightarrow c$$

$$S_3 \sim T_3 \qquad S_3 \sim T_3 \qquad S_3 \sim T_3$$
$$1 \leftrightarrow b \qquad\quad 1 \leftrightarrow c \qquad\quad 1 \leftrightarrow c$$
$$2 \leftrightarrow c \qquad\quad 2 \leftrightarrow a \qquad\quad 2 \leftrightarrow b$$
$$3 \leftrightarrow a \qquad\quad 3 \leftrightarrow b \qquad\quad 3 \leftrightarrow a$$

(c) 24, (d) $n!$.

7. $n(S) + n(P) = 33 + 8 = 41$ 9. Yes

section 1–4, page 8.

1. (a) $\{1, 2, 4, 8, 16, 32, 64, 128\}$. (b) $\{1, 2, 4, 5, 8, 10, 16, 20, 40, 80\}$. (c) $\{1, 2, 4, 5, 8, 10, 16, 20, 32, 40, 64, 80, 128\}$. (d) $\{1, 2, 4, 8, 16\}$. (e) Yes. (f) $T \cup A = A$; $T \cap A = T$; $T \cup B = \{1, 2, 4, 5, 8, 10, 16, 20, 32, 40, 80\}$; $T \cap B = \{1, 2, 4, 8, 16\}$.

3. $a + b - c$

5. (a) $\{6, 7, 8, 9\}$.   (b) $\{1, 2, 4, 6, 9\}$.   (c) $\{1, 2, 3, 4, 5, 6\}$.
(d) $\{1, 2, 4, 6, 7, 8, 9\}$.   (e) $\{1, 2, 4, 6, 7, 8, 9\}$.   (f) $\{7, 8, 9\}$.
(g) $\varnothing$.   (h) $\{6, 9\}$.   (i) $\{6, 9\}$.   (j) $\{6\}$.   (k) $\varnothing$.

7. *Part 1.* If $x \in (A \cap B)$, then $x \in A$ by definition of the intersection of two sets. Thus, $A \cap B \subseteq A$.   *Part 2.* If $x \in A$, then since $A \subseteq B$ we have $x \in B$. Thus, $x \in (A \cap B)$ and $A \subseteq (A \cap B)$. Hence, $A \cap B = A$.

9. *Part 1.* If $x \in [A \cup (B \cap C)]$, then $x \in A$ or $x \in (B \cap C)$. If $x \in A$, then $x \in (A \cup B)$ and $x \in (A \cup C)$ so $x \in [(A \cup B) \cap (A \cup C)]$. If $x \notin A$, then $x \in (B \cap C)$. Consequently, $x \in B$ and $x \in C$ which implies that $x \in (A \cup B)$ and $x \in (A \cup C)$. Hence, $x \in [(A \cup B) \cap (A \cup C)]$.   *Part 2.* If $x \in [(A \cup B) \cap (A \cup C)]$, then $x \in (A \cup B)$ and $x \in (A \cup C)$. If $x \in A$, then $x \in [A \cup (B \cap C)]$. If $x \notin A$, then $x \in B$ and $x \in C$ so $x \in (B \cap C)$. Thus, $x \in [A \cup (B \cap C)]$ and $[(A \cup B) \cap (A \cup C)] \subseteq [A \cup (B \cap C)]$. Parts 1 and 2 prove the theorem.

11. $S = N$

13. (a) $\{1, 2, 3, 4, 5, 6\}$.   (b) $\{1, 2, 3, 6\}$.   (c) $\{1, 2, 3, 4, 5, 6, 7, 8\}$.
(d) $\{6\}$.   (e) $\{4, 6\}$.   (f) $\{1, 2, 3, 4, 6\}$.

section 2–2, page 15.

1. Addition, subtraction, multiplication, and division.

3. Yes. No. Yes. No.

5. No. No. Yes. No.

7. Yes. No. Yes. No.

9. (a) is true, since $2 + 6 = 8$.   (b) is false, since $7 + (-4) = 3$.
(c) is true by definition of $\leqslant$.   (d) is false, since $3 \leqslant 3$ but it is false that $3 < 3$.

section 2–3, page 22.

1. No.   Let $x = 0$.

3. (a) 28 and -3.   (b) 3 and 13/6.   (c) 167/24 and $-55/48$.
(d) 106/21 and $-38/21$.

5. $y - x$ is the distance between two points. $(y - x)/3$ is 1/3 the distance. $x + (y - x)/3 = (2x + y)/3$ is the coordinate of the point.

7. $[(n - k)x + ky]/n$ is the coordinate of the end of the kth segment.

9. No. If $-3/5 > -16/27$, then $3/5 < 16/27$ and $81 < 80$, a contradiction.

11. If $(a + c) < (b + c)$, then $(a + c) + (-c) < (b + c) + (-c)$ by Theorem 2–3. By the associative property of addition and the additive identity property, $a < b$.

13. $(a/b) + (x/y) = c/d$ implies $ad + (xbd/y) = cb$. Since ad and bc are integers, $bc - ad$ is an integer.

section 2–5, page 27.

1. Assume a rational number exists whose square is 3. Let p/q be the rational expressed as a fraction where p and q have no common factors except 1. If $(p/q)^2 = 3$, then $3p^2 = q^2$, and q^2 is a multiple of 3. That is, 3 is a factor of $q \times q$. Therefore, 3 is a factor of q and $q = 3r$ where r is an integer. Then, $3p^2 = (3r)^2 = 9r^2$ and $p^2 = 3r^2$. We conclude that p^2 had 3 as a factor so p has 3 as a factor, a contradiction.

section 2–6, page 31.

1. Let $xy = 0$. If $x = 0$, the theorem is proved. If $x \neq 0$, then there exists a multiplicative inverse x^{-1}. Thus, $x^{-1}(xy) = x^{-1}(0) = 0$ and $(x^{-1}x)y = 1(y) = y = 0$.

3. Given: $xz = yz$. Since $z \neq 0$, there exists a multiplicative inverse z^{-1}. Hence, $(xy)z^{-1} = (yz)z^{-1}$ and $x(zz^{-1}) = y(zz^{-1})$. Therefore, $x = y$.

5. If $x < y$, then $x + (-x) < y + (-x)$ and $0 < y + (-x)$. Furthermore, $(-y) + 0 < (-y) + [y + (-x)]$; $(-y) < [(-y) + y] + (-x)$; and $-y < -x$.

7. $1 \neq 0$ by the field properties. If $1 < 0$, then $1(1) > 1(0)$ and $1 > 0$, a contradiction. Thus, $1 > 0$.

9. Obviously, $x^{-1} \neq 0$. If $x^{-1} < 0$, then $x(x^{-1}) < x(0)$ and $1 < 0$, a contradiction. Thus $x^{-1} > 0$.

11. If $x < y$, then $x + w < y + w$. If $w < z$, then $y + w < y + z$. By the transitive property inequality, $x + w < y + z$.

13. $(x^{-1})(x^{-1})^{-1} = 1$ since $(x^{-1})^{-1}$ is the multiplicative inverse of x^{-1}. Thus, $x[(x^{-1})(x^{-1})^{-1}] = x(1)$; $[x(x^{-1})](x^{-1})^{-1} = x$; $1(x^{-1})^{-1} = x$; and $(x^{-1})^{-1} = x$.

15. If $x < 0$ and $y < 0$, then $xy > 0$ and $1/xy > 0$. If $x < y$, then $(1/xy)x < (1/xy)y$ and $1/y < 1/x$.

section 3–1, page 37.

1. $x < -5/2$ 3. $x \leq -1/120$ 5. $-1/3 < x < 5/2$

7. $x < -11/6$ or $x > -2/17$ 9. $-3/4 < x < 0$

11. $x < -3/4$ or $-1/5 < x < 2/5$ 13. $-8 < x < -2/3$ or $x > 4/5$.

15. $0 < d \leq 9/13$

section 3–2, page 40.

1.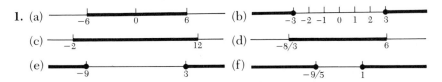

3. *Part 1.* If $a > 0$ and $b > 0$, then $a/b > 0$. Thus, $|a| = a$, $|b| = b$, and $|a/b| = a/b$. Consequently, $|a|/|b| = a/b$.   *Part 2.* If $a > 0$ and $b < 0$, then $a/b < 0$. Thus, $|a| = a$, $|b| = -b$, and $|a/b| = -a/b$. Consequently, $|a|/|b| = a/b$.   *Part 3.* See Part 2.

5. $\{3, -11\}$ 7. $\{6, 4/5\}$

9. (a) $\{x \mid x < -2 \text{ or } x > 1\}$. (b) No solution.

11. $\{x \mid x \text{ is any real number}\}$

13. $\left\{ x \mid x > \dfrac{-7 + \sqrt{505}}{12} \quad \text{or} \quad x < \dfrac{-7 - \sqrt{505}}{12} \right\}$

15. $0 < d < 9t/(3t + 5)$

17. $|x| = |-y + (x + y)| \le |-y| + |x + y|$. Thus, $|x| - |-y| \le |x + y|$ and $|x| - |y| \le |x + y|$.

19. If $x \ge 0$, $|x| = x$. Thus, $|x|^2 = |x| \, |x| = x \cdot x = x^2$. If $x \le 0$, then $|x| = -x$. Thus, $|x|^2 = |x| \, |x| = (-x)(-x) = x^2$.

section 4–1, page 47.

1. $D_f = \{3, -2, 5, -1\}$; $R_f = \{5, 7, -5, -4, -1\}$

3. $D_h = \{3\}$; $R_h = \{y \mid y \text{ is a real number}\}$

5. $D_G = \{x \mid x \text{ is a real number}\} = R_G$

7. $D_v = \{x \mid x \text{ is a real number}\}$; $R_v = \{x \mid x \text{ is a non-negative real number}\}$.

9. $z = \{(x, y) \mid 6x + 8y = 61\}$

11. Since $\sqrt{(x-1)^2 + (y+3)^2} = \sqrt{(x-8)^2 + (y-2)^2}$ implies that $7x + 5y = 29$, we know that $7x + 5y = 29$ is the equation of the perpendicular bisector. $(-3, 10)$ is on the line, since $(-3, 10)$ satisfies the equation. Second solution: show

$$\sqrt{(1+3)^2 + (-3-10)^2} = \sqrt{(8+3)^2 + (2-10)^2}$$

13. $\sqrt{117} + \sqrt{104} + \sqrt{137} \approx 32.72$

15. (a) $(5, 10)$.   (b) $(5, 21/2)$.   (c) $(2, 3)$.

17. 19

19. $\left(\dfrac{x_1 + 2x_2}{3}, \dfrac{y_1 + 2y_2}{3} \right)$

21. mn

23. $A = B$. If $A \ne B$, there is a $t \in A$ and $t \notin B$ (or $t \in B$ and $t \notin A$). If $t \in A$, let $b \in B$. Then, $(t, b) \in A \times B$ but $(t, b) \notin B \times A$. Therefore, $A \times B \ne B \times A$.

section 4–2, page 53.

1. (a) $G, f, g, h, v, w,$ and u are functions.   (b) The inverses of $G, f, g, h,$ and u are functions.

3. $D_f = \{x | x \geq -7/2\}; \ R_f = \{y | y \geq 0\}.$

$f^{-1} = \{(t, f^{-1}(t)) | f^{-1}(t) = (t^2 - 7)/2 \text{ where } t \geq 0\}. \ D_{f^{-1}} = R_f \text{ and } R_{f^{-1}} = D_f.$

5. $f^{-1}(t) = \dfrac{3t + 6}{2t - 3}$ for $t \neq 3/2.$

Graph:

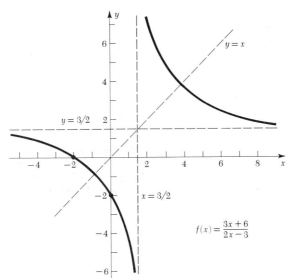

7. $D_F = \{x | x \neq 0\}; \ R_F = \{y | y \neq 1\}. \ F^{-1}(x) = 2/(x - 1)$

9. (a) Yes. (b) $\sqrt{(x - 0)^2 + (y - 4)^2} = |y|$ if and only if $x^2 + y^2 - 8y + 16 = y^2$. Thus, points (x, y) satisfy the given conditions if and only if they satisfy $x^2 - 8y + 16 = 0.$

11. (a) It is symmetric to the y-axis. (b) It is symmetric to the origin.
(c) $F(x) = x^2, \ G(x) = x^3, \ h(x) = x^2 + 2x.$

13. $a = -d$

15. (a) Yes. No. (b) $\sigma(3) = 4, \ \sigma(6) = 12, \ \sigma(5) = 6, \ \sigma(17) = 18,$
$\sigma(28) = 56, \ \sigma(496) = 992, \ \sigma(m) = 1 + m.$
(c) $(1 + m)(1 + n) = (1 + m + n + mn).$ (d) No. (e) Yes.

section 4–3, page 57.

1. (b) $|b - a|.$ (c) 0. (d) $(0, 5).$

3. $\{(x, y) | 2x - 3y = -21\}$

5. $\{(x, y) | y = 9\}$

7. Let P_1 and P_2 be two different points on one line and P_3 and P_4 be two different points on the other line. Form similar right triangles with sides parallel to the coordinate axes and P_1P_2 the hypotenuse of one triangle and P_3P_4 the hypotenuse of the other. Use the fact that lengths of the sides are proportional.

9. (a) $t = -9$. (b) $(-9, -36)$ are the coordinates of the point of intersection of the two lines.

11. The points on the y-axis, except $(0, 3)$.

13. $y = -x - 1$

section 4–5, page 61.

1. (b) $\{x | x \geqslant -3\}$. (c) $\{x | x \leqslant -3\}$. (d) No maximum; the minimum value of f is -18.

3. (b) $\{x | x \geqslant 1/2\}$. (c) $\{x | x \leqslant 1/2\}$. (d) No maximum; the minimum value of the function is $3/4$.

5. (b) $\{x | x \geqslant -b/2a\}$. (c) $\{x | x \leqslant -b/2a\}$. (d) No maximum; the minimum value is $(4ac - b^2)/4a$.

7. Perpendicular distance from (x, y) to the line $y = -10$ is $|y + 10|$. The distance from (x, y) to $(-1, -6)$ is $\sqrt{(x + 1)^2 + (y + 6)^2}$. Assume that $|y + 10| \neq \sqrt{(x + 1)^2 + (y + 6)^2}$. Then, $y^2 + 20y + 100 \neq x^2 + 2x + 1 + y^2 + 12y + 36$ and $y \neq (x^2 + 2x - 63)/8$, a contradiction since (x, y) is on the graph of g.

section 4–6, page 65.

1. (a) 3. (b) No. (c) $\{x | x \geqslant 4\}$. (d) $\emptyset$

3. (a) $f \circ g$ is defined by $f(g(x)) = 5x + 22$, or $f \circ g = \{(x, 5x + 22) | x$ is a real number$\}$. (b) $g \circ f = \{(x, 5x + 10) | x$ is a real number$\}$.

5. (a) $D_{f/g} = \{2, 3, 4, 5\}$; $f/g = \{(2, 0), (3, 4), (4, 1/2), (5, 1/3)\}$.
   (b) $D_{g/f} = \{3, 4, 5\}$; $g/f = \{(3, 1/4), (4, 2), (5, 3)\}$.
   (c) $D_{f \circ g} = \{1, 2, 4, 5\}$; $f \circ g = \{(1, 1), (2, 0), (4, 2), (5, -4)\}$.
   (d) $D_{g \circ f} = \{0, 4, 5\}$; $g \circ f = \{(0, 0), (4, 2), (5, 0)\}$.

7. (a) $f(1 \times 1) = f(1) + f(1)$; thus, $f(1) = 2f(1)$. Hence, $f(1) = 0$.
   (b) $f(-1 \times -1) = f(-1) + f(-1)$; thus, $f(1) = 2f(-1)$ and $0 = 2f(-1)$. Hence, $f(-1) = 0$.
   (c) $f(-x) = f(-1 \times x) = f(-1) + f(x) = 0 + f(x) = f(x)$.

9. $f(g(x)) = 3g(x) + 7$. $8x^2 + 15x - 19 = 3g(x) + 7$. Solving for $g(x)$, $g(x) = 1/3(8x^2 + 15x - 26)$.

section 5–2, page 69.

1. Let $\log_b x = u$ and $\log_b = v$. Then, $b^u = x$ and $b^v = y$. $x/y = b^u/b^v = b^{u-v}$. Thus, $\log_b x/y = u - v = \log_b x - \log_b y$.

3. (a) 3. (b) 3. (c) 0.01. (d) 100. (e) 2. (f) 4. (g) 7.
   (h) 5. (i) -2. (j) -4.

5. (a) 1.3010. (b) 2.3010. (c) $0.3010 - 1$. (d) $0.3010 - 2$.
   (e) 0.6990. (f) 1.3980. (g) 0.6020. (h) 1.9030. (i) 0.8060.
   (j) 0.1505. (k) 0.3495. (l) 0.5000.

7. $2 \log x + 3 \log x = 10$; $\log x = 2$; $x = 100$.

9. No.

11. (a) 5.   (b) 1,000.   (c) 6.   (d) 10.

13. $D_f = \{x | x > 0\}$; $R_f = \{x | x \text{ is a real number}\}$.

Section 5–3, page 73.

1. 9.286×10^{-8} 3. 0.4648   5. 0.328

7. 4.524   9. 0.9478

section 6–3, page 78.

1. 15 inches.   3. $s = 20(129\pi)/180 \approx 45.03$

5. (a) $14\pi/5$.   (b) $r = 7/5$ and $A = \pi r^2 = 49\pi/25$.

7. (a) I.   (b) II.   (c) IV.   (d) quadrantal.   (e) quadrantal.
   (f) II.

9. (a) $(1, 0)$.   (b) $(0, 1)$.   (c) $(0, 1)$.   (d) $(-1, 0)$.   (e) $(0, -1)$.
   (f) $(\sqrt{2}/2, \sqrt{2}/2)$.   (g) $(-\sqrt{2}/2, -\sqrt{2}/2)$.   (h) $(0, -1)$.
   (i) $(-\sqrt{2}/2, -\sqrt{2}/2)$.   (j) $(-\sqrt{2}/2, -\sqrt{2}/2)$.

11. $16\pi/3$

section 6–4, page 81.

1. Let $P(0, a)$ and $Q(0, b)$ be any two distinct points on the positive y-axis and let θ be the measure of an angle in standard position with positive y-axis as terminal side. Sin $\theta = a/a = b/b = 1$; cos $\theta = 0/a = 0/b = 0$; tan θ is undefined.

5. (a) $(-1, 1)$.   (b) $(-\infty, -1) \cup (1, +\infty)$.   (c) $(-\infty, +\infty)$.
   (d) $(-\infty, +\infty)$.   (e) $(-\infty, -1) \cup (1, +\infty)$.

7. (a) -1.   (b) 0.   (c) -1.   (d) 0.

9. (a) $\sqrt{3/7}$.   (b) $-2/\sqrt{7}$.   (c) $\sqrt{3}/-2$.   (d) $\sqrt{7/3} = \sqrt{21}/3$.
   (e) $\sqrt{7}/-2$.   (f) $-2/\sqrt{3}$.   (g) 1.

11. Let P be any point on the terminal side of an angle in standard position with measure θ and let r be the distance of P from the origin. By the Pythagorean Theorem, $x^2 + y^2 = r^2$. If $x \neq 0$, $1 + (y/x)^2 = (r/x)^2$ and $1 + (\tan \theta)^2 = (\sec \theta)^2$. Consequently, $(\tan \theta)^2 < (\sec \theta)^2$. If $x = 0$, θ is not in the domain of both the functions.

13.

function	I quadrant	II quadrant	III quadrant	IV quadrant
sin	+	+	−	−
cos	+	−	−	+
tan	+	−	+	−
csc	+	+	−	−
sec	+	−	−	+
cot	+	−	+	−

section 6–5, page 86.

1. (a) 2π.   (b) 2π.   (c) 2π.   (d) π.   (e) π.

5. Increases on $[(2k-1)\pi, 2k\pi]$ where k is an integer. Decreases on $[2k\pi, (2k+1)\pi]$.

7. Function never increases. Function decreases on $(k\pi, (k+1)\pi)$ where k is an integer.

9. Cosine and secant.

section 6–6, page 92.

3. (a), (b), (d), and (f) are identities. Solution set for (c) is $\{0, -3/2\}$. Solution set for (e) is $\{-4\}$. Solution set for (g) is ϕ. [Hint for (g): Consider $x \leq -1$, $-1 \leq x \leq -1/2$, $x \geq -1/2$.]

5. $\cos 2\theta = \cos^2 \theta - \sin^2 \theta = (1 - \sin^2 \theta) - \sin^2 \theta = 1 - 2 \sin^2 \theta$

7. $1 - \tan^4 \theta = (1 - \tan^2 \theta)(1 + \tan^2 \theta) = \left(1 - \dfrac{\sin^2 \theta}{\cos^2 \theta}\right) \sec^2 \theta$

$$= \left(\dfrac{\cos^2 \theta - \sin^2 \theta}{\cos^2 \theta}\right) \dfrac{1}{\cos^2 \theta} = \dfrac{\cos 2\theta}{\cos^4 \theta}$$

9. $\cos(90° - \theta) = \cos 90° \cos \theta + \sin 90° \sin \theta = \sin \theta$

11. $\dfrac{1}{\csc \theta + \cot \theta} = \dfrac{1}{\csc \theta + \cot \theta} \cdot \dfrac{\csc \theta - \cot \theta}{\csc \theta - \cot \theta}$

$$= \dfrac{\csc \theta - \cot \theta}{\csc^2 \theta - \cot^2 \theta} = \csc \theta - \cot \theta.$$

13. $\cos 75° = \cos(45° + 30°) = \cos 45° \cos 30° - \sin 45° \sin 30°$
$= (\sqrt{2}/2)(\sqrt{3}/2) - (\sqrt{2}/2)(1/2) = (\sqrt{2}/4)(\sqrt{3} - 1)$

15. (a) $\sin 15° = \sin(45° - 30°) = \sin 45° \cos 30° - \cos 45° \sin 30°$
$= (\sqrt{2}/2)(\sqrt{3}/2) - (\sqrt{2}/2)(1/2) = (\sqrt{2}/4)(\sqrt{3} - 1)$
(b) $\cos 30° = 1 - 2 \sin^2 15°$

$$\dfrac{\sqrt{3}}{2} = 1 - 2 \sin^2 15°, \quad \sin^2 15° = \dfrac{2 - \sqrt{3}}{4}$$

$$\sin 15° = \sqrt{\dfrac{2 - \sqrt{3}}{4}}. \text{ Since } (\sqrt{3} - 1)^2 = 4 - 2\sqrt{3},$$

$$\sqrt{\dfrac{2 - \sqrt{3}}{4}} = \sqrt{\dfrac{4 - 2\sqrt{3}}{8}} = \dfrac{\sqrt{4 - 2\sqrt{3}}}{2\sqrt{2}} = \dfrac{\sqrt{2}}{2}(\sqrt{3} - 1).$$

17. Yes: $\dfrac{\cos^2 \theta}{1 - \sin \theta} + \dfrac{\cos^2 \theta}{1 + \sin \theta} = \cos^2 \theta \left(\dfrac{1 + \sin \theta + 1 - \sin \theta}{1 - \sin^2 \theta}\right)$

$$= \dfrac{2 \cos^2 \theta}{1 - \sin^2 \theta} = 2.$$

19. $\cos(\alpha + \beta) = \cos \alpha \cos \beta - \sin \alpha \sin \beta$
$\cos(\alpha - \beta) = \cos \alpha \cos \beta - \sin \alpha \sin \beta$
$\cos(\alpha - \beta) - \cos(\alpha - \beta) = -2 \sin \alpha \sin \beta$

21. $\sin \theta = 2/7$, $\cos^2 \theta = 1 - \sin^2 \theta = 1 - (4/49) = (45/49)$.
Thus, $\cos \theta = -3\sqrt{5}/7$. $\tan \theta = \sin \theta / \cos \theta = 2/-3\sqrt{5} = -2\sqrt{5}/15$.
$\csc \theta = 1/\sin \theta = 7/2$.

section 6–7, page 94.

1. $\sin 2\theta = \sin(\theta + \theta) = \sin\theta\cos\theta + \cos\theta\sin\theta = 2\sin\theta\cos\theta$

3. Let $\alpha + \beta = \theta$ and $\alpha - \beta = \phi$. Thus, $\alpha = (\theta + \phi)/2$ and $\beta = (\theta - \phi)/2$.
$\text{Sin}(\alpha + \beta) = \sin\alpha\cos\beta + \cos\alpha\sin\beta$; $\sin(\alpha - \beta) = \sin\alpha\cos\beta - \cos\alpha\sin\beta$;
$\sin(\alpha + \beta) - \sin(\alpha - \beta) = 2\cos\alpha\sin\beta$. Hence, $\sin\theta - \sin\phi = 2\cos(\theta + \phi)/2$
$\sin(\theta - \phi)/2$.

5. $\tan(\theta - \phi) = \dfrac{\sin(\theta - \phi)}{\cos(\theta - \phi)} = \dfrac{\sin\theta\cos\phi - \cos\theta\sin\phi}{\cos\theta\cos\phi + \sin\theta\sin\phi}$

$\qquad = \dfrac{\dfrac{\sin\theta\cos\phi}{\cos\theta\cos\phi} - \dfrac{\cos\theta\sin\phi}{\cos\theta\cos\phi}}{1 + \dfrac{\sin\theta\sin\phi}{\cos\theta\cos\phi}}$

$\qquad = \dfrac{\tan\theta + \tan\phi}{1 + \tan\theta\tan\phi}.$

7. $\sin(\theta + \phi)\sin(\theta + \phi) = (\sin\theta\cos\phi + \cos\theta\sin\phi)(\sin\theta\cos\phi - \cos\theta\sin\phi)$
$\qquad = \sin^2\theta\cos^2\phi - \cos^2\theta\sin^2\phi$
$\qquad = \sin^2\theta(1 - \sin^2\phi) - (1 - \sin^2\theta)\sin^2\phi$
$\qquad = \sin^2\theta - \sin^2\phi$

9. $\dfrac{\sin\theta + \sin 2\theta}{1 + \cos\theta + \cos 2\theta} = \dfrac{\sin\theta + 2\sin\theta\cos\theta}{1 + \cos\theta + 2\cos^2\theta - 1}$

$\qquad = \dfrac{\sin\theta(1 + 2\cos\theta)}{\cos\theta(1 + 2\cos\theta)} = \tan\theta$

11. $\dfrac{\cos 3\theta}{\sin\theta} + \dfrac{\sin 3\theta}{\cos\theta} = \dfrac{\cos 3\theta\cos\theta + \sin 3\theta\sin\theta}{\sin\theta\cos\theta}$

$\qquad = \dfrac{2\cos(3\theta - \theta)}{2\sin\theta\cos\theta} = \dfrac{2\cos 2\theta}{\sin 2\theta}$
$\qquad = 2\cot 2\theta$

13. $\sec 2\theta - \tan 2\theta = \dfrac{1}{\cos 2\theta} - \dfrac{\sin 2\theta}{\cos 2\theta} = \dfrac{1 - \sin 2\theta}{\cos 2\theta}$

$\qquad = \dfrac{1 - 2\sin\theta\cos\theta}{1 - 2\sin^2\theta}$

15. $\sin 3\theta = \sin(2\theta + \theta) = \sin 2\theta\cos\theta + \cos 2\theta\sin\theta$
$\qquad = 2\sin\theta\cos^2\theta + (1 - 2\sin^2\theta)\sin\theta$
$\qquad = 2\sin\theta(1 - \sin^2\theta) + \sin\theta - 2\sin^3\theta.$
$\qquad = 3\sin\theta - 4\sin^3\theta$

17. $\dfrac{\tan^2\theta}{1 + \sec\theta} + 1 = \dfrac{\sec^2\theta - 1}{\sec\theta + 1} + 1 = \sec\theta - 1 + 1 = \sec\theta$

19. $\dfrac{\sin 3\theta}{1 - \cos 3\theta} = \dfrac{\sin 3\theta/\cos 3\theta}{(1/\cos 3\theta) - 1} = \dfrac{\tan 3\theta}{\sec 3\theta - 1}$

section 6–8, page 100.

1. $\beta = 90° - 28° = 62°$, $a = 20\tan 28° = 10.63$, $c = 20\sec 28° = 22.65$.

3. $\beta = 90° - 39° = 51°$, $a = 36\sin 39° = 22.66$, $b = 36\cos 39° = 22.98$.

5. $\alpha = 90° - 68° = 22°$, $c = 40\csc 68° = 16.16$, $a = 40\cot 68° = 43.13$.

7. $\beta = 90° - 28°48', = 61°12', a = 2.37 \tan 28°48' = 1.303,$
$c = 2.37 \sec 28°48' = 2.704.$

9. $b = \sqrt{56^2 - 23^2} = 51.06, \alpha = 24°15', \beta = 65°45'.$

section 6–9, page 104.

3. $\beta = 25°55'$

5. $a = 44.3$

7. $a = 18.5, \beta = 72°8'$

9. No triangle.

section 6–10, page 107.

1. $x = \pi/2 + 2k\pi$, k an integer   **3.** $x = 2k\pi, \pi/2 + 2k\pi$

5. $x = 45° + 180°k, 116°34' + 180°k$ **7.** $x = k\pi, \pi/2 + k\pi$

9. $x = 3\pi/4, 9\pi/8, 21\pi/8, 15\pi/4, 33\pi/8, 45\pi/8.$ In general, $x = (3\pi/4) - 3k\pi$
or $x = (-3\pi/8) - (3k\pi/2).$

11. $x = \pi/2 + k\pi, 7\pi/6 + 2k\pi, 11\pi/6 + 2k\pi$ **13.** $k\pi < x < \pi/4 + k\pi$

section 6–11, page 109.

3. (a) 30°.   (b) 45°.   (c) −45°.   (d) −45°.   (e) 30°.   (f) 30°.

5. (a) 1/2.   (b) $\sqrt{3}/3$.   (c) $\sqrt{3}/2$.   (d) 45°.

7. (a) If $-\pi/2 \leqslant \theta_1 \leqslant \pi/2$ and $-\pi/2 \leqslant \theta_2 \leqslant \pi/2$, then $\sin \theta_1 = \sin \theta_2$ if and
only if $\theta_1 = \theta_2$. Since $\sin(\text{arc} \sin(-x)) = -x$ and $\sin[-(\text{arc} \sin x)]$
$= -\sin(\text{arc} \sin x) = -x$, arc $\sin(-x) = -\text{arc} \sin x$.   (b) If $0 \leqslant \theta_1 \leqslant \pi$
and $0 \leqslant \theta_2 \leqslant \pi$, then $\cos \theta_1 = \cos \theta_2$ if and only if $\theta_1 = \theta_2$. Since $\cos$
$(\text{arc} \cos(-x)) = -x$ and

$$\cos(\pi - \text{arc} \cos x) = \cos \pi \cos(\text{arc} \cos x) + \sin \pi \sin(\text{arc} \cos x)$$
$$= -\cos(\text{arc} \cos x) = -x,$$

$\pi - \text{arc} \cos x = \text{arc} \cos (-x).$

section 7–2, page 115.

1. I. $n = 1.$ $1^5 - 1 = 0$, and 0 has 5 as a factor.
   II. Assume 5 is a factor of $k^5 - k$; thus, $k^5 - k = 5t$ where t is an integer.
   Furthermore,

$$(k+1)^5 - (k+1) = k^5 + 5k^4 + 10k^3 + 10k^2 + 5k + 1 - k - 1$$
$$= (k^5 - k) + 5(k^4 + 2k^3 + 2k^2 + k)$$
$$= 5(t + k^4 + 2k^3 + 2k^2 + k).$$

   Hence, 5 is a factor of $(k+1)^5 - (k+1).$

3. I. $n = 1.$ $\dfrac{\sin 2^1 \theta}{2^1 \sin \theta} = \dfrac{2 \sin \theta \cos \theta}{2 \sin \theta} = \cos \theta.$

II. Assume $(\cos \theta)(\cos 2\theta) \ldots (\cos 2^{k-1} \theta) = \dfrac{\sin 2^k \theta}{2^k \sin \theta}$.

Then,

$$(\cos \theta)(\cos 2\theta)(\cos 2^2\theta) \ldots (\cos 2^{k-1} \theta)(\cos 2^k \theta) = \frac{\sin 2^k \theta}{2^k \sin \theta}(\cos 2^k \theta)$$
$$= \frac{2(\sin 2^k \theta)}{2^{k+1} \sin \theta} = \frac{\sin 2^{k+1} \theta}{2^{k+1} \sin \theta}.$$

5.   I. $n = 1.$ $x^2 - y^2$ has $(x + y)$ as a factor.

   II. Assume $x^{2k} - y^{2k}$ has $(x + y)$ as a factor. Then,

$$x^{2(k+1)} - y^{2(k+1)} = x^{2k+2} - y^{2k+2}$$
$$= x^2(x^{2k}) - x^2(y^{2k}) + x^2(y^{2k}) - y^2(y^{2k})$$
$$= x^2(x^{2k} - y^{2k}) + y^{2k}(x^2 - y^2).$$

Since $(x^{2k} - y^{2k})$ and $(x^2 - y^2)$ each has $(x + y)$ as a factor, the sum has $(x + y)$ as a factor.

7.   I. $n = 1.$ $\cos \pi = (-1)^1 = -1.$

   II. Assume $\cos k\,\pi = (-1)^k.$ Then,

$$\cos (k + 1)\pi = \cos (k\pi + \pi) = \cos k\pi \cos \pi - \sin k\pi \sin \pi$$
$$= (-1)^k(-1)$$
$$= (-1)^{k+1}.$$

9.   I. $n = 1.$ $1/5 + 1/3 + 7/15 = 3/15 + 5/15 + 7/15 = 1$, an integer.

   II. Assume $k^5/5 = (k^3/3) + (7k/15)$ is an integer. Then,

$$\frac{(k+1)^5}{5} + \frac{(k+1)^3}{3} + \frac{7(k+1)}{15} = \frac{k^5 + 5k^4 + 10k^3 + 10k^2 + 5k + 1}{5}$$
$$+ \frac{k^3 + 3k^2 - 3k + 1}{3} + \frac{7k + 7}{15}$$
$$= \frac{k^5}{5} + \frac{k^3}{3} + \frac{7k}{15} + (k^4 + 2k^3 + 2k^2 + k)$$
$$+ (k^2 + k) + (1/5 + 1/3 + 7/15).$$

Since each term in parentheses in the sum is an integer, the sum is an integer.

10.   I. $n = 1.$ $1/7 + 1/3 + 11/21 = 3/21 + 7/21 + 11/21 = 1.$

   II. Assume $k^7/7 + k^3/3 + 11k/21$ is an integer. Then,

$$\frac{(k+1)^7}{7} + \frac{(k+1)^3}{3} + \frac{11(k+1)}{21} = \left(\frac{k^7}{7} + \frac{k^3}{3} + \frac{11k}{21}\right)$$
$$+ (k^6 + 3k^5 + 5k^4 + 5k^3 + 3k^2 + k) + (k^2 + k) + (1/7 + 1/3 + 11/21).$$

Since each term in parentheses in the sum is an integer, the sum is an integer.

11.   I. $n = 1.$ $6^3 + 7^3 = 559 = 43(13)$ has 43 as a factor.

   II. Assume that $6^{k+2} + 7^{2k+1}$ has 43 as a factor. Then,

$$k^{k+3} + 7^{2k+3} = 6(6^{k+1}) + 6(7^{2k+1}) - 6(7^{2k+1}) + 49(7^{2k+1})$$
$$= 6(6^{k+1} + 7^{2k+1}) + 7^{2k+1}(43).$$

Since $6(6^{k+1} + 7^{2k+1})$ and $7^{2k+1}(43)$ each has 43 as a factor, the sum has 43 as a factor.

12. I. Let $A_1 = \{a_1\}$ and $B_1 = \{b_1\}$. The only one-to-one correspondence is given by $a_1 \leftrightarrow b_1$. Thus, the number of one-to-one correspondences is 1!, or 1.

   II. Let $A_k = \{a_1, a_2, a_3, \ldots, a_k\}$ and $B_k = \{b_1, b_2, b_3, \ldots, b_k\}$. Assume there are a total of $k!$ one-to-one correspondences between A_k and B_k. Now, consider the sets $A_{k+1} = \{a_1, a_2, a_3, \ldots, a_k, a_{k+1}\}$ and $B_{k+1} = \{b_1, b_2, b_3, \ldots, b_k, b_{k+1}\}$. The elements b_{k+1} can correspond to any one of the $(k+1)$ elements in A_{k+1}. When b_{k+1} corresponds to, say, a_3, there are $k!$ one-to-one correspondences between the remaining k elements in each set. Since b_{k+1} can correspond to $(k+1)$ different elements in A_{k+1}, there are $(k+1)k! = (k+1)!$ different one-to-one correspondences between the two sets with $(k+1)$ elements.

13. Let $S = \{x | x$ is a positive integer and $P(x)$ is false$\}$. If S is not empty. Let t be the least integer in S; that is, t is the smallest positive integer such that $P(t)$ is false. Then, $P(y)$ is true for every positive integer $y < t$, and by hypothesis (b) we have that $P(t)$ is true. This contradiction proves that $P(n)$ is true for every positive integer.

14. Let $S = \{x | x$ is an integer and $P(x)$ is false$\}$. If S is not empty, there exists a smallest integer t such that $P(t)$ is false. By hypothesis (a), $P(n)$ is true for every integral power of 2. Hence, there exists some positive integer v such that $2^v > t$. Let d be the difference $2^v - t$; that is, $d = 2^v - t$. Now, if $P(t+1)$ is true, by hypothesis (b) we would have that $P(t)$ is true. This is a contradiction and $P(t+1)$ is false. If $P(t+1)$ is false, by a similar argument we could conclude that $P(t+2)$, $p(t+3)$, $\ldots$, $P(t+d)$ are false. However, since $t + d = 2^v$, this would imply that $P(2^v)$ is false, in contradiction to hypothesis (a). Thus $P(n)$ is true for every positive integer.

section 8-1, page 118.

1. $S_1 = 3$, $S_2 = 7$, $S_3 = 11$, $S_4 = 15$, $S_5 = 19$, $S_6 = 23$

3. $-1, 0, -1, 0, -1, 0, -1, 0, -1, 0$; $t_{99} = -1$

5. $4, 9, 16, 25$; 400

7. (a) $t_3 = 3$, $t_4 = 5$, $t_5 = 8$, $t_6 = 13$, $t_7 = 21$, $t_8 = 34$.

   (b) $s_1 = t_2{}^2 - t_1 t_3 = 4 - (1)(3) = 1$, $s_2 = t_3{}^2 - t_2 t_4 = -1$, $s_3 = 1$, $s_4 = -1$, $s_5 = 1$, $s_6 = -1$, $s_7 = 1$.

   (c) $s_n = (-1)^{n-1}$.

   (d) Use mathematical induction. Hint:
        Assume $s_k = t_{k+1}{}^2 - t_k t_{k+2} = (-1)^{k-1}$. Thus, $t_{k+1}{}^2 - (t_{k+2} - t_{k+1}) t_{k+2} = (-1)^{k-1}$ since $t_k = t_{k+2} - t_{k+1}$ Consequently, $-t_{k+1}{}^2 + t_{k+2}{}^2 - t_{k+1} t_{k+2} = (-1)^k$.
        Now

$$s_{k+1} = t_{k+2}{}^2 - t_{k+1} t_{k+3}$$
$$= t_{k+2}{}^2 - t_{k+1} (t_{k+1} + t_{k+2})$$
$$= t_{k+2}{}^2 - t_{k+1}{}^2 - t_{k+1} t_{k+2}$$
$$= (-1)^k.$$

section 8–2, page 124.

1. $\sum_{n=1}^{n} 5n = 5 \sum_{n=1}^{n} n = 5 \dfrac{(27)(28)}{2} = 1{,}890$

3. $\sum_{n=1}^{100} (3n^2 + 1) = 3 \sum_{n=1}^{100} n^2 + \sum_{n=1}^{100} 1 = \dfrac{3(100)(101)(201)}{6} + 100 = 1{,}015{,}150$

5. $\sum_{n=1}^{50} \dfrac{1}{n(n+1)} = -\sum_{n=1}^{50} \left(\dfrac{1}{n+1} - \dfrac{1}{n} \right) = -\left(\dfrac{1}{51} - \dfrac{1}{1} \right) = \dfrac{50}{51}$

7. $4 \sum_{n=1}^{k} n^3 = \sum_{n=1}^{k} [n^4 - (n-1)^4] + 6 \sum_{n=1}^{k} n^2 - \sum_{n=1}^{k} 4n + \sum_{n=1}^{k} 1.$

Thus,

$$\sum_{n=1}^{k} n^3 = 1/4 \left[k^4 + \dfrac{6k(k+1)(2k+1)}{6} - \dfrac{4k(k+1)}{2} + k \right]$$

$$= \dfrac{k^2(k+1)^2}{4} = \left(\sum_{n=1}^{k} n \right)^2.$$

9. $\sum_{n=1}^{k} (3n^3 - 3n^2 + 1) = 3 \sum_{n=1}^{k} n^3 - 3 \sum_{n=1}^{k} n^2 + \sum_{n=1}^{k} 1$

$$= \dfrac{3\,k^2(k+1)^2}{4} - \dfrac{3k(k+1)(2k+1)}{6} + k$$

$$= \dfrac{k[3k(k+1)^2 - 2(k+1)(2k+1) + 4]}{4}$$

$$= \dfrac{k(3k^3 + 2k^2 - 3k + 2)}{4}$$

11. Use mathematical induction. Hint:

Assume $\sum_{n=1}^{u} (-1)^{n-1} n^2 = (-1)^{u-1} \sum_{n=1}^{u} n$. Then,

$$\sum_{n=1}^{u+1} (-1)^{n-1} n^2 = \left(\sum_{n=1}^{u} (-1)^{n-1} n^2 \right) + (-1)^u (u+1)^2$$

$$= (-1)^{u-1} \sum_{n=1}^{u} n + (-1)^u (u+1)^2$$

$$= (-1)^u \left[(u+1)^2 - \dfrac{u(u+1)}{2} \right]$$

$$= (-1)^u \dfrac{(u+1)(u+2)}{2}$$

$$= (-1)^u \sum_{n=1}^{u+1} n.$$

section 8–3, page 129.

1. $100 = \dfrac{22[2(3) + 21d]}{2}$, $d = 34/21k$

3. $\sigma_{37} = \dfrac{37[2(5) + 36(3)]}{2}$, $\sigma_{37} = 2{,}183$

5. $100 = \dfrac{2(2^8 - 1)}{2 - 1}$, $a = 100/255 = 20/51$

7. $\displaystyle\sum_{n=1}^{8} (3n + 2^n) = 3 \sum_{n=1}^{8} n + \sum_{n=1}^{8} 2n = \dfrac{3(8)(9)}{2} = 2(2^8 - 1) = 618$

9. (b) $6 = 2 \times 3$; $28 = 2^2 \times 7$; $496 = 2^4 \times 31$;
　　　$8{,}128 = 2^6 \times 127$; $33{,}550{,}336 = 2^{12} \times 8{,}191$.
　　(d) 1 and $2^p - 1$.
　　(e) $1, 2, 2^2, 2^3, 2^4, \ldots, 2^{p-1}$.
　　(f) $1, 2, 2^2, 2^3, \ldots, 2^{p-1}, (2^p - 1), 2(2^p - 1), 2^2(2^p - 1), 2^3(2^p - 1), \ldots,$
　　　$2^{p-1}(2^p - 1)$.
　　(g) $\sigma(n) = 1 + 2 + 2^2 + 2^3 + \cdots + 2^{p-1} + 2^p - 1 + 2^{p+1} - 2 + 2^{p+2} - 2^2$
　　　　　　　　$+ 2^{2p+3} - 2^3 + \cdots + 2^{2p-1} - 2^{p-1}$
　　　　　　$= 2^p + 2^{p+1}$
　　　　　　$= 2^{p+2} + \cdots + 2^{2p-1}$
　　　　　　$= \dfrac{2^p[2^p - 1]}{2 - 1}$
　　　　　　$= 2[2^{p-1}(2^p - 1)]$
　　　　　　$= 2n$.

section 9–1, page 133.

1. $1/52$　　　**3.** $24^2 + 24^3 = 14{,}400$　　　**5.** $36; 6; 1/6$

7. $Pr(\text{vote yes}) = 88/190$　　　**9.** $0/n = 0;\ n/n = 1$　　　**11.** $Pr(3) = 1/7$

section 9–2, page 137.

1. $(40)_1 + (40)_2 + (40)_3 = 60{,}880$

3. $\dbinom{13}{2} \cdot \dbinom{39}{3} = 712{,}842$　　　**5.** $\dbinom{10}{2} \cdot \dbinom{12}{3} = 9{,}900$

7. R can be chosen to serve on the committee in $\dbinom{N}{R}$ ways;

　　$(N - R)$ members can be rejected for service in $\dbinom{N}{N - R}$ ways.

9. $\dbinom{4}{1,2,1} = 12$. Perhaps three will be recognized: REED, DEER in English
　　and ERDE in German. $\dbinom{11}{1,4,4,2} > 24$

section 9–3, page 141.

1. $\displaystyle\sum_{n=0}^{n} (-1)^r \dbinom{n}{r} = (1 - 1)^n = 0$

3. The entire term is $\dbinom{8}{2} (2a)^2(b)^6 = 112a^2b^6$.

5. The sum is $(3+2)^5 = 3{,}125$.

7. Entries are symmetrical with respect to a center term (if n is even) or to two center terms (if n is odd).

section 9–4, page 144.

1. $\binom{12}{2} = 66$; $6/66 = 1/11$ **3.** $6^3 = 216$

5. $\{(G,G),(G,D),(D,G),(D,D)\}$ where D = defective bulb, G = good bulb.

7. $.10 + .15 = .25$

9. $\{H, TH, TTH, TTTH, TTTT\}$, with probabilities 1/2, 1/4, 1/8, 1/16, 1/16, respectively.

section 9–5, page 148.

1. $PR(A \cup B) = 6/36 + 11/36 - 2/36 = 5/12$

3. (a) .23.   (b) .47.   (c) .25.

5. $3/7$; $3/7$; $3/7$ **7.** .5   **9.** 1/4

11. $\frac{1}{2}\left(\frac{a}{a+b} + \frac{c}{c+d}\right)$; $\frac{a+c}{a+b+c+d}$; if $a/b = c/d$ or $a + b = c + d$.

13. $p^{10} \div p^9 = p$; no.

section 9–6, page 153.

1. $\binom{4}{4}(.3)^4(.7)^0 = .0081$

3. $\binom{5}{2}\left(\frac{1}{6}\right)^2\left(\frac{5}{6}\right)^3$, or, approximately, .161.

5. $1 - (1/2)^n > .98$ if $n \geqslant 6$.

7. $1 - (.95)^{30} - 1.5(.95)^{29}$, or approximately .447.

9. $15/64$; $15/63$

section 10–1, page 158.

1. $a\left(x - \dfrac{b}{3a}\right)^3 + b\left(x - \dfrac{b}{a}\right)^2 + c\left(x - \dfrac{b}{a}\right) + d = 0$

$ax^3 - bx^2 + \dfrac{b^2}{3a}x - \dfrac{b^3}{9a^2} + bx^2 - \dfrac{2b^2}{a}x + \dfrac{b^3}{a^2} + cx - \dfrac{bc}{a} + d = 0$

$ax^3 + \left(\dfrac{b^2}{3a} - \dfrac{2b^2}{a} + c\right)x - \dfrac{b^3}{9a^2} + \dfrac{b^3}{a^2} - \dfrac{bc}{a} + d = 0$

$x^3 + \dfrac{3ac - 5b^2}{3a^2}x + \dfrac{8b^3 - 9abc + 9a^2d}{9a^3} = 0$

$P = \dfrac{3ac - 5b^2}{3a^2}$ and $q = \dfrac{8b^3 - 9abc + 9a^2d}{9a^3}.$

section 10–3, page 161.

1. (a) $(-3, 11)$.   (b) $(-6\sqrt{3}, 5/3)$.   (c) $(-6, 2)$.   (d) $(4, 7)$.
(e) $(8, 11)$.   (f) $(1, -4\sqrt{3})$.

3. $(a, b)(1, 0) = (a \times 1 - b \times 0, a \times 0 + b \times 1) = (a, b)$.

5. (a) $\pi/2$, 1.   (b) π, 1.   (c) $\frac{3\pi}{2}$, 1.   (d) $\frac{5\pi}{4}$, $\sqrt{2}$.   (e) $\pi/3$, 2.

(f) $\frac{5\pi}{6}$, 2.

section 10–4, page 163.

1. $(a, b)(c, d) = (ac - bd, ad + bc)$, $(c, d)(a, b) = (ca - db, cb + da)$, and
$(ac - bd, ad + bc) = (ca - db, cb + da)$.

3. $(a, b) + (-a, -b) = (a + (-a), b + (-b)) = (0, 0)$

5. $(a, b) \left(\dfrac{a}{a^2 + b^2}, \dfrac{-b}{a^2 + b^2} \right) = \left(\dfrac{a^2}{a^2 + b^2} - \dfrac{-ab}{a^2 + b^2} + \dfrac{ba}{a^2 + b^2} \right)$
$= (1, 0)$

section 10–5, page 167.

1. *Part 1.* $z^1 = \cos \theta + i \sin \theta$
Part 2. Assume

$$(\cos \theta + i \sin \theta)^k = \cos k\theta + i \sin k\theta.$$

Then,

$$
\begin{aligned}
(\cos \theta + i \sin \theta)^{k+1} &= (\cos \theta + i \sin \theta)^k (\cos \theta + i \sin \theta) \\
&= (\cos k\theta + i \sin k\theta)(\cos \theta + i \sin \theta) \\
&= (\cos k\theta \cos \theta - \sin k\theta \sin \theta) \\
&\quad + i (\sin k\theta \cos \theta + \cos k\theta \sin \theta) \\
&= \cos (k\theta + \theta) + i \sin (k\theta + \theta) \\
&= \cos (k+1)\theta + i \sin (k+1)\theta.
\end{aligned}
$$

3. (a) $(3+i)^4 - 6(3+i)^3 + 7(3+i)^2 + 18(3+i) - 30 = 81 + 108i - 54 - 12i$
$+ 1 - 162 + 54 + 6i + 63 + 42i - 7 + 54 + 18i - 30 = 0$.

5. $z = a + 0i$ when $a \geqslant 0$; that is, non-negative reals.

7. $a = -29/26$, $b = 359/78$

section 10–6, page 169.

1. $-8i$.   **3.** $1024i$.   **5.** -64.   **7.** $32\sqrt{2} - 32i\sqrt{2}$.

9. $2^{1/4}(\cos 22.5° + i \sin 22.5°)$; $2^{1/4}(\cos 202.5° + i \sin 202.5°)$

11. $2^{1/2}(\cos 22.5° + i \sin 22.5°)$; $2^{1/2}(\cos 202.5° + i \sin 202.5°)$

13. $2^{1/3}(\cos 50° + i \sin 50°)$; $2^{1/3}(\cos 170° + i \sin 170°)$; $2^{1/3}(\cos 290° + i \sin 290°)$

15. $(\cos 67.5° + i \sin 67.5°)$; $(\cos 157.5° + i \sin 157.5°)$;
$(\cos 247.5° + i \sin 247.5°)$; $(\cos 337.5° + i \sin 337.5°)$

17. 3; $-(3/2) + (3i\sqrt{3}/2)$; $-(3/2) - (3i\sqrt{3}/2)$

section 11–1, page 174.

1. $\sqrt{450-9} + \sqrt{900} \neq 9$. $\sqrt{9} + \sqrt{36} = 9$.   Thus, $x_2 = 18$ is the only solution.

3. $x^2 - 5x + 6 = 0$

5. (a) $r_1 = 2, r_2 = 1/3$.   (b) $r_1 = (1/5) + (2/5^i)$, $r_2 = (1/5) - (2/5^i)$.

7. $r_1 = 1 - i$, $r_2 = -2 - i$

9. (a) 13.   (b) $\dfrac{58 + 5\sqrt{123}}{2}$.

11. $x = \pi/2 + 2k\pi$, k an integer.

13. $x = 3$

section 11–3, page 178.

1. $(x+1)(x-2)(2x+1)$

3. $(3x-2)(2x+1)(5x+3)$ or $30\left(x - \dfrac{2}{3}\right)\left(x + \dfrac{1}{2}\right)\left(x + \dfrac{3}{5}\right)$.

5. $x_1 = -2$, $x_2 = \dfrac{-1 + i\sqrt{3}}{2}$, $x_3 = \dfrac{-1 - i\sqrt{3}}{2}$

7. $x_1 = -1$, $x_2 - \dfrac{-101 + \sqrt{10{,}921}}{24}$, $x_3 = \dfrac{-101 - \sqrt{10{,}921}}{24}$

9. $x = \pi/6 + 2k\pi$ and $x = 5\pi/6 + 2k\pi$, k an integer.

11. $x_1 = 5/3$, $x_2 = (-1 + i\sqrt{3})/2$, $x_3 = (-1 - i\sqrt{3})/2$

13. $10^x = 1/2$, $10^x = 2$, $10^x = 1/5$. Thus,
$x_1 = -0.3010$, $x_2 = 0.3010$, $x_3 = -0.6990$.

15. $k = (-9 \pm 5\sqrt{43})/72$.   3 would have to be a factor of 11.

17. $x_1 = 4 + i\sqrt{2}$, $x_2 = 4 - i\sqrt{2}$, $x_3 = (3 + \sqrt{5})/2$, $x_4 = (3 - \sqrt{5})/2$

19. $x_1 = \arcsin 1/2$, $x_2 = \arcsin \sqrt{2}/2$, $x_3 = \arcsin -\sqrt{2}/2$

21. $x = \arctan -1$; that is, $x = 3\pi/4 + k\pi$, k an integer.

section 12–2, page 184.

1. (a) $d = \sqrt{85}$, $(-5/2, 4)$.   (b) $d = 5$, $(15/2, 5)$.
(c) $d = \sqrt{137}/3$, $(-1/18, 5/9)$.   (d) $d = \sqrt{67}$, $(3\sqrt{3}/2, 1)$.

3. (a) $-2/9$.   (b) $4/3$.   (c) $-4/7$.   (d) $-8\sqrt{3}/3$.

5. Let $A(-3, 4)$, $B(6, -2)$, $C(-6, 6)$ be the three points.   (a) Prove that
$M_{AB} = M_{BC}$; $-2/3 = -2/3$.   (b) Prove that $d_{CA} + d_{AB} = d_{CB}$;
$\sqrt{13} + \sqrt{117} = \sqrt{208}$, $\sqrt{13} + 3\sqrt{13} = 4\sqrt{13}$.

7. Let $(t, 0)$ be on the x-axis. Then,
$\sqrt{(t-1)^2 + 3^2} = \sqrt{(t-3)^2 + 5^2}$; $t = 6$. The point is $(6, 0)$.

9. $17/7, 37/7$ or $11/7, 33/7$.

11. $(0, 56/5)$

13. Use slopes or prove the diagonals bisect each other.

15. (a) A $(22/3, 6)$, B $(4, -4)$, C $(10, 4)$. $M_{AB} = 3$. $M_{AC} = -3/4$, $M_{BC} = 4/3$.

Since $M_{AC} = -1/M_{BC}$, $C = 90°$. $\tan B = \dfrac{3 - 4/3}{1 + 3\,(4/3)} = 1/3$.

$B \approx 26°34'$; $A \approx 63°26'$.

17. $(-37/7, 81/28)$

section 12–3, page 189.

1. (a) x − intercept − $(5, 0)$; y − intercept − $(0, 3)$; area − 15/2 square units.
(b) $(11/5, 0)$; $(0, -11/4)$; 121/40 square units.

3. (a) $x - 2y = 13$.
(c) $120x + 100y = -177$.
(b) $2x + 3y = -31$.
(d) $\sqrt{3}\,x - y = 3\sqrt{3} - 8$.

5. (a) $18x - 7y = -13$.
(c) $291x - 210y = 488$.
(b) $4x + 3y = 19$.
(d) $2x + 7y = 18$.

7. (a) $3x - 7y = -56$.
(c) $105x - 189y = 205$.
(b) $2x + 3y = 6$.

9. (a) $7x + 3y = -34$.
(c) $63x + 35y = 17$.
(b) $3x - 2y = -4$.

11. (a) $4x - 30y = 121$.   (b) $26x + 20y = -77$.   (c) $y = 12$.

15. $(-4613/625, 1684/625)$; $d = 34/25$

section 12–6, page 207.

1. (x, y) satisfies the first equation if and only if the point (x, y) is on the ellipse in Fig. 12–20. Squaring both sides and simplifying yields second equation.

3.

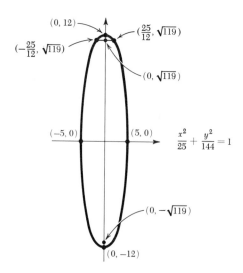

$(0, 12)$ $\left(\dfrac{25}{12}, \sqrt{119}\right)$

$\left(-\dfrac{25}{12}, \sqrt{119}\right)$

$(0, \sqrt{119})$

$(-5, 0)$ $(5, 0)$ $\dfrac{x^2}{25} + \dfrac{y^2}{144} = 1$

$(0, -\sqrt{119})$

$(0, -12)$

5. $\dfrac{x^2}{4} + \dfrac{y^2}{\left(\dfrac{5}{3}\right)^2} = 1$

$\left(-\dfrac{\sqrt{11}}{3}, \dfrac{25}{18}\right)$

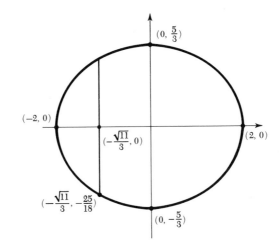

7. $\dfrac{x^2}{3^2} + \dfrac{y^2}{2^2} = 1$

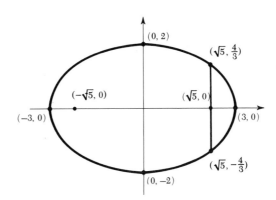

9. $x^2 + \dfrac{y^2}{4^2} = 1$

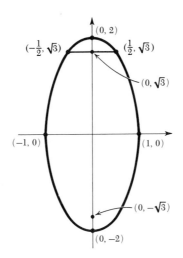

11. (a) Note: $\dfrac{x^2}{a^2} + \dfrac{y^2}{a^2 - c^2} = 1$. Solve for y^2 and substitute.

(b) $\dfrac{a}{c} > 1$

13. $\dfrac{x^2}{25} + \dfrac{y^2}{9} = 1$ **15.** $\dfrac{x^2}{36} + \dfrac{y^2}{20} = 1$ **17.** $\left(\dfrac{x+5}{3}\right)^2 + \left(\dfrac{y-1}{2}\right)^2 = 1$

19. $\sqrt{(x-11)^2 + (y-11)^2} + \sqrt{(x-3)^2 + (y-3)^2} = 10$

section 12–7, page 211.

1. See Ex. 1, p. 4.

3. $\dfrac{x^2}{9} - \dfrac{y^2}{16} = 1$

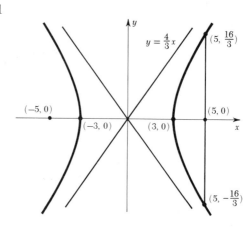

5. $\dfrac{y^2}{8^2} - \dfrac{x^2}{15^2} = 1$

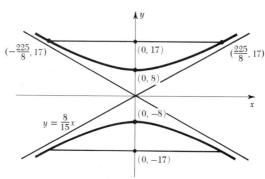

7. $\dfrac{x^2}{1/2} - y^2 = 1$

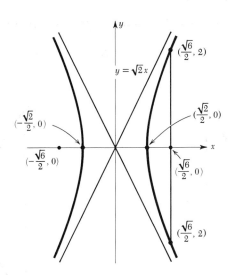

9. $\dfrac{x^2}{2^2} - y^2 = 1$

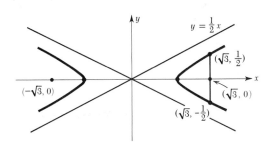

11. $\dfrac{y^2}{1/9} - x^2 = 1$

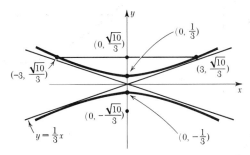

13. $\dfrac{x^2}{36} - \dfrac{y^2}{28} = 1$ 15. $x^2 - y^2 = 4$

section 12–8, page 213.

1. Square both sides of (1) and simplify to obtain (2).

3. $y^2 = 8x$ **5.** $y^2 = -32x$

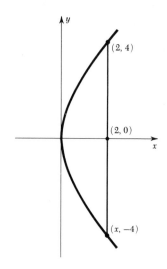

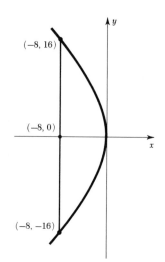

7. $y^2 = x$ **9.** $x^2 = 20y$

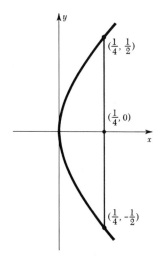

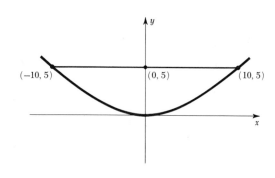

11. $x^2 = -36y$

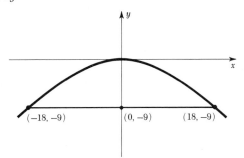

(−18, −9)   (0, −9)   (18, −9)

13. $(y-4)^2 = 8(x+3)$ 15. $(x-5)^2 = 12(y-5)$

section 12–9, page 218.

1. $\sqrt{89}$ 3. $(\sqrt{149})/3$

7. $A(5, 7, 13)$, $B(-1, 6, 8)$, $C(3, 87)$. Consider $d_{AB} = \sqrt{62}$, $d_{BC} = \sqrt{21}$, $d_{AC} = \sqrt{41}$, $(d_{BC})^2 + (d_{AC})^2 = (d_{AB})^2$.

9. (a) S is the plane perpendicular to the line segment with P and Q as end points passing through the midpoint of the segment, $8x + 10y - 4z = 67$.
(b) $(4, 11/2, 5)$.   (c) yes.

11. $8x + 5y - 9z = 1$

section 13–1, page 225.

1. $1, 1, a^2 + b^2, x^2 - 5x + 11$

3. (i) $x = 57/58$, $y = -16/58$

(ii) Not applicable: $\begin{vmatrix} 3 & 9 \\ 1 & 3 \end{vmatrix} = 0$

(iii) $x = 0$, $y = 0$
(iv) $x = -763/3739$, $y = 3835/3739$

5. (i) $\begin{vmatrix} 1001 & 99 \\ 999 & 101 \end{vmatrix} = \begin{vmatrix} 1000+1 & 100-1 \\ 1000-1 & 100+1 \end{vmatrix}$

$= \begin{vmatrix} 1000 & 100 \\ 1000 & 100 \end{vmatrix} + \begin{vmatrix} 1 & 100 \\ -1 & 100 \end{vmatrix} + \begin{vmatrix} 1000 & -1 \\ 1000 & 1 \end{vmatrix} + \begin{vmatrix} 1 & -1 \\ -1 & 1 \end{vmatrix}$
$= 0 + 200 + 2000 + 0 = 2200$

(ii) $\begin{vmatrix} -450 & 360 \\ 15 & -8 \end{vmatrix} =$ (Add $30 \times R_2$ to R_1)

$\begin{vmatrix} 0 & 120 \\ 15 & -8 \end{vmatrix} = -1800$

7. $\begin{vmatrix} x_1 & y_1 \\ x_2 & y_2 \end{vmatrix}$

9. If elementary vector theory is permitted, we have:
$(x_1, y_1) \cdot (a, b) = (x_1, y_1) \cdot (c, d) = 0 \leftrightarrow (a, b) = k(c, d) \leftrightarrow a = kc,$
$b = kd \leftrightarrow a = kcd, \; bd = kcd \leftrightarrow ad = bc \leftrightarrow ad - bc = 0 \leftrightarrow \begin{vmatrix} a & b \\ c & d \end{vmatrix} = 0.$

(i) Assume (x_1, y_1) is a solution, $x_1 \neq 0$. Therefore
$$ax_1 + by_1 = 0 \atop cx_1 + dy_1 = 0 \; {\to} \; {adx_1 + bdy_1 = 0 \atop bcx_1 + bdy_1 = 0}$$
$$\to adx_1 - bcx_1 = 0 \to (ad - bc)x_1 = 0.$$
Since $x_1 \neq 0$, $ad - bc = \begin{vmatrix} a & b \\ c & d \end{vmatrix} = 0$

(ii) Assume $\begin{vmatrix} a & b \\ c & d \end{vmatrix} = 0$; then $ad - bc = 0$. If $a = b = c = d = 0$, then any pair (x, y) is a solution. Therefore, assume $d \neq 0$; then $(d, -c) \neq (0, 0)$, $a(d) + b(-c) = 0$, and $c(d) + d(-c) = 0$.

11. (i) $b_1 \begin{vmatrix} b_2 & c_2 \\ b_3 & c_3 \end{vmatrix} - b_2 \begin{vmatrix} b_1 & c_1 \\ b_3 & c_3 \end{vmatrix} + b_3 \begin{vmatrix} b_1 & c_1 \\ b_2 & c_2 \end{vmatrix}$
$= b_1(b_2 c_3 - b_3 c_2) - b_2(b_1 c_3 - b_3 c_1) + b_2(b_1 c_2 - b_2 c_1)$
$= b_1 b_2 c_3 - b_1 b_3 c_2 - b_1 b_2 c_3 + b_2 b_3 c_1 + b_1 b_3 c_2 - b_2 b_3 c_1$
$= (b_1 b_2 c_3 - b_1 b_2 c_3) + (b_2 b_3 c_1 - b_2 b_3 c_1) + (b_1 b_3 c_2 - b_1 b_3 c_2) = 0$

(ii) $c_1 \begin{vmatrix} b_2 & c_2 \\ b_3 & c_3 \end{vmatrix} - c_2 \begin{vmatrix} b_1 & c_1 \\ b_3 & c_3 \end{vmatrix} + c_3 \begin{vmatrix} b_1 & c_1 \\ b_2 & c_2 \end{vmatrix}$
$= c_1(b_2 c_3 - b_3 c_2) - c_2(b_1 c_3 - b_3 c_1) + c_3(b_1 c_2 - b_2 c_1)$
$= b_2 c_1 c_3 - b_3 c_1 c_2 - b_1 c_2 c_3 + b_3 c_1 c_2 + b_1 c_2 c_3 - b_2 c_1 c_3$
$= (b_2 c_1 c_3 - b_2 c_1 c_3) + (b_3 c_1 c_2 - b_3 c_1 c_2) + (b_1 c_2 c_3 - b_1 c_2 c_3) = 0$

section 13–2, page 230.

1. $1, 70, 10, -abc, a^3 + b^3 + c^3 - 3abc$

3. (a) $x = 58/131$; $y = 91/131$; $z = 48/131$.   (b) $x = -7/5$; $y = 9/5$; $z = -12/5$.

(c) Not applicable: $\begin{vmatrix} 4 & 4 & -1 \\ 3 & -1 & 2 \\ 1 & 5 & -3 \end{vmatrix} = 0.$

5. $x(y_1 - y_2) - y(x_1 - x_2) + (x_1 y_2 - x_2 y_1) = 0$. Considering x_1, x_2, y_1, y_2 constants, this is a linear equation in x and y. Substituting, we find that (x_1, y_1) and (x_2, y_2) are solutions.

section 13–3, page 239.

1–8. Apply direct computation to each general case.

9. $\begin{vmatrix} a & b & c \\ b & c & a \\ c & a & b \end{vmatrix} = \begin{vmatrix} a+b+c & a+b+c & a+b+c \\ b & c & a \\ c & a & b \end{vmatrix} = (a+b+c) \begin{vmatrix} 1 & 1 & 1 \\ b & c & a \\ c & a & b \end{vmatrix}$

Expanding by the first row:

$(a + b + c)([bc - a^2] - [b^2 - ac] + [ab - c^2])$
$$= (a + b + c)(ac + bc + ab - a^2 - b^2 - c^2).$$

11. $\begin{vmatrix} x-y & y-z & z-x \\ y-z & z-x & x-y \\ z-x & x-y & y-z \end{vmatrix}$ $\quad$ (adding row 3 to row 2) $\quad = \begin{vmatrix} x-y & y-z & z-x \\ y-x & z-y & x-z \\ z-x & x-y & y-z \end{vmatrix}$

$= (-1) \begin{vmatrix} x-y & y-z & z-x \\ x-y & y-z & z-x \\ z-x & x-y & y-z \end{vmatrix} = 0,$ since row $1 =$ row 2.

13. $\begin{vmatrix} 1 & 1 & 1 \\ a & b & c \\ a^3 & b^3 & c^3 \end{vmatrix} = \begin{vmatrix} 1 & 0 & 0 \\ a & b-a & c-a \\ a^3 & b^3-a^3 & c^3-a^3 \end{vmatrix} = \begin{vmatrix} b-a & c-a \\ b^3-a^3 & c^3-a^3 \end{vmatrix}$ (expand by row 1)

$\qquad = (b-a)(c-a) \begin{vmatrix} 1 & 1 \\ b^2+ab+a^2 & c^2+ac+a^2 \end{vmatrix}$

$\qquad = (b-a)(c-a)(c^2+ac+a^2-b^2-ab-a^2)$

$\qquad = (b-a)(c-a)([c-b][c+b]+a[c-b])$

$\qquad = (b-a)(c-a)(c-b)(a+b+c)$

15. By property $8(i)$, the first equation is 0. By $8(ii)$, the other two equations are 0.

section 13-4, page 248.

1. (a) $\{(-131/63, -53/63, 35/63)\}$—three planes intersecting in one point.
   (b) $\emptyset$—two planes intersecting in a line parallel to the third.
   (c) $\{(t, (4-122t)/13, (-5-10t)/13)|t$ is a real number$\}$—three planes intersecting in one line.
   (d) $\emptyset$—two planes intersecting in a line parallel to the third.
   (e) $\{(0,0,0)\}$—three planes intersecting at the origin.
   (f) $\{(x, y, z)|x+y-z=0\}$—three coinciding planes through the origin.
   (g) $\{(x, y, z)|x=0, y+z=0\}$—three planes intersecting in the line $y=-z$ in YZ plane.
   (h) $\{(x, y, z)|x=1/3, y+z=2/3\}$—three planes intersecting in a line.
   (i) $\emptyset$—two parallel planes and a transverse plane.
   (j) $\{(-1, t, t-5)|t$ is a real number$\}$—two coinciding planes; third intersecting in a line.

3. Let (x, y, z) be any solution to equations (1). Then $u=x-x_1, v=y-y_1,$ $w=z-z_1$ satisfies (2). Hence $x=u+x_1, y=v+y_1, z=w+z_1.$

5. The three planes coincide.

7. (a) $\{(x, y, z, t)|x=r, y=(12-7r)/5, z=-(3+2r)/5, t=(4r-4)/5, r$ real$\}$.
   (b) $\{(29/19, 15/19, 26/19)\}$.
   (c) $\{(x, y, z, t)|x=r, y=s, z=(-15r+5s)/2, t=(-7r+s)/2\}$.
   (d) $\{(-1, 2, r, -4, 3-r) \begin{vmatrix} r, s \text{ real} \\ r \text{ is real} \end{vmatrix}\}.$

section 13-5, page 253.

1. (a) -4.   (b) 21.   (c) 1.

3. Subtract row 1 from each row; expand by column 1; factor binomial out of each row; go back to (a).

5. $(a+b+c+d)(a-c)[(a-b)(c-d)+(b+c-c-a)(c-d)]$

section 14–2, page 260.

1. (a) $[-5, 8]$.   (b) $[9, -2]$.   (c) $\sqrt{13}$.   (d) $\sqrt{74}$.

3. $\vec{A} + \vec{B} = [a_1, b_1] + [a_2, b_2] = [a_1 + a_2, b_1 + b_2]$
$$= [a_2 + a_1, b_2 + b_1] = [a_2, b_2] + [a_1, b_1] = \vec{B} + \vec{A}$$

5. $|C \cdot \vec{A}| = |C[a_1, b_1]| = |[ca_1, cb_1]|$
$$= \sqrt{c^2 a_1{}^2 + c^2 b_1{}^2} = \sqrt{c^2(a_1{}^2 + b_1{}^2)} = c\sqrt{a_1{}^2 + b_1{}^2} = c|\vec{A}|$$

section 14–2, page 264.

1. (a) $|\vec{PQ}| = \sqrt{4^2 + 5^2} = \sqrt{41}$.   (b) $|\vec{PR}| = \sqrt{1^2 + 12^2} = \sqrt{145}$.

(c) $\cos \theta \dfrac{\vec{PQ} \cdot \vec{PR}}{|\vec{PQ}||\vec{PR}|} = \dfrac{[-5, 4] \cdot [-1, -12]}{\sqrt{41} \sqrt{145}} = \dfrac{5 - 48}{\sqrt{41} \sqrt{145}} = \dfrac{-43}{\sqrt{5945}} \approx 0.558$

(d) $\vec{RQ} \cdot \vec{RP} = [-4, 16] \cdot [1, 12] = 188$

3. $[x, y] = [2 + 7t, 5 + 3t]$ implies $x = 2 + 7t$ and $y = 5 + 3t$. Thus, $3x - 6 = 21t$ and $7y - 35 = 21t$. Consequently $3x - 6 = 7y - 35$, and $3x - 7y = -29$ is the equation of the line.

5. The side opposite $\vec{B}$ in the parallelogram formed with $\vec{A}$ and $\vec{B}$ as sides.

7. The line segment with the tips of vectors $\vec{A}$ and $\vec{B}$ as end points.

9. $[1, 3] = s[3, 8] + t[5, -2]$; $[1, 3] = [3s + 5t, 8s - 2t]$; thus, $1 = 3s + 5t$ and $3 = 8s - 2t$. Solving the two equations $s = 17/46$, $t = -1/46$.

section 14–3, page 266.

1. (a) $\vec{A} \cdot \vec{B} = [2, 1, 3] \cdot [-2, -1, 2] = -4 - 1 + 6 = 1$

(b) $|\vec{A}| = \sqrt{14}$, $\cos \alpha = 2/\sqrt{14}$, $\cos \beta = 1/\sqrt{14}$, $\cos \delta = 3/\sqrt{14}$

(c) $|\vec{B}| = 3$, $\cos \alpha = -2/3$, $\cos \beta = -1/3$, $\cos \delta = 2/3$. Thus,
$$\alpha = 131° 50', \quad \beta = 109° 30', \quad \delta = 48° 10'$$

(d) $\cos \theta = \vec{A} \cdot \vec{B}/|\vec{A}||\vec{B}| = 1/(3\sqrt{14})$. Thus, $\theta \approx 84° 20'$

3. $\vec{A} = [1, 3, 8], \vec{B} = [2, 5, 1]$, $\cos \theta = \dfrac{\vec{A} \cdot \vec{B}}{|\vec{A}||\vec{B}|} = \dfrac{25}{\sqrt{74} \sqrt{30}} = \dfrac{25}{2\sqrt{555}}$

5. Geometric interpretation. The lengths of the diagonals of a rectangle are equal.

$|\vec{A} - \vec{B}|^2 = (\vec{A} - \vec{B})(\vec{A} - \vec{B}) = \vec{A} \cdot \vec{A} - 2\vec{A} \cdot \vec{B} + \vec{B} \cdot \vec{B}$

$|\vec{A} + \vec{B}|^2 = (\vec{A} + \vec{B})(\vec{A} + \vec{B}) = \vec{A} \cdot \vec{A} + 2\vec{A} \cdot \vec{B} + \vec{B} \cdot \vec{B}$

$|\vec{A} - \vec{B}|^2 = |\vec{A} + \vec{B}|^2$ if and only if $-\vec{A} \cdot \vec{B} = \vec{A} \cdot \vec{B}$; that is, $\vec{A} \cdot \vec{B} = 0$

7. Let $P(p_1, p_2, p_3)$ and $Q(q_1, q_2\ q_3)$ be two points in the plane. Thus, $ap_1 + bp_2 + cp_3 = d$ and $aq_1 + bq_2 + cq_3 = d$. Hence, $(p_1 - q_1)a + (p_2 - q_2)b + (p_3 - q_3)c = 0$. But $\vec{QP} = [p_1 - q_1, p_2 - q_2, p_3 - q_3]$; therefore, $\vec{QP} \cdot [a, b, c] = 0$ and the vectors are perpendicular. We conclude the vector $[a, b, c]$ is perpendicular to the plane containing the vector $\vec{QP}$.

section 15–3, page 279.

1. 0   **3.** $\dfrac{v(x) - v(t)}{x - t}$ is the average acceleration between times

t and x. $v'(t)$ is the acceleration at time t.   **5.** $-\dfrac{1}{25}$

7. (a) $f'(x) = 3x^2$ (b) $f'(x) = \dfrac{1}{2} x^{-1/2}$ (c) $f'(x) = \dfrac{1}{3} x^{-2/3}$

9. (i) 2.71828   **11.** 2   **13.** 73

section 15–4, page 288.

1. 17   **3.** 10   **5.** 27   **7.** 3
9. Given $\epsilon > 0$, show that $|(3x + 2) - 8| < \epsilon$ whenever $|x - 2| < \epsilon/3 = \delta$.

11. −3   **13.** Yes   **15.** $x = 5, -4$ **17.** $\dfrac{\sqrt{57}}{3} = t$ **19.** $\dfrac{3}{4} = t$

21. $\dfrac{4}{3} = t$ **23.** Let $\lim\limits_{x \to t} \dfrac{f(x)}{g(x)} = L$, a real number.

$$\text{Then } \lim_{x \to t} f(x) = \lim_{x \to t} \frac{f(x)}{g(x)} \cdot \lim_{x \to t} g(x) = L \cdot 0 = 0.$$

section 15–5, page 291.

1. $f'(x) = 36x^2 + 5$ **3.** $f'(x) = 20x^3 - 26x$ **5.** $f'(x) = \dfrac{5}{2} x^4 - 42$

7. $f'(x) = 3x^2 - 12x + 7$ **9.** $f'(x) = 0$ **11.** $f'(x) = 15(5x + 1)^2$
13. $f'(x) = 4x(x^2 + 4)$ **15.** $f'(x) = 3 > 0$ for all x
17. $f'(x) = 0$ for all x

19. $f'(x) = 3x^2 - 6 \begin{cases} > 0 \text{ if } |x| > \sqrt{2} \\ = 0 \text{ if } |x| = \sqrt{2} \\ < 0 \text{ if } |x| < \sqrt{2} \end{cases}$

21. $h = f - g = f + (-1) \cdot g$.
Therefore, $h' = f' + [(-1) \cdot g]' = f' + (-1) \cdot g' = f' - g'$.

section 15–6, page 293.

1. $f'(x) = 4x^3 + 6x + 6$
3. $f'(x) = 2(x^3 + 7x^2 + 3x + 11)(3x^2 + 14x + 3)$
5. $f'(x) = 3(3x^5 + 7x^2 - 2)^2 (15x^4 + 14x)$
7. $f'(x) = 5x^4 + 8x^3 + 36x^2 + 26x + 33$
9. $f'(x) = 3(x^3 - 5x + 1)^2 (3x^2 - 5)$
11. $f'(x) = 30x^2 - 78x + 20$
13. (a) Express h as $u(v(w(z)))$ and use Theorem 15–9.
  (b) $h'(x) = 2(3x^2 + 11)(5x - 11)(x^3 + 7)$
    $+ (2x + 3)(6x)(5x - 11)(x^3 + 7)$
    $+ (2x + 3)(3x^2 + 11)(5)(x^3 + 7)$
    $+ (2x + 3)(3x^2 + 11)(5x - 11)(3x^2)$
  (c) Use part (a) where $u = v = w = z$.
  (d) $h'(x) = 4(3x^3 + 7x + 2)(9x^2 + 7)$

15. If $n = 1$, $h(x) = f(x)$. Therefore $h'(x) = 1 \cdot [f(x)]^0 \cdot f'(x) = f'(x)$.
Assume $[f(x)^k]' = k \cdot [f(x)]^{k-1} \cdot f'(x)$. Let $h(x) = [f(x)]^{k+1}$
$= [f(x)]^k \cdot f(x)$. Therefore, $h'(x) = [f(x)]^k f'(x) + f(x) \cdot k[f(x)]^{k-1} \cdot f'(x)$
$= (k + 1)[f(x)]^k \cdot f'(x)$. In Exercise 15, let $h(x) = [f(x)]^n$
for $f(x) = x$.

section 15–7, page 295.

1. $f'(x) = -x^{-2}$ **3.** $f'(x) = -2x^{-3}$ **5.** $f'(x) = -\dfrac{(3x^2 + 2)}{(x^3 + 2x + 1)^2}$

7. $f'(2) = \dfrac{50}{121}$

9. $f'(x)$ is > 0 if $x \in (-\infty, -9) \cup (-1, \infty)$
$= 0$ if $x \in \{-9, -1\}$
< 0 if $x \in (-9, -1)$ and $x \neq -5$.

11. True for $p \geqslant 0$. If $p < 0$, $-p > 0$ and $h(x) = \dfrac{1}{[g(x)]^{-p}}$. Therefore,
$h'(x) = \dfrac{p[g(x)]^{-p-1}g'(x)}{[g(x)]^{-2p}} = p[g(x)]^{p-1}g'(x)$.

13. $f'(x) = \dfrac{-13}{(2x - 1)^2}$ **15.** $\dfrac{(-4)(x^2 + x + 2)(2x + 1)}{(x^2 + 2)^3}$

section 15–8, page 298.

1. Let $f(x) = x^{p'}$. Then, $h(x) = f(g(x))$ and $h'(x) = f'(g(x)) \cdot g'(x) = p[g(x)]^{p-1} \cdot g'(x)$.

3. $t'(x) = (x^2 + 1)^{1/2}(4x^2 + 1)$ **5.** $f'(x) = 32x(2x^2 + 1)^7$

7. $h'(x) = \dfrac{1}{2(x + 1)^{1/2}(x + 2)^{3/2}}$ **9.** $h'(x) = 2 \cdot \dfrac{x^2 + x - 1}{(2x + 1)^2}$

11. $g'(x) = (12x^4 + 2x)(3x^3 + 1)^{-1/3}$

13. $f'(x) = 2(7x^2 + x + 7)/(x^2 + 1)^{1/2} + (98x + 14x^2)/(x^2 + 1)$

15. $f'(x) = \dfrac{4}{3}(2x + (x^2 + 1)^{1/2})^{1/3}\left(2 + \dfrac{x}{x^2 + 1}\right)$

section 15–9, page 302.

1. $f^{(1)}(x) = 6x^5 - 15x^2 + 12x - 2$ **3.** $y^{(1)} = 3x - 12x + 11$
    $f^{(2)}(x) = 30x^4 - 30x + 12$ $y^{(2)} = 6x - 12$
    $f^{(3)}(x) = 120x^3 - 30$ $y^{(3)} = 6$

5. $g^{(1)}(x) = \dfrac{4}{3}(4x+3)^{-1/3}$

$g^{(2)}(x) = -\dfrac{16}{9}(4x+3)^{-4/3}$

$g^{(3)}(x) = \dfrac{256}{27}(4x+3)^{-2/3}$

7. $G^{(1)}(u) = \dfrac{1}{2}(u+1)^{-1/2}(3u+2)$

$G^{(2)}(u) = \dfrac{1}{4}(u+1)^{-3/2}(3u+4)$

$G^{(3)}(u) = -\dfrac{3}{8}(u+1)^{-5/2}(u+2)$

9. $F^{(1)}(x) = nx^{n-1}$
$F^{(2)}(x) = n(n-1)x^{n-2}$
$F^{(3)}(x) = n(n-1)(n-2)x^{n-3}$

11. $y'(x) = x^{-1/2}$

$y''(x) = -\dfrac{1}{2}x^{-3/2}$

13. $y' = \dfrac{x}{2\sqrt{x^2+16}}{}^{-1/2}$

$y'' = 8(x^2+16)^{-3/2}$

15. $y' = -\dfrac{3x^2+2x+33}{(3x+1)^2}$

$y'' = \dfrac{-196}{(3x+1)^3}$

17. Defines two functions, $y_1(x) = 2-x$ and $y_2(x) = -2-x$ such that $y'_1(x) = y'_2(x) = -1$ for all x.

section 15–11, page 307.

1. Increasing. Concave down: $(0, \infty)$.
Decreasing. Concave up: $(-\infty, 0)$. Inflection point: $(0, 0)$.

3. Increasing. $(-\infty, 0) \cup (2, \infty)$. Decreasing: $(0, 2)$.
Concave down: $(-\infty, 1)$. Concave up: $(1, \infty)$.
Inflection point: $(1, -2)$.

5. Increasing. $\left(-\infty, \dfrac{-5-\sqrt{73}}{6}\right) \cup \left(\dfrac{-5+\sqrt{73}}{6}, \infty\right)$.

Decreasing. $\left(\dfrac{-5-\sqrt{73}}{6}, \dfrac{-5+\sqrt{73}}{6}\right)$.

Concave down: $\left(-\infty, -\dfrac{5}{6}\right)$. Concave up: $\left(-\dfrac{5}{6}, \infty\right)$.

Inflection point: $\left(-\dfrac{5}{6}, \dfrac{539}{54}\right)$.

7. Increasing. $(-\infty, 0) \cup \left(\dfrac{7}{6}, \infty\right)$. Decreasing. $\left(0, \dfrac{7}{6}\right)$.

Concave down: $\left(-\infty, \dfrac{7}{12}\right)$. Concave up: $\left(\dfrac{7}{12}, \infty\right)$.

Inflection point: $\left(\dfrac{7}{12}, \dfrac{343}{5184}\right)$.

9. $-\dfrac{1}{8}$ **11.** $\dfrac{1}{5}$

section 15–12, page 313.

1. (a) $\{x|x < -1\}$, $\{x|x > 6\}$ (b) $-1 < x < 6$

 (c) $\left(\dfrac{5}{2}, \dfrac{-299}{4}\right)$ (d) $\{x|x > 5/2\}$ (e) $\{x|x < 5/2\}$

 (f) $f(6)$ (g) $f(-1)$ (h) none   (i) none

3. (a) $\{x|x < -5/3\}$, $\{x|x > 1/2\}$ (b) $-5/3 < x < 1/2$

 (c) $\left(\dfrac{7}{12}, f\left(\dfrac{7}{12}\right)\right)$ (d) $\{x|x > 7/12\}$ (e) $\{x|x < 7/12\}$

 (f) $f(1/2)$ (g) $f(-5/3)$ (h) none   (i) none

5. (a) $x < -\sqrt{2}$, $x > \sqrt{2}$ (b) $0 < x < \sqrt{2}$, $-\sqrt{2}, < x < 0$
 (c) none   (d) $x > 0$ (e) $x < 0$ (f) $f(\sqrt{2})$ (g) $f(-\sqrt{2})$
 (h) none   (i) none

7. (a) $3 < x < 4$ (b) $x > 4$ (c) none   (d) none
 (e) $x > 3$ (f) $f(3)$ (g) $f(4)$ (h) $f(4)$ (i) none

9. (a) $x < -11/3$, $x > -11/3$ (b) $\varnothing$ (c) none   (d) $x < -11/3$
 (e) $x > -11/3$ (f) none   (g) none   (h) none   (i) none

11. (a) $x < -1/3$, $x > 29/9$ (b) $-1/3 < x < 29/9$

 (c) $\left(\dfrac{13}{9}, f\left(\dfrac{13}{9}\right)\right)$ (d) $x > \dfrac{13}{9}$ (e) $x < \dfrac{13}{9}$ (f) $f\left(\dfrac{29}{9}\right)$

 (g) $f(-1/3)$ (h) none   (i) none

13. Row to a point on shore that is $\sqrt{3}$ mi. from closest point on shore, then walk to destination:

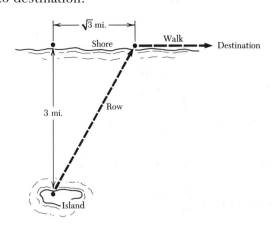

15. Radius, $\dfrac{R\sqrt{6}}{3}$; height, $\dfrac{2R\sqrt{3}}{2}$.

section 15–14, page 319.

1. $dy = 3x^2 dx$ **3.** $dy = (x + 3)^{-1/2}(2x^2 + 3)\ dx$
5. (a) 27.324 (b) 27.325297728 **7.** (a) $5.0267 \approx \sqrt[3]{127}$
(b) $33.04 \approx (2.013)^5$ **9.** 3.24

section 15–15, page 322.

1. 23.99 mph. **3.** $\dfrac{26}{25} \cdot \left(\dfrac{2}{3\pi}\right)^{1/3}$ **5.** $75\pi\ \dfrac{\text{sq. ft.}}{\text{sec.}}$

7. $\dfrac{25}{72}\dfrac{\text{in.}}{\text{sec.}}$ **9.** $8 \cdot 15 - 4.05\pi$

section 15–16, page 324.

1 and 3. Use differentiation properties in section 15.

5. $\dfrac{3}{5} x^{5/3} + C$ **7.** $x^3 - 3x^2 + 7x + C$ **9.** $2x^4 - 2x^3 + 11x + C$

11. $\dfrac{1}{4} (3x + 5)^4 + C$ **13.** $\dfrac{1}{5} (7x - 3)^5 + C$ **15.** $\dfrac{1}{5} (x^3 - 2)^5 + C$

17. $\dfrac{5}{252} (6x^3 + 11)^{14/5}$ **19.** $\dfrac{3}{16} (4x^2 + 2x + 11)^{8/3}$

section 16–1, page 330.

1. (a) 84 (b) 98 (c) $42 + 49\ \dfrac{n - 1}{n}$ (d) $42 + 49\ \dfrac{n + 1}{n}$

(e) For large n, $\dfrac{n - 1}{n}$ and $\dfrac{n + 1}{n}$ are close to 1. Both $L(P, f)$ and

$U(P,f)$, therefore, are close to $42 + 49 = 91$.

3. Show that $U(P, f) = \sum\limits_{k=1}^{n} \left(2 + k'\dfrac{4}{n}\right)^2 \left(\dfrac{4}{n}\right)$. Using the summation prop-

erties to simplify will give the desired result.

section 16–3, page 336.

1. 0. $f(x) = x^3$ is an "odd" function ($f(-x) = -f(x)$) so that its integral

over any interval $[-a, a]$ is zero, since $\displaystyle\int_{-a}^{0} f = -\int_{0}^{a} f$, as is geometri-

cally evident.

3. $\dfrac{44}{3}$ 5. $\dfrac{7}{8}$ 7. $-\dfrac{9106}{7}$ 9. $\dfrac{363}{10}$ 11. $\dfrac{7}{3}$ 13. 324

15. $\displaystyle\int_{-a}^{a} f(x) = \int_{-a}^{0} f(x) + \int_{0}^{a} f(x) = \int_{-a}^{0} f(-x) + \int_{0}^{a} f(x).$

Let $P(x)$ be an antiderivative of $f(x)$ and show that $-P(-x)$ is an anti-derivative of $f(-x)$. Then

$$\int_{-a}^{0} f(-x) = [-P(-0)] - [-P(-(-a))] = P(a) - P(0) = \int_{0}^{a} f(x).$$

Therefore, $\displaystyle\int_{-a}^{a} f(x) = 2\int_{0}^{a} f(x).$

17. $\dfrac{1}{6}$ 19. 36   21. $\dfrac{1}{2}$ 23. 36   25. $\dfrac{50}{3}$

section 16–4, page 341.

1. $\tan x \sec x$ 3. $-\csc x^2$ 5. $\sin 2x - \dfrac{\cos x}{2\sqrt{1 - \sin x}}$

7. $3 \sec^2 3x$ 9. $-3 \sin 6x$ 11. $-\sin(\sin x) \cdot \cos x$ 13. 0

15. $-\dfrac{3}{4} \sin^2 2x + \cos^4 x$ 17. 2   19. $\dfrac{\sin^4 x}{4} + C$ 21. $\dfrac{\tan 3x}{3} + C$

23. $-\dfrac{2}{3}(1 + \cos^2 x)^{3/2}$ 25. $-\sec x$ 27. $32(27 - \sqrt{3})/135$

29. $2\sqrt{1 + \sec^2} + C$ 31. See first page of this section.

section 16–5, page 345.

1. Max: $x = \dfrac{3\pi}{4}$. Min: $\dfrac{7\pi}{4}$. Inflection: $x = \dfrac{\pi}{4}, \dfrac{5\pi}{4}$.

Concave up: $\left(0, \dfrac{\pi}{4}\right) \cup \left(\dfrac{5\pi}{4}, 2\pi\right)$. Concave down: $\left(\dfrac{\pi}{4}, \dfrac{5\pi}{4}\right)$.

3. Max: $x = \pi$. Min: $x = 0$. Inflection: $x = 0, \pi$. Concave down: $(0, \pi)$.

5. Max: $x = \pi$. Min: $x = 0$. Inflection: $x = \dfrac{\pi}{2}$.

Concave up: $\left(0, \dfrac{\pi}{2}\right)$. Concave down: $\left(\dfrac{\pi}{2}, \pi\right)$.

7. $\pi - 2 \arctan 2$ $(\approx .90)$ 9. 2   11. $\sqrt{3} - 1$

13. 0.47943; error $< .00001$.

TABLE 1. FOUR PLACE LOGARITHMS

	Mantissas										Proportional Parts								
N	0	1	2	3	4	5	6	7	8	9	1	2	3	4	5	6	7	8	9
10	0000	0043	0086	0128	0170	0212	0253	0294	0334	0374	4	8	12	17	21	25	29	33	37
11	0414	0453	0492	0531	0569	0607	0645	0682	0719	0755	4	8	11	15	19	23	26	30	34
12	0792	0828	0864	0899	0934	0969	1004	1038	1072	1106	3	7	10	14	17	21	24	28	31
13	1139	1173	1206	1239	1271	1303	1335	1367	1399	1430	3	6	10	13	16	19	23	26	29
14	1461	1492	1523	1553	1584	1614	1644	1673	1703	1732	3	6	9	12	15	18	21	24	27
15	1761	1790	1818	1847	1875	1903	1931	1959	1987	2014	3	6	8	11	14	17	20	22	25
16	2041	2068	2095	2122	2148	2175	2201	2227	2253	2279	3	5	8	11	13	16	18	21	24
17	2304	2330	2355	2380	2405	2430	2455	2480	2504	2529	2	5	7	10	12	15	17	20	22
18	2553	2577	2601	2625	2648	2672	2695	2718	2742	2765	2	5	7	9	12	14	16	19	21
19	2788	2810	2833	2856	2878	2900	2923	2945	2967	2989	2	4	7	9	11	13	16	18	20
20	3010	3032	3054	3075	3096	3118	3139	3160	3181	3201	2	4	6	8	11	13	15	17	19
21	3222	3243	3263	3284	3304	3324	3345	3365	3385	3404	2	4	6	8	10	12	14	16	18
22	3424	3444	3464	3483	3502	3522	3541	3560	3579	3598	2	4	6	8	10	12	14	16	17
23	3617	3636	3655	3674	3692	3711	3729	3747	3766	3784	2	4	6	7	9	11	13	15	17
24	3802	3820	3838	3856	3874	3892	3909	3927	3945	3962	2	4	5	7	9	11	12	14	16
25	3979	3997	4014	4031	4048	4065	4082	4099	4116	4133	2	4	5	7	9	10	12	14	16
26	4150	4166	4183	4200	4216	4232	4249	4265	4281	4298	2	3	5	7	8	10	11	13	15
27	4314	4330	4346	4362	4378	4393	4409	4425	4440	4456	2	3	5	6	8	9	11	12	14
28	4472	4487	4502	4518	4533	4548	4564	4579	4594	4609	2	3	5	6	8	9	11	12	14
29	4624	4639	4654	4669	4683	4698	4713	4728	4742	4757	1	3	4	6	7	9	10	12	13
30	4771	4786	4800	4814	4829	4843	4857	4871	4886	4900	1	3	4	6	7	9	10	11	13
31	4914	4928	4942	4955	4969	4983	4997	5011	5024	5038	1	3	4	5	7	8	10	11	12
32	5051	5065	5079	5092	5105	5119	5132	5145	5159	5172	1	3	4	5	7	8	9	11	12
33	5185	5198	5211	5224	5237	5250	5263	5276	5289	5302	1	3	4	5	7	8	9	11	12
34	5315	5328	5340	5353	5366	5378	5391	5403	5416	5428	1	2	4	5	6	8	9	10	11
35	5441	5453	5465	5478	5490	5502	5514	5527	5539	5551	1	2	4	5	6	7	9	10	11
36	5563	5575	5587	5599	5611	5623	5635	5647	5658	5670	1	2	4	5	6	7	8	10	11
37	5682	5694	5705	5717	5729	5740	5752	5763	5775	5786	1	2	4	5	6	7	8	9	11
38	5798	5809	5821	5832	5843	5855	5866	5877	5888	5899	1	2	3	5	6	7	8	9	10
39	5911	5922	5933	5944	5955	5966	5977	5988	5999	6010	1	2	3	4	5	7	8	9	10
40	6021	6031	6042	6053	6064	6075	6085	6096	6107	6117	1	2	3	4	5	6	8	9	10
41	6128	6138	6149	6160	6170	6180	6191	6201	6212	6222	1	2	3	4	5	6	7	8	9
42	6232	6243	6253	6263	6274	6284	6294	6304	6314	6325	1	2	3	4	5	6	7	8	9
43	6335	6345	6355	6365	6375	6385	6395	6405	6415	6425	1	2	3	4	5	6	7	8	9
44	6435	6444	6454	6464	6474	6484	6493	6503	6513	6522	1	2	3	4	5	6	7	8	9
45	6532	6542	6551	6561	6571	6580	6590	6599	6609	6618	1	2	3	4	5	6	7	8	9
46	6628	6637	6646	6656	6665	6675	6684	6693	6702	6712	1	2	3	4	5	6	7	7	8
47	6721	6730	6739	6749	6758	6767	6776	6785	6794	6803	1	2	3	4	5	6	7	7	8
48	6812	6821	6830	6839	6848	6857	6866	6875	6884	6893	1	2	3	4	5	6	7	7	8
49	6902	6911	6920	6928	6937	6946	6955	6964	6972	6981	1	2	3	4	4	5	6	7	8
50	6990	6998	7007	7016	7024	7033	7042	7050	7059	7067	1	2	3	3	4	5	6	7	8
51	7076	7084	7093	7101	7110	7118	7126	7135	7143	7152	1	2	3	3	4	5	6	7	8
52	7160	7168	7177	7185	7193	7202	7210	7218	7226	7235	1	2	3	3	4	5	6	7	7
53	7243	7251	7259	7267	7275	7284	7292	7300	7308	7316	1	2	2	3	4	5	6	6	7
54	7324	7332	7340	7348	7356	7364	7372	7380	7388	7396	1	2	2	3	4	5	6	6	7
N	0	1	2	3	4	5	6	7	8	9	1	2	3	4	5	6	7	8	9

TABLE 1. FOUR PLACE LOGARITHMS

N	0	1	2	3	4	5	6	7	8	9	1 2 3	4 5 6	7 8 9
	Mantissas										Proportional Parts		
55	7404	7412	7419	7427	7435	7443	7451	7459	7466	7474	1 2 2	3 4 5	5 6 7
56	7482	7490	7497	7505	7513	7520	7528	7536	7543	7551	1 2 2	3 4 5	5 6 7
57	7559	7566	7574	7582	7589	7597	7604	7612	7619	7627	1 1 2	3 4 5	5 6 7
58	7634	7642	7649	7657	7664	7672	7679	7686	7694	7701	1 1 2	3 4 4	5 6 7
59	7709	7716	7723	7731	7738	7745	7752	7760	7767	7774	1 1 2	3 4 4	5 6 7
60	7782	7789	7796	7803	7810	7818	7825	7832	7839	7846	1 1 2	3 4 4	5 6 6
61	7853	7860	7868	7875	7882	7889	7896	7903	7910	7917	1 1 2	3 3 4	5 6 6
62	7924	7931	7938	7945	7952	7959	7966	7973	7980	7987	1 1 2	3 3 4	5 5 6
63	7993	8000	8007	8014	8021	8028	8035	8041	8048	8055	1 1 2	3 3 4	5 5 6
64	8062	8069	8075	8082	8089	8096	8102	8109	8116	8122	1 1 2	3 3 4	5 5 6
65	8129	8136	8142	8149	8156	8162	8169	8176	8182	8189	1 1 2	3 3 4	5 5 6
66	8195	8202	8209	8215	8222	8228	8235	8241	8248	8254	1 1 2	3 3 4	5 5 6
67	8261	8267	8274	8280	8287	8293	8299	8306	8312	8319	1 1 2	3 3 4	5 5 6
68	8325	8331	8338	8344	8351	8357	8363	8370	8376	8382	1 1 2	3 3 4	4 5 6
69	8388	8395	8401	8407	8414	8420	8426	8432	8439	8445	1 1 2	3 3 4	4 5 6
70	8451	8457	8463	8470	8476	8482	8488	8494	8500	8506	1 1 2	3 3 4	4 5 6
71	8513	8519	8525	8531	8537	8543	8549	8555	8561	8567	1 1 2	3 3 4	4 5 6
72	8573	8579	8585	8591	8597	8603	8609	8615	8621	8627	1 1 2	3 3 4	4 5 6
73	8633	8639	8645	8651	8657	8663	8669	8675	8681	8686	1 1 2	2 3 4	4 5 5
74	8692	8698	8704	8710	8716	8722	8727	8733	8739	8745	1 1 2	2 3 4	4 5 5
75	8751	8756	8762	8768	8774	8779	8785	8791	8797	8802	1 1 2	2 3 3	4 5 5
76	8808	8814	8820	8825	8831	8837	8842	8848	8854	8859	1 1 2	2 3 3	4 4 5
77	8865	8871	8876	8882	8887	8893	8899	8904	8910	8915	1 1 2	2 3 3	4 4 5
78	8921	8927	8932	8938	8943	8949	8954	8960	8965	8971	1 1 2	2 3 3	4 4 5
79	8976	8982	8987	8993	8998	9004	9009	9015	9020	9025	1 1 2	2 3 3	4 4 5
80	9031	9036	9042	9047	9053	9058	9063	9069	9074	9079	1 1 2	2 3 3	4 4 5
81	9085	9090	9096	9101	9106	9112	9117	9122	9128	9133	1 1 2	2 3 3	4 4 5
82	9138	9143	9149	9154	9159	9165	9170	9175	9180	9186	1 1 2	2 3 3	4 4 5
83	9191	9196	9201	9206	9212	9217	9222	9227	9232	9238	1 1 2	2 3 3	4 4 5
84	9243	9248	9253	9258	9263	9269	9274	9279	9284	9289	1 1 2	2 3 3	4 4 5
85	9294	9299	9304	9309	9315	9320	9325	9330	9335	9340	1 1 2	2 3 3	4 4 5
86	9345	9350	9355	9360	9365	9370	9375	9380	9385	9390	1 1 2	2 3 3	4 4 5
87	9395	9400	9405	9410	9415	9420	9425	9430	9435	9440	1 1 2	2 3 3	4 4 5
88	9445	9450	9455	9460	9465	9469	9474	9479	9484	9489	0 1 1	2 2 3	3 4 4
89	9494	9499	9504	9509	9513	9518	9523	9528	9533	9538	0 1 1	2 2 3	3 4 4
90	9542	9547	9552	9557	9562	9566	9571	9576	9581	9586	0 1 1	2 2 3	3 4 4
91	9590	9595	9600	9605	9609	9614	9619	9624	9628	9633	0 1 1	2 2 3	3 4 4
92	9638	9643	9647	9652	9657	9661	9666	9671	9675	9680	0 1 1	2 2 3	3 4 4
93	9685	9689	9694	9699	9703	9708	9713	9717	9722	9727	0 1 1	2 2 3	3 4 4
94	9731	9736	9741	9745	9750	9754	9759	9763	9768	9773	0 1 1	2 2 3	3 4 4
95	9777	9782	9786	9791	9795	9800	9805	9809	9814	9818	0 1 1	2 2 3	3 4 4
96	9823	9827	9832	9836	9841	9845	9850	9854	9859	9863	0 1 1	2 2 3	3 4 4
97	9868	9872	9877	9881	9886	9890	9894	9899	9903	9908	0 1 1	2 2 3	3 4 4
98	9912	9917	9921	9926	9930	9934	9939	9943	9948	9952	0 1 1	2 2 3	3 3 4
99	9956	9961	9965	9969	9974	9978	9983	9987	9991	9996	0 1 1	2 2 3	3 3 4
N	0	1	2	3	4	5	6	7	8	9	1 2 3	4 5 6	7 8 9

TABLE 2

FOUR–PLACE VALUES OF FUNCTIONS AND RADIANS

Degrees	Radians	Sin	Cos	Tan	Cot	Sec	Csc		
0° 00'	.0000	.0000	1.0000	.0000	——	1.000	——	1.5708	**90° 00'**
10	029	029	000	029	343.8	000	343.8	679	50
20	058	058	000	058	171.9	000	171.9	650	40
30	.0087	.0087	1.0000	.0087	114.6	1.000	114.6	1.5621	30
40	116	116	.9999	116	85.94	000	85.95	592	20
50	145	145	999	145	68.75	000	68.76	563	10
1° 00'	.0175	.0175	.9998	.0175	57.29	1.000	57.30	1.5533	**89° 00'**
10	204	204	998	204	49.10	000	49.11	504	50
20	233	233	997	233	42.96	000	42.98	475	40
30	.0262	.0262	.9997	.0262	38.19	1.000	38.20	1.5446	30
40	291	291	996	291	34.37	000	34.38	417	20
50	320	320	995	320	31.24	001	31.26	388	10
2° 00'	.0349	.0349	.9994	.0349	28.64	1.001	28.65	1.5359	**88° 00'**
10	378	378	993	378	26.43	001	26.45	330	50
20	407	407	992	407	24.54	001	24.56	301	40
30	.0436	.0436	.9990	.0437	22.90	1.001	22.93	1.5272	30
40	465	465	989	466	21.47	001	21.49	243	20
50	495	494	988	495	20.21	001	20.23	213	10
3° 00'	.0524	.0523	.9986	.0524	19.08	1.001	19.11	1.5184	**87° 00'**
10	553	552	985	553	18.07	032	18.10	155	50
20	582	531	983	582	17.17	·002	17.20	126	40
30	.0611	.0610	.9981	.0612	16.35	1.002	16.38	1.5097	30
40	640	640	980	641	15.60	002	15.64	068	20
50	669	669	978	670	14.92	002	14.96	039	10
4° 00'	.0698	.0698	.9976	.0699	14.30	1.002	14.34	1.5010	**86° 00'**
10	727	727	974	729	13.73	003	13.76	981	50
20	756	756	971	758	13.20	003	13.23	952	40
30	.0785	.0785	.9969	.0787	12.71	1.003	12.75	1.4923	30
40	814	814	967	816	12.25	003	12.29	893	20
50	844	843	964	846	11.83	004	11.87	864	10
5° 00'	.0873	.0872	.9962	.0875	11.43	1.004	11.47	1.4835	**85° 00'**
10	902	901	959	904	11.06	004	11.10	806	50
20	931	929	957	934	10.71	004	10.76	777	40
30	.0960	.0958	.9954	.0963	10.39	1.005	10.43	1.4748	30
40	989	987	951	992	10.08	005	10.13	719	20
50	.1018	.1016	948	.1022	9.788	005	9.839	690	10
6° 00'	.1047	.1045	.9945	.1051	9.514	1.006	9.567	1.4661	**84° 00'**
10	076	074	942	080	9.255	006	9.309	632	50
20	105	103	939	110	9.010	006	9.065	603	40
30	.1134	.1132	.9936	.1139	8.777	1.006	8.834	1.4573	30
40	164	161	932	169	8.556	007	8.614	544	20
50	193	190	929	198	8.345	007	8.405	515	10
7° 00'	.1222	.1219	.9925	.1228	8.144	1.008	8.206	1.4486	**83° 00'**
10	251	248	922	257	7.953	008	8.016	457	50
20	280	276	918	287	7.770	008	7.834	428	40
30	.1309	.1305	.9914	.1317	7.596	1.009	7.661	1.4399	30
40	338	334	911	346	7.429	009	7.496	370	20
50	367	363	907	376	7.269	009	7.337	341	10
8° 00'	.1396	.1392	.9903	.1405	7.115	1.010	7.185	1.4312	**82° 00'**
10	425	421	899	435	6.968	010	7.040	283	50
20	454	449	894	465	6.827	011	6.900	254	40
30	.1484	.1478	.9890	.1495	6.691	1.011	6.765	1.4224	30
40	513	507	886	524	6.561	012	6.636	195	20
50	542	536	881	554	6.435	012	6.512	166	10
9° 00'	.1571	.1564	.9877	.1584	6.314	1.012	6.392	1.4137	**81° 00'**
		Cos	Sin	Cot	Tan	Csc	Sec	Radians	Degrees

From A. Spitzbart and R. H. Bardell, *College Algebra and Plane Trigonometry*. Reading, Mass.: Addison-Wesley Publishing Company, 1955. Reprinted by permission.

TABLE 2

FOUR-PLACE VALUES OF FUNCTIONS AND RADIANS

Degrees	Radians	Sin	Cos	Tan	Cot	Sec	Csc		
9° 00′	.1571	.1564	.9877	.1584	6.314	1.012	6.392	1.4137	81° 00′
10	600	593	872	614	197	013	277	108	50
20	629	622	868	644	084	013	166	˙079	40
30	.1658	.1650	.9863	.1673	5.976	1.014	6.059	1.4050	30
40	687	679	858	703	871	014	5.955	1.4021	20
50	716	708	853	733	769	015	855	992	10
10° 00′	.1745	.1736	.9848	.1763	5.671	1.015	5.759	1.3963	80° 00′
10	774	765	843	793	576	016	665	934	50
20	804	794	838	823	485	016	575	904	40
30	.1833	.1822	.9833	.1853	5.396	1.017	5.487	1.3875	30
40	862	851	827	883	309	018	403	846	20
50	891	880	822	914	226	018	320	817	10
11° 00′	.1920	.1908	.9816	.1944	5.145	1.019	5.241	1.3788	79° 00′
10	949	937	811	974	066	019	164	759	50
20	978	965	805	.2004	4.989	020	089	730	40
30	.2007	.1994	.9799	.2035	4.915	1.020	5.016	1.3701	30
40	036	.2022	793	065	843	021	4.945	672	20
50	065	051	787	095	773	022	876	643	10
12° 00′	.2094	.2079	.9781	.2126	4.705	1.022	4.810	1.3614	78° 00′
10	123	108	775	156	638	023	745	584	50
20	153	136	769	186	574	024	682	555	40
30	.2182	.2164	.9763	.2217	4.511	1.024	4.620	1.3526	30
40	211	193	757	247	449	025	560	497	20
50	240	221	750	278	390	026	502	468	10
13° 00′	.2269	.2250	.9744	.2309	4.331	1.026	4.445	1.3439	77° 00′
10	298	278	737	339	275	027	390	410	50
20	327	306	730	370	219	028	336	381	40
30	.2356	.2334	.9724	.2401	4.165	1.028	4.284	1.3352	30
40	385	363	717	432	113	029	232	323	20
50	414	391	710	462	061	030	182	294	10
14° 00′	.2443	.2419	.9703	.2493	4.011	1.031	4.134	1.3265	76° 00′
10	473	447	696	524	3.962	031	086	235	50
20	502	476	689	555	914	032	039	206	40
30	.2531	.2504	.9681	.2586	3.867	1.033	3.994	1.3177	30
40	560	532	674	617	821	034	950	148	20
50	589	560	667	648	776	034	906	119	10
15° 00′	.2618	.2588	.9659	.2679	3.732	1.035	3.864	1.3090	75° C0′
10	647	616	652	711	689	036	822	061	50
20	676	644	644	742	647	037	782	032	40
30	.2705	.2672	.9636	.2773	3.606	1.038	3.742	1.3003	30
40	734	700	628	805	566	039	703	974	20
50	763	728	621	836	526	039	665	945	10
16° 00′	.2793	.2756	.9613	.2867	3.487	1.040	3.628	1.2915	74° 00′
10	822	784	605	899	450	041	592	886	50
20	851	812	596	931	412	042	556	857	40
30	.2880	.2840	.9588	.2962	3.376	1.043	3.521	1.2828	30
40	909	868	580	994	340	044	487	799	20
50	938	896	572	.3026	305	045	453	770	10
17° 00′	.2967	.2924	.9563	.3057	3.271	1.046	3.420	1.2741	73° 00′
10	996	952	555	089	237	047	388	712	50
20	.3025	979	546	121	204	048	356	683	40
30	.3054	.3007	.9537	.3153	3.172	1.049	3.326	1.2654	30
40	083	035	528	185	140	049	295	625	20
50	113	062	520	217	108	050	265	595	10
18° 00′	.3142	.3090	.9511	.3249	3.078	1.051	3.236	1.2566	72° 00′
		Cos	Sin	Cot	Tan	Csc	Sec	Radians	Degrees

382

TABLE 2

FOUR-PLACE VALUES OF FUNCTIONS AND RADIANS

Degrees	Radians	Sin	Cos	Tan	Cot	Sec	Csc		
18° 00'	.3142	.3090	.9511	.3249	3.078	1.051	3.236	1.2566	**72° 00'**
10	171	118	502	281	047	052	207	537	50
20	200	145	492	314	018	053	179	508	40
30	.3229	.3173	.9483	.3346	2.989	1.054	3.152	1.2479	30
40	258	201	474	378	960	056	124	450	20
50	287	228	465	411	932	057	098	421	10
19° 00'	.3316	.3256	.9455	.3443	2.904	1.058	3.072	1.2392	**71° 00'**
10	345	283	446	476	877	059	046	363	50
20	374	311	436	503	850	060	021	334	40
30	.3403	.3338	.9426	.3541	2.824	1.061	2.996	1.2305	30
40	432	365	417	574	798	062	971	275	20
50	462	393	407	607	773	063	947	246	10
20° 00'	.3491	.3420	.9397	.3640	2.747	1.064	2.924	1.2217	**70° 00'**
10	520	448	387	673	723	065	901	188	50
20	549	475	377	706	699	066	878	159	40
30	.3578	.3502	.9367	.3739	2.675	1.068	2.855	1.2130	30
40	607	529	356	772	651	069	833	101	20
50	636	557	346	805	628	070	812	072	10
21° 00'	.3665	.3584	.9336	.3839	2.605	1.071	2.790	1.2043	**69° 00'**
10	694	611	325	872	583	072	769	1.2014	50
20	723	638	315	906	560	074	749	985	40
30	.3752	.3665	.9304	.3939	2.539	1.075	2.729	1.1956	30
40	782	692	293	973	517	076	709	926	20
50	811	719	283	.4006	496	077	689	897	10
22° 00'	.3840	.3746	.9272	.4040	2.475	1.079	2.669	1.1868	**68° 00'**
10	869	773	261	074	455	080	650	839	50
20	898	800	250	108	434	081	632	810	40
30	.3927	.3827	.9239	.4142	2.414	1.082	2.613	1.1781	30
40	956	854	228	176	394	084	595	752	20
50	985	881	216	210	375	085	577	723	10
23° 00'	.4014	.3907	.9205	.4245	2.356	1.086	2.559	1.1694	**67° 00'**
10	043	934	194	279	337	088	542	665	50
20	072	961	182	314	318	089	525	636	40
30	.4102	.3987	.9171	.4348	2.300	1.090	2.508	1.1606	30
40	131	.4014	159	383	282	092	491	577	20
50	160	041	147	417	264	093	475	548	10
24° 00'	.4189	.4067	.9135	.4452	2.246	1.095	2.459	1.1519	**66° 00'**
10	218	094	124	487	229	096	443	490	50
20	247	120	112	522	211	097	427	461	40
30	.4276	.4147	.9100	.4557	2.194	1.099	2.411	1.1432	30
40	305	173	088	592	177	100	396	403	20
50	334	200	075	628	161	102	381	374	10
25° 00'	.4363	.4226	.9063	.4663	2.145	1.103	2.366	1.1345	**65° 00'**
10	392	253	051	699	128	105	352	316	50
20	422	279	038	734	112	106	337	286	40
30	.4451	.4305	.9026	.4770	2.097	1.108	2.323	1.1257	30
40	480	331	013	806	081	109	309	228	20
50	509	358	001	841	066	111	295	199	10
26° 00'	.4538	.4384	.8988	.4877	2.050	1.113	2.281	1.1170	**64° 00'**
10	567	410	975	913	035	114	268	141	50
20	596	436	962	950	020	116	254	112	40
30	.4625	.4462	.8949	.4986	2.006	1.117	2.241	1.1083	30
40	654	488	936	.5022	1.991	119	228	054	20
50	683	514	923	059	977	121	215	1.1025	10
27° 00'	.4712	.4540	.8910	.5095	1.963	1.122	2.203	1.0996	**63° 00'**
		Cos	Sin	Cot	Tan	Csc	Sec	Radians	Degrees

TABLE 2

FOUR-PLACE VALUES OF FUNCTIONS AND RADIANS

Degrees	Radians	Sin	Cos	Tan	Cot	Sec	Csc		
27° 00′	.4712	.4540	.8910	.5095	1.963	1.122	2.203	1.0996	**63° 00′**
10	741	566	897	132	949	124	190	966	50
20	771	592	884	169	935	126	178	937	40
30	.4800	.4617	.8870	.5206	1.921	1.127	2.166	1.0908	30
40	829	643	857	243	907	129	154	879	20
50	858	669	843	280	894	131	142	850	10
28° 00′	.4887	.4695	.8829	.5317	1.881	1.133	2.130	1.0821	**62° 00′**
10	916	720	816	354	868	134	118	792	50
20	945	746	802	392	855	136	107	763	40
30	.4974	.4772	.8788	.5430	1.842	1.138	2.096	1.0734	30
40	.5003	797	774	467	829	140	085	705	20
50	032	823	760	505	816	142	074	676	10
29° 00′	.5061	.4848	.8746	.5543	1.804	1.143	2.063	1.0647	**61° 00′**
10	091	874	732	581	792	145	052	617	50
20	120	899	718	619	780	147	041	588	40
30	.5149	.4924	.8704	.5658	1.767	1.149	2.031	1.0559	30
40	178	.950	689	696	756	151	020	530	20
50	207	975	675	735	744	153	010	501	10
30° 00′	.5236	.5000	.8660	.5774	1.732	1.155	2.000	1.0472	**60° 00′**
10	265	025	646	812	720	157	1.990	443	50
20	294	050	631	851	709	159	980	414	40
30	.5323	.5075	.8616	.5890	1.698	1.161	1.970	1.0385	30
40	352	100	601	930	686	163	961	356	20
50	381	125	587	969	.675	165	951	327	10
31° 00′	.5411	.5150	.8572	.6009	1.664	1.167	1.942	1.0297	**59° 00′**
10	440	175	557	048	653	169	932	268	50
20	469	200	542	088	643	171	923	239	40
30	.5498	.5225	.8526	.6128	1.632	1.173	1.914	1.0210	30
40	527	250	511	168	621	175	905	181	20
50	556	275	496	208	611	177	896	152	10
32° 00′	.5585	.5299	.8480	.6249	1.600	1.179	1.887	1.0123	**58° 00′**
10	614	324	465	289	590	181	878	094	50
20	643	348	450	330	580	184	870	065	40
30	.5672	.5373	.8434	.6371	1.570	1.186	1.861	1.0036	30
40	701	398	418	412	560	188	853	1.0007	20
50	730	422	403	453	550	190	844	977	10
33° 00′	.5760	.5446	.8387	.6494	1.540	1.192	1.836	.9948	**57° 00′**
10	789	471	371	536	530	195	828	919	50
20	818	495	355	577	520	197	820	890	40
30	.5847	.5519	.8339	.6619	1.511	1.199	1.812	.9861	30
40	876	544	323	661	501	202	804	832	20
50	905	568	307	703	1.492	204	796	803	10
34° 00′	.5934	.5592	.8290	.6745	1.483	1.206	1.798	.9774	**56° 00′**
10	963	616	274	787	473	209	781	745	50
20	992	640	258	830	464	211	773	716	40
30	.6021	.5664	.8241	.6873	1.455	1.213	1.766	.9687	30
40	050	688	225	916	446	216	758	657	20
50	080	712	208	959	437	218	751	628	10
35° 00′	.6109	.5736	.8192	.7002	1.428	1.221	1.743	.9599	**55° 00′**
10	138	760	175	046	419	223	736	570	50
20	167	783	158	089	411	226	729	541	40
30	.6196	.5807	.8141	.7133	1.402	1.228	1.722	.9512	30
40	225	831	124	177	.393	231	715	483	20
50	254	854	107	221	385	233	708	454	10
36° 00′	.6283	.5878	.8090	.7265	1.376	1.236	1.701	.9425	**54° 00′**
		Cos	Sin	Cot	Tan	Csc	Sec	Radians	Degrees

TABLE 2

FOUR–PLACE VALUES OF FUNCTIONS AND RADIANS

Degrees	Radians	Sin	Cos	Tan	Cot	Sec	Csc		
36° 00′	.6283	.5878	.8090	.7265	1.376	1.236	1.701	.9425	**54° 00′**
10	312	901	073	310	368	239	695	396	50
20	341	925	056	355	360	241	688	367	40
30	.6370	.5948	.8039	.7400	1.351	1.244	1.681	.9338	30
40	400	972	021	445	343	247	675	308	20
50	429	995	004	490	335	249	668	279	10
37° 00′	.6458	.6018	.7986	.7536	1.327	1.252	1.662	.9250	**53° 00′**
10	487	041	969	581	319	255	655	221	50
20	516	065	951	627	311	258	649	192	40
30	.6545	.6088	.7934	.7673	1.303	1.260	1.643	.9163	30
40	574	111	916	720	295	263	636	134	20
50	603	134	898	766	288	266	630	105	10
38° 00′	.6632	.6157	.7880	.7813	1.280	1.269	1.624	.9076	**52° 00′**
10	661	180	862	860	272	272	618	047	50
20	690	202	844	907	265	275	612	.9018	40
30	.6720	.6225	.7826	.7954	1.257	1.278	1.606	.8988	30
40	749	248	808	.8002	250	281	601	959	20
50	778	271	790	050	242	284	595	930	10
39° 00′	.6807	.6293	.7771	.8098	1.235	1.287	1.589	.8901	**51° 00′**
10	836	316	753	146	228	290	583	872	50
20	865	338	735	195	220	293	578	843	40
30	.6894	.6361	.7716	.8243	1.213	1.296	1.572	.8814	30
40	923	383	698	292	206	299	567	785	20
50	952	406	679	342	199	302	561	756	10
40° 00′	.6981	.6428	.7660	.8391	1.192	1.305	1.556	.8727	**50° 00′**
10	.7010	450	642	441	185	309	550	698	50
20	039	472	623	491	178	312	545	668	40
30	.7069	.6494	.7604	.8541	1.171	1.315	1.540	.8639	30
40	098	517	585	591	164	318	535	610	20
50	127	539	566	642	157	322	529	581	10
41° 00′	.7156	.6561	.7547	.8693	1.150	1.325	1.524	.8552	**49° 00′**
10	185	583	528	744	144	328	519	523	50
20	214	604	509	796	137	332	514	494	40
30	.7243	.6626	.7490	.8847	1.130	1.335	1.509	.8465	30
40	272	648	470	899	124	339	504	436	20
50	301	670	451	952	117	342	499	407	10
42° 00′	.7330	.6691	.7431	.9004	1.111	1.346	1.494	.8378	**48° 00′**
10	359	713	412	057	104	349	490	348	50
20	389	734	392	110	098	353	485	319	40
30	.7418	.6756	.7373	.9163	1.091	1.356	1.480	.8290	30
40	447	777	353	217	085	360	476	261	20
50	476	799	333	271	079	364	471	232	10
43° 00′	.7505	.6820	.7314	.9325	1.072	1.367	1.466	.8203	**47° 00′**
10	534	841	294	380	066	371	462	174	50
20	563	862	274	435	060	375	457	145	40
30	.7592	.6884	.7254	.9490	1.054	1.379	1.453	.8116	30
40	621	905	234	545	048	382	448	087	20
50	650	926	214	601	042	386	444	058	10
44° 00′	.7679	.6947	.7193	.9657	1.036	1.390	1.440	.8029	**46° 00′**
10	709	967	173	713	030	394	435	999	50
20	738	988	153	770	024	398	431	970	40
30	.7767	.7009	.7133	.9827	1.018	1.402	1.427	.7941	30
40	796	030	112	884	012	406	423	912	20
50	825	050	092	942	006	410	418	883	10
45° 00′	.7854	.7071	.7071	1.000	1.000	1.414	1.414	.7854	**45° 00′**
		Cos	Sin	Cot	Tan	Csc	Sec	Radians	Degrees

385

TABLE 3. SQUARES, CUBES, AND ROOTS

Roots of numbers other than those given directly may be found by the following relations:

$$\sqrt{100n} = 10\sqrt{n}; \quad \sqrt{1000n} = 10\sqrt{10n}; \quad \sqrt{\frac{1}{10}n} = \frac{1}{10}\sqrt{10n}; \quad \sqrt{\frac{1}{100}n} = \frac{1}{10}\sqrt{n},$$

$$\sqrt{\frac{1}{1000}n} = \frac{1}{100}\sqrt{10n}; \quad \sqrt[3]{1000n} = 10\sqrt[3]{n}; \quad \sqrt[3]{10,000n} = 10\sqrt[3]{10n}; \quad \sqrt[3]{100,000n} =$$

$$10\sqrt[3]{100n}; \quad \sqrt[3]{\frac{1}{10}n} = \frac{1}{10}\sqrt[3]{100n}; \quad \sqrt[3]{\frac{1}{100}n} = \frac{1}{10}\sqrt[3]{10n}; \quad \sqrt[3]{\frac{1}{1000}n} = \frac{1}{10}\sqrt[3]{n}.$$

n	n^2	$\sqrt{n}$	$\sqrt{10n}$	n^3	$\sqrt[3]{n}$	$\sqrt[3]{10n}$	$\sqrt[3]{100n}$
1	1	1.000 000	3.162 278	1	1.000 000	2.154 435	4.641 589
2	4	1.414 214	4.472 136	8	1.259 921	2.714 418	5.848 035
3	9	1.732 051	5.477 226	27	1.442 250	3.107 233	6.694 330
4	16	2.000 000	6.324 555	64	1.587 401	3.419 952	7.368 063
5	25	2.236 068	7.071 068	125	1.709 976	3.684 031	7.937 005
6	36	2.449 490	7.745 967	216	1.817 121	3.914 868	8.434 327
7	49	2.645 751	8.366 600	343	1.912 931	4.121 285	8.879 040
8	64	2.828 427	8.944 272	512	2.000 000	4.308 869	9.283 178
9	81	3.000 000	9.486 833	729	2.080 084	4.481 405	9.654 894
10	100	3.162 278	10.00000	1 000	2.154 435	4.641 589	10.00000
11	121	3.316 625	10.48809	1 331	2.223 980	4.791 420	10.32280
12	144	3.464 102	10.95445	1 728	2.289 428	4.932 424	10.62659
13	169	3.605 551	11.40175	2 197	2.351 335	5.065 797	10.91393
14	196	3.741 657	11.83216	2 744	2.410 142	5.192 494	11.16689
15	225	3.872 983	12.24745	3 375	2.466 212	5.313 293	11.44714
16	256	4.000 000	12.64911	4 096	2.519 842	5.428 835	11.69607
17	289	4.123 106	13.03840	4 913	2.571 282	5.539 658	11.93483
18	324	4.242 641	13.41641	5 832	2.620 741	5.646 216	12.16440
19	361	4.358 899	13.78405	6 859	2.668 402	5.748 897	12.38562
20	400	4.472 136	14.14214	8 000	2.714 418	5.848 035	12.59921
21	441	4.582 576	14.49138	9 261	2.758 924	5.943 922	12.80579
22	484	4.690 416	14.83240	10 648	2.802 039	6.036 811	13.00591
23	529	4.795 832	15.16575	12 167	2.843 867	6.126 926	13.20006
24	576	4.898 979	15.49193	13 824	2.884 499	6.214 465	13.38866
25	625	5.000 000	15.81139	15 625	2.924 018	6.299 605	13.57209
26	676	5.099 020	16.12452	17 576	2.962 496	6.382 504	13.75069
27	729	5.196 152	16.43168	19 683	3.000 000	6.463 304	13.92477
28	784	5.291 503	16.73320	21 952	3.036 589	6.542 133	14.09460
29	841	5.385 165	17.02939	24 389	3.072 317	6.619 106	14.26043
30	900	5.477 226	17.32051	27 000	3.107 233	6.694 330	14.42250
31	961	5.567 764	17.60682	29 791	3.141 381	6.767 899	14.58100
32	1 024	5.656 854	17.88854	32 768	3.174 802	6.839 904	14.73613
33	1 089	5.744 563	18.16590	35 937	3.207 534	6.910 423	14.88806
34	1 156	5.830 952	18.43909	39 304	3.239 612	6.979 532	15.03695
35	1 225	5.916 080	18.70829	42 875	3.271 066	7.047 299	15.18294
36	1 296	6.000 000	18.97367	46 656	3.301 927	7.113 787	15.32619
37	1 369	6.082 763	19.23538	50 653	3.332 222	7.179 054	15.46680
38	1 444	6.164 414	19.49359	54 872	3.361 975	7.243 156	15.60491
39	1 521	6.244 998	19.74842	59 319	3.391 211	7.306 144	15.74061
40	1 600	6.324 555	20.00000	64 000	3.419 952	7.368 063	15.87401
41	1 681	6.403 124	20.24846	68 921	3.448 217	7.428 959	16.00521
42	1 764	6.480 741	20.49390	74 088	3.476 027	7.488 872	16.13429
43	1 849	6.557 439	20.73644	79 507	3.503 398	7.547 842	16.26133
44	1 936	6.633 250	20.97618	85 184	3.530 348	7.605 905	16.38643
45	2 025	6.708 204	21.21320	91 125	3.556 893	7.663 094	16.50964
46	2 116	6.782 330	21.44761	97 336	3.583 048	7.719 443	16.63103
47	2 209	6.855 655	21.67948	103 823	3.608 826	7.774 980	16.75069
48	2 304	6.928 203	21.90890	110 592	3.634 241	7.829 735	16.86865
49	2 401	7.000 000	22.13594	117 649	3.659 306	7.883 735	16.98499
50	2 500	7.071 068	22.36068	125 000	3.684 031	7.937 005	17.09976

Handbook of Chemistry & Physics, 46th Edition. Reprinted by courtesy of The Chemical Rubber Company, Cleveland, Ohio, publishers.

TABLE 3. SQUARES, CUBES, AND ROOTS

n	n^2	$\sqrt{n}$	$\sqrt{10n}$	n^3	$\sqrt[3]{n}$	$\sqrt[3]{10n}$	$\sqrt[3]{100n}$
50	2 500	7.071 068	22.36068	125 000	3.684 031	7.937 005	17.09976
51	2 601	7.141 428	22.58318	132 651	3.708 430	7.989 570	17.21301
52	2 704	7.211 103	22.80351	140 608	3.732 511	8.041 452	17.32478
53	2 809	7.280 110	23.02173	148 877	3.756 286	8.092 672	17.43513
54	2 916	7.348 469	23.23790	157 464	3.779 763	8.143 253	17.54411
55	3 025	7.416 198	23.45208	166 375	3.802 952	8.193 213	17.65174
56	3 136	7.483 315	23.66432	175 616	3.825 862	8.242 571	17.75808
57	3 249	7.549 834	23.87467	185 193	3.848 501	8.291 344	17.86316
58	3 364	7.615 773	24.08319	195 112	3.870 877	8.339 551	17.96702
59	3 481	7.681 146	24.28992	205 379	3.892 996	8.387 207	18.06969
60	3 600	7.745 967	24.49490	216 000	3.914 868	8.434 327	18.17121
61	3 721	7.810 250	24.69818	226 981	3.936 497	8.480 926	18.27160
62	3 844	7.874 008	24.89980	238 328	3.957 892	8.527 019	18.37091
63	3 969	7.937 254	25.09980	250 047	3.979 057	8.572 619	18 46915
64	4 096	8.000 000	25.29822	262 144	4.000 000	8.617 739	18.56636
65	4 225	8.062 258	25.49510	274 625	4.020 726	8.662 391	18.66256
66	4 356	8.124 038	25.69047	287 496	4.041 240	8.706 588	18.75777
67	4 489	8.185 353	25.88436	300 763	4.061 548	8.750 340	18.85204
68	4 624	8.246 211	26.07681	314 432	4.081 655	8.793 659	18.94536
69	4 761	8.306 624	26.26785	328 509	4.101 566	8.836 556	19.03778
70	4 900	8.366 600	26.45751	343 000	4.121 285	8.879 040	19.12931
71	5 041	8.426 150	26.64583	357 911	4.140 818	8.921 121	19.21997
72	5 184	8.485 281	26.83282	373 248	4.160 168	8.962 809	19.30979
73	5 329	8.544 004	27.01851	389 017	4.179 339	9.004 113	19.39877
74	5 476	8.602 325	27.20294	405 224	4.198 336	9.045 042	19.48695
75	5 625	8.660 254	27.38613	421 875	4.217 163	9.085 603	19.57434
76	5 776	8.717 798	27.56810	438 976	4.235 824	9.125 805	19 66095
77	5 929	8.774 964	27.74887	456 533	4.254 321	9.165 656	19.74681
78	6 084	8.831 761	27.92848	474 552	4.272 659	9.205 164	19.83192
79	6 241	8.888 194	28.10694	493 039	4.290 840	9.244 335	19.91632
80	6 400	8.944 272	28.28427	512 000	4.308 869	9.283 178	20.00000
81	6 561	9 000 000	28.46050	531 441	4.326 749	9.321 698	20.08299
82	6 724	9.055 385	28.63564	551 368	4.344 481	9.359 902	20.16530
83	6 889	9.110 434	28.80972	571 787	4.362 071	9.397 796	20.24694
84	7 056	9.165 151	28.98275	592 704	4.379 519	9.435 388	20.32793
85	7 225	9.219 544	29.15476	614 125	4.396 830	9.472 682	20.40828
86	7 396	9.273 618	29.32576	636 056	4.414 005	9.509 685	20.48800
87	7 569	9.327 379	29.49576	658 503	4.431 048	9.546 403	20.56710
88	7 744	9.380 832	29.66479	681 472	4.447 960	9.582 840	20.64560
89	7 921	9.433 981	29.83287	704 969	4.464 745	9.619 002	20.72351
90	8 100	9.486 833	30.00000	729 000	4.481 405	9.654 894	20.80084
91	8 281	9.539 392	30.16621	753 571	4.497 941	9.690 521	20.87759
92	8 464	9.591 663	30.33150	778 688	4.514 357	9.725 888	20.95379
93	8 649	9.643 651	30.49590	804 357	4.530 655	9.761 000	21.02944
94	8 836	9.695 360	30.65942	830 584	4.546 836	9.795 861	21.10454
95	9 025	9.746 794	30.82207	857 375	4.562 903	9.830 476	21.17912
96	9 216	9.797 959	30.98387	884 736	4.578 857	9.864 848	21.25317
97	9 409	9.848 858	31.14482	912 673	4.594 701	9.898 983	21.32671
98	9 604	9.899 495	31.30495	941 192	4.610 436	9.932 884	21.39975
99	9 801	9.949 874	31.46427	970 299	4.626 065	9.966 555	21.47229
100	10 000	10.00000	31.62278	1 000 000	4.641 589	10.00000	21.54435

index

Velocity, 272
Venn diagram, 145
Vertex of an angle, 75
Vertical asymptote, 193
Void set, 4

Well-ordering property, 13
Whole numbers, 13

x-axis, 42
x-coordinate, 43

y-axis, 42
y-coordinate, 43
y-intercept, 56

Zero, division by, 14
Zero vector, 257